3b
A Secondary Mathematics Core Curriculum

MATH
Connections®

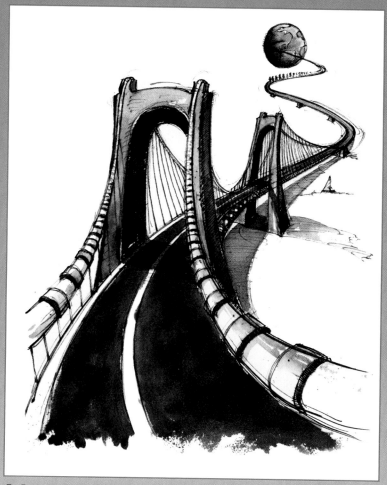

Advanced Algebra, Functions, and Modeling

William P. Berlinghoff
Clifford Sloyer
Eric F. Wood

IT's ABOUT TIME®
HERFF JONES EDUCATION DIVISION

IT's ABOUT TIME ®

HERFF JONES EDUCATION DIVISION
84 Business Park Drive
Armonk, NY 10504
Phone (914)273-2233
Fax (914)273-2227
www.ITS-ABOUT-TIME.com

President
Tom Laster

Creative/Art Director
John Nordland

Director of Product Development
Barbara Zahm

Cover Illustration
Robert Conge

Illustrations
Dennis Falcon

Editorial Coordinator
Monica T. Rodriguez

Production Specialist
Bernardo Saravia

MATH *Connections*®: *A Secondary Mathematics Core Curriculum* was developed under the National Science Foundation Grant No. ESI-9255251 awarded to the Connecticut Business and Industry Association.

ISBN # 1-58591-373-1
ISBN # 1-58591-374-X (Year 3, 2 Book Set)
4 5 6 VH 09 08 07 06

This project was supported, in part,
by the

National Science Foundation
Opinions expressed are those of the authors
and not necessarily those of the Foundation.

Welcome to **MATH** *Connections*®!

This book was written for you. It is designed to provide you with mathematical experiences that will excite your curiosity, stimulate your imagination, and challenge your skills. It bridges mathematics with the real world of people, business and everyday life. It isn't finished until you take an active part in the interesting problems and projects that invite you to explore important mathematical ideas. You'll want to discuss these ideas with other students, your teacher and your family. You might find that not all your ideas work, but try again, perhaps a different approach will work—that is all part of learning. And the learning is up to you!

<u>In the Margins</u> **The Learning Outcomes** are in the margins of the first page of each section. These will alert you to the major topic. The **Thinking Tip** in the margins will help you in gathering your ideas and in solving problems. **About Words** will show you how some words we use in mathematics relate to words you already know and use every day. **About Symbols** will explain particular notations and their use in mathematics.

<u>In the Text</u> A **Word to Know** and A **Phrase to Know** appear in the text and signal particularly important definitions. Similarly, A **Fact to Know** signals an important mathematical result.

<u>In the Profiles</u> you will meet people in various careers and professions who use mathematics in their everyday work.

<u>In the Appendices</u> at the back of your book you'll find some more sections to assist with learning and problem solving.

- Appendix A: Using a TI-84 Plus (TI-83 Plus) Graphing Calculator
- Appendix B: Using a Spreadsheet
- Appendix C: Programming the TI-82 (TI-83)
- Appendix D: Linear Programming With Excel
- Glossary
- Index

From time to time you'll see these graphic icons that call you to action.

Do this now
Identifies questions for you to answer.

Discuss this
Identifies questions for you to discuss as a class or in groups.

Write this
Usually requires you to gather information or reflect on a particular topic.

How MATH Connections takes you to the real world.

MATH *Connections* begins with you!
Each **MATH** *Connections* chapter introduces a concept
by asking you to think about what you already know.
You bring a lot of your life experiences into the classroom
and with **MATH** *Connections* those experiences
are strengths.

Provides a solid foundation in mathematics.
Building on your knowledge, **MATH** *Connections*
connects your experiences with comprehensive
mathematics. You'll learn algebra, geometry, statistics,
probability, trigonometry, discrete mathematics plus
dynamic programming, linear programming and
optimization techniques.

Relates the mathematics to real situations.
As you learn the mathematics, you will apply it
to real situations from hundreds of professions
and careers ranging from architecture to
micro-surgery to managing a grocery store.
Whether it is at home, in games, in sports or
at work .... **MATH** *Connections* connects
mathematics to the real world of
science, literature, art; and the
things you do every day.

Think math. Do math. Talk math. Write math.

Ultimately, math is a language that can help you in every aspect of your life. And with **MATH** *Connections* you really make mathematics your own by exploring, looking for patterns and reasoning things out. Whether you are working on your own, in small groups or as a class to solve problems, with **MATH** *Connections*, you will achieve a real understanding of mathematics.

Classroom tested for excellence.

MATH *Connections* works! **MATH** *Connections* was field-tested by more than 5000 students like yourself, in more than 100 high school classrooms. During the 4-year field test, it was continuously refined by its developers and high school teachers. And year after year it has proven to make the learning of mathematics more effective and more enjoyable. Plus, bottom line, **MATH** *Connections* students score higher on state and national tests.

Prepares you for your future.

Whether you plan to pursue a career in the sciences, the fine arts, or sports .... **MATH** *Connections* prepares you for the real world and your future.

Algebra, geometry, probability, trigonometry, statistics, discrete mathematics, dynamic and linear programming, optimization...

MATH *Connections* ties these all together.
Just like bridge cables that sustain and connect the span of a bridge, **MATH** *Connections* supports and relates to what you do in school, at home, in games, in sports, in college and at work to make you stronger in math and stronger in life.

MATH *Connections* TEAM

PRINCIPAL INVESTIGATORS

June G. Ellis, Director

Robert A. Rosenbaum
Wesleyan University

Robert J. Decker
University of Hartford

SENIOR WRITERS

William P. Berlinghoff
Colby College, Maine

Clifford Sloyer
University of Delaware

Robert W. Hayden
Plymouth State College,
New Hampshire

THE STAFF

Robert Gregorski
Associate Director

Lorna Rojan
Program Manager

Carolyn Mitchell
Administrative Assistant

THE CONTRIBUTORS

Don Hastings (retired)
Stratford Public Schools

Kathleen Bavelas
Manchester Community-
Technical College

George Parker
E. O. Smith High School,
Storrs

Linda Raffles
Glastonbury High School

Joanna Shrader Panning
Middletown High School

Frank Corbo
Staples High School, Westport

Thomas Alena
Talcott Mountain Science Center,
Avon

William Casey
Bulkeley High School, Hartford

Sharon Heyman
Bulkeley High School, Hartford

Helen Knudson
Choate Rosemary Hall, Wallingford

Mary Jo Lane (retired)
Granby Memorial High School

Lori White Moroso
Beth Chana Academy for Girls,
Orange

John Pellino
Talcott Mountain Science Center,
Avon

Pedro Vasquez, Jr.
Multicultural Magnet School,
Bridgeport

Thomas Willmitch
Talcott Mountain Science Center,
Avon

Leslie Paoletti
Greenwich Public Schools

Robert Fallon (retired)
Bristol Eastern High School

Table of Contents

MATH *Connections* Team

Welcome to **MATH** *Connections*!

Charles Bressinger
If It Absolutely Has To Get There

Coordinating the delivery of more than three million packages each day in 211 countries using 40,500 vehicles and 610 aircraft is certainly challenging — and definitely rewarding. It may even find you a soul mate.

Charles Bressinger, a technical fellow in the Operation Research (OR) department of Federal Express, handles everything from system form analysis, routing, to runway operations and the forecasting of future volume of deliveries. "Over the years the company has moved from purely air to both ground and air delivery," explains Charles. "We make decisions and tackle problems that affect millions of people and companies. Deciding where and how to move a package has real impact."

FedEx has also had a real impact on Charles. He began as an intern at FedEx more than 20 years ago and has never left.

In fact, Charles met his wife, with whom he has two children, in OR (she now works in a different department of Federal Express).

"At FedEx we devise three alternative transportation options for each shipment," explains Charles. "This allows us to consider weather, routing and traffic conditions before choosing the fastest, safest and most cost-effective route. We make all our own models and computer programs," he continues, "and develop large linear programs for long-term flight schedules."

The most difficult aspect of Charles' work is an unavoidable one. "The business is always changing. It keeps things interesting. Thankfully, I have the opportunity to work as a consultant for many areas of the company. I've worked with maintenance and engineers, with forecasting, even with the runway crews. I have a wide range of activities and that is what I enjoy."

Optimization: Math Does It Better

CHAPTER

5

5.1 Dynamic Programming

Learning Outcomes

After studying this section you will be able to:

Use Dynamic Programming to solve block diagram problems

Compare the time required for a computer using the Exhaustive Search method versus Dynamic Programming

Explain how working backwards can be an efficient problem-solving tool.

During the last 50 years, powerful new ideas have emerged in mathematics. Many of these ideas have resulted from the introduction of computers into everyday life and into the work place. Names like Linear Programming, Dynamic Programming, Geometric Programming, and Graph Theory have become household words to the many people who work daily with mathematics. In this chapter you will be introduced to the basic ideas of Linear Programming, Dynamic Programming, and Graph Theory.

In Chapter 4, you were introduced to a set of problems involving block diagrams. Our objective in that chapter was to learn how to count the number of paths and the number of operations involved in solving such problems. As you'll recall, some of the solutions discussed in Chapter 4 would take a computer, capable of performing 100,000 operations per second, more than 2 million years to solve.

The method we used in Chapter 4 for finding the quickest route involved looking at the time for each of the possible paths and then finding one that required the smallest amount of time. This method is known as the *Brute Force* method or the *Exhaustive Search* method. It should be clear that this method is not very efficient for solving block diagram problems. Even a 30 by 30 problem is not a big problem when one considers the routing of fire trucks or ambulances in cities like San Francisco, California, or Phoenix, Arizona.

5.1

1. Jon Greedee, a student at Fermi's School of Science, claims to have a better method for solving block diagram problems. He illustrates his method with the following example given in Display 5.1:

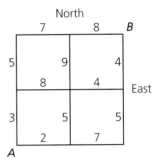

Display 5.1

Jon states that we can find the quickest path by simply starting at *A* and at each corner take the block which requires the least amount of time. In this example, starting at *A*, we should go east one block because 2 is smaller than 3. This is shown in Display 5.2.

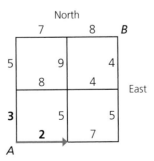

Display 5.2

At the next corner, we have a choice of 5 or 7, and since 5 is smaller than 7, we should go north one block. See Display 5.3.

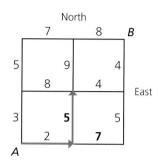

Display 5.3

At the next corner we should go east one block since 4 is smaller than 9. Finally, we must go north one block to reach B. See Display 5.4.

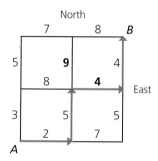

Display 5.4

(i) Jon claims that ENEN gives the quickest path from A to B. Is Jon correct?

(ii) Use Jon's method (known as a Greedy Algorithm) to find a route from A to B in the following problem in Display 5.5.

Is your path the quickest path from A to B?

North
7   8   B
5| 4| 6
  2   7   East
3| 5| 5
  4   7
A

Display 5.5

(iii) Is Jon's method more efficient than looking at all possible paths from *A* to *B*? Why?

(iv) Do you think Jon's method will work with any block diagram problem? If your answer is Yes, give an argument as to why you think it will work. If your answer is No, give an example to show that it does not always work.

2. How many corners, including *A* and *B*, are there in a

(i) 2 by 2 block diagram problem?

(ii) 3 by 3 block diagram problem?

(iii) 10 by 10 block diagram problem?

(iv) 30 by 30 block diagram problem?

It should be clear that there is a need to find more efficient ways to solve block diagram problems. One efficient method was discovered in 1950 by mathematician Richard Bellman. In order to illustrate Bellman's ideas, we return to a 2 by 2 block diagram problem as shown in Display 5.6.

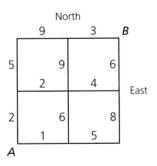

Display 5.6

Suppose one arrives at the corner circled in Display 5.7.

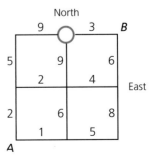

Display 5.7

We have no choice but to go east. It takes 3 minutes to reach B. This information is indicated in Display 5.8.

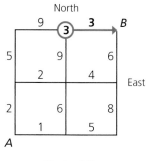

Display 5.8

In Display 5.9, three more corners are circled along with the times required to reach B and the directions indicated by arrows.

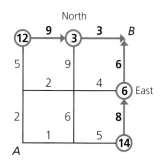

Display 5.9

There are four circled corners in Display 5.9. Note there is one path for each one. If we should arrive at the corner of the empty circle in Display 5.10, we will need to decide in which direction to travel.

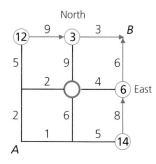

Display 5.10

At this corner we have to make a decision of whether to go east or north. If we move north from the empty circle, it will take $9 + 3 = 12$ minutes to reach B. If we move east from the empty circle, it will take $4 + 6 = 10$ minutes to reach B. Clearly we want to move east, *should we arrive at this corner.* This information is given in Display 5.11.

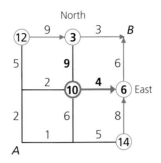

Display 5.11

Another decision will have to be made *should we arrive at the corner of the empty circle in Display 5.12.*

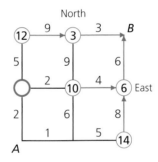

Display 5.12

If we move north from the empty circle it will take $5 + 12 = 17$ minutes to reach B, but if we move east from the circle it will take $2 + 10 = 12$ minutes to reach B. Thus, we want to move east. This information is given in Display 5.13.

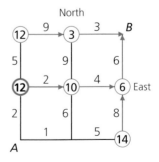

Display 5.13

1. Which numbers should go in the empty circles in Display 5.14? What are the appropriate directions to follow?

5.2

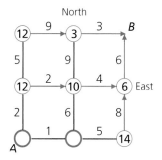

Display 5.14

2. How can you use the diagram that results from question 1 above to find a quickest path from A to B? What is the quickest path in this case? Would you get the same answer if you were to list all possible paths from A to B along with the times, and look for a quickest path? Would you get the same answer if you used Jon Greedee's method?

3. Just to make sure you have the idea of this process, find a quickest path from A to B in the following 3 by 3 block diagram problem. Your teacher will give you a copy of Display 5.15.

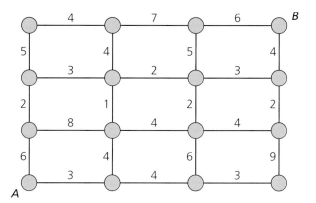

Display 5.15

In order to get some idea of the efficiency of this procedure, let's look at the number of operations needed. First, note in Display 5.16 that no additions were necessary at corners D and F, and only one addition was needed at each of the corners C and E.

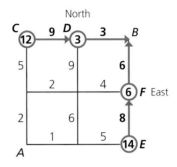

Display 5.16

In Display 5.17, two additions $(4 + 6$ and $9 + 3)$ were needed at corner G. Also, we had to compare the results $(10$ and $12)$ which we will count as an operation. Thus, at corner G, three operations were required.

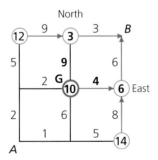

Display 5.17

The same comment can be made about all of the remaining corners in Display 5.17. At each remaining corner, three operations are needed. Our conclusion is the following: Using Bellman's Process, at each corner of a block diagram problem, *no more than three operations are needed.* This process is known as *Dynamic Programming*.

Problem Set: 5.1

1. Explain why less than 3000 operations are needed to solve a 30 by 30 block diagram problem using Dynamic Programming.

2. If a computer performs 100,000 operations per second, how long will it take this computer to solve a 30 by 30 block diagram problem using Dynamic Programming? You've answered the following question before. How long will it take this computer to solve the same problem using the Brute Force method looking at all possible paths? Are you impressed?

For questions 3 and 4, your teacher will give you a copy of Display 5.18 and 5.19.

3. Use Dynamic Programming to find the quickest route from *A* to *B* in the block diagram problem of Display 5.18.

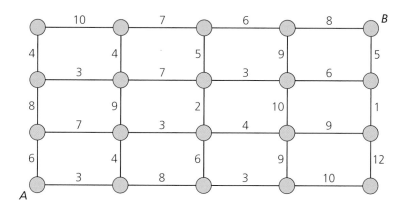

Display 5.18

4. (a) How many paths are there from *A* to *B* in Display 5.19?

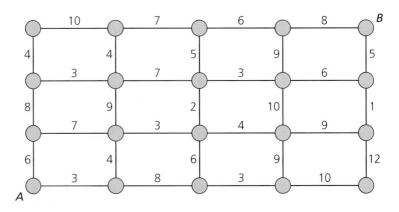

Display 5.19

(b) Using Dynamic Programming we decide that an optimal path must end in EN. How many paths from *A* to *B* end in EN?

(c) How many paths from *A* to *B* are eliminated when a decision is made to end the path in EN?

5.2 Introduction to Linear Programming: You Think You Have a Problem?

Linear Programming is one of the most widely used areas of mathematics. As a mathematical tool for doing things better, Linear Programming evolved as a result of many large and complex military problems that arose during World War II. It was soon discovered, however, that this tool was extremely powerful in solving a diversified set of problems in business and government work. In this section, as well as the three which follow, you will be introduced to the mathematical ideas involved with Linear Programming.

In 1989, the city of San Francisco began using mathematics to schedule the shifts worked by police officers. As a result, the police department of that city began saving 11 million dollars a year while at the same time increasing their services to the community. Let's look at a situation which involves ideas like those used in San Francisco.

Situation 1 A police department requires a certain number of officers on duty for each day of the week. The minimum number of officers needed each day is given in Display 5.20.

Day of the Week	Number of Officers Needed
Monday	18
Tuesday	12
Wednesday	15
Thursday	14
Friday	15
Saturday	20
Sunday	17

Display 5.20

What reasons can you give as to why a police department would need a different number of officers available on each day of the week?

5.3

Union rules state that each officer must work five consecutive days and then have two days off. For example, an officer who begins work on Thursday will work every day up to and including the following Monday, but then have Tuesday and Wednesday off.

One possible schedule which meets the requirements in Display 5.20, and the union rules, is given in Display 5.21.

Day	Number of Officers Beginning Work on This Day
Monday	6
Tuesday	4
Wednesday	2
Thursday	6
Friday	2
Saturday	7
Sunday	0

Display 5.21

We will use Display 5.22 to show that all the requirements in Display 5.20 are satisfied.

Day	Number of Officers on Duty
Monday	21
Tuesday	19
Wednesday	?
Thursday	?
Friday	?
Saturday	?
Sunday	?

Display 5.22

Observe from Display 5.20 that at least 18 officers must be on duty on Monday. The above schedule meets that requirement since 21 officers will be on duty. The number 21 is obtained by adding the number of officers beginning work on Thursday, Friday, Saturday, Sunday, and Monday. That is, $6 + 2 + 7 + 0 + 6 = 21$.

1. Copy and complete Display 5.22 by filling in the appropriate numbers into the ? slots. Are the requirements of Display 5.20 satisfied? How do you know?

5.4

2. The police department wants to minimize the total number of officers that must be hired. The schedule in Display 5.21 requires that 27 officers be hired. Do you think you can meet the daily requirements with less than 27 officers? Well, here's your chance to try. Fill in a schedule similar to but different from that of Display 5.21. Make a table similar to Display 5.22 to check the requirements.

   How many officers must be hired for your schedule? Is your schedule any better than that of Display 5.21? Why or why not? How does your schedule compare with those of other students in the class?

3. Explain why the schedule in Display 5.23 is *not* an acceptable schedule.

Day	Number of Officers Beginning Work on This Day
Monday	6
Tuesday	4
Wednesday	2
Thursday	6
Friday	1
Saturday	7
Sunday	0

Display 5.23

The problem faced by the San Francisco Police Department involved minimizing the number of officers hired. With this in mind, one wanted to find the best possible schedule (if there is such a thing). Similar problems, faced by many companies, involve finding the best way to do something so that costs are small and profits are large.

In recent years an oil company began using new mathematical ideas (discussed in this chapter) for finding how to blend incoming crude oils into unleaded regular, unleaded plus, and super unleaded gasolines. The results save the oil company more than 30 million dollars each year.

The problems faced by the oil company form a small fraction of all the blending problems that have been solved using new ideas in mathematics. A former student of this author recently went to work for a quarry in Maryland. During the first eight months this student increased the profits of the company by more than $300,000 by finding a less costly but higher quality blend of materials for making blacktop roads. The following situation has the flavor of such blending problems:

Situation 2 A quarry has three different sizes of stones: S_1, S_2, and S_3. The stones are used in the production of two concrete mixes, C_1 and C_2. Each day the quarry has available a stock of 8000 tons of S_1, 12,000 tons of S_2, and 5000 tons of S_3. Each mix of concrete uses different percentages of the stones (given in Display 5.24 below), plus appropriate amounts of other materials such as sand. There is an abundant amount of other materials available. The net profit on a ton of each type of concrete is also given in the table. How many tons of each type of concrete mix should the company make each day to maximize the total profit?

Concrete	S_1	S_2	S_3	Other	Profit Per Ton
C_1	60%	15%	10%	15%	$7
C_2	15%	35%	40%	10%	$9

Display 5.24

For this problem, one possible production schedule is the following:

Make 9000 tons of C_1

and

Make 8000 tons of C_2

which gives a profit of $135,000.

One can check that this schedule does not use more than the available stones by looking at Display 5.25.

Tons Concrete Needed	S_1 Tons Needed	S_2 Tons Needed	S_3 Tons Needed
C_1 9000	5400	1350	900
C_2 8000	1200	2800	?
Totals Needed	6600	4150	?

Display 5.25

Observe that this solution requires 6600 tons of S_1 and 8000 tons are available. This solution requires 4150 tons of S_2 and 12,000 tons are available.

5.5

1. Find the number of tons of S_3 needed for mix C_2 and the total number of tons of S_3 needed for this production schedule. Are there a sufficient number of tons of S_3 available to meet this schedule?

2. Another production schedule is the following:

   Make 10,000 tons of C_1
   and
   Make 8000 tons of C_2

   (a) Using a table similar to Display 5.25, show that this schedule is a possible production schedule.

   (b) What is the profit from this schedule?

3. Make up another schedule. Check that your schedule does not use more than the available stones by constructing a table similar to Display 5.25. What is the profit from your schedule? Remember you are trying to make the profit as large as possible. How does the profit from your schedule compare with those of other students in the class?

4. Explain why the following schedule is impossible to implement:

   Make 12,000 tons of C_1
   and
   Make 10,000 tons of C_2

Problem Set: 5.2

1. Entebe hears that the Mountaineer Hiking Club is taking a trip on Saturday. He wants to make some money. He thinks he can sell lunches to the hikers for their trip if he can box the lunches to fit in their backpacks. He has two types of lunch. The Thirsty Hiker Lunch contains three cans of soda and two sandwiches. The Hungry Hiker Lunch contains three sandwiches and two cans of soda. Sodas cost him 50 cents each and sandwiches cost him $2 each. He sells the Thirsty Hiker Lunch for $6 and the Hungry Hiker Lunch for $9.

   (a) Summarize this information in a table. There should be one row each for the two types of lunch. There should be columns for the number of sodas in each type of lunch, the number of sandwiches in each type of lunch, the cost to Entebe, the selling price, and the profit for each type of lunch.

   Entebe only has storage space for 30 cans of soda and 24 sandwiches. He is able to sell all the lunches he can store.

   (b) Can Entebe make and sell six Thirsty Hiker Lunches and four Hungry Hiker Lunches? Check this by making a table with rows for each kind of lunch and a row of totals. Make a column for the number of lunches of each type, the number of sodas needed, the number of sandwiches needed, and the profit. If Entebe cannot sell this combination of lunches, explain why. If he can, find the total profit.

   (c) Can Entebe make and sell five Thirsty Hiker Lunches and six Hungry Hiker Lunches? Make an appropriate table. If Entebe cannot sell this combination of lunches, explain why. If he can, find the total profit.

   (d) One of the plans you investigated in (b) and (c) worked. Can you find another plan that works but gives a larger profit? If you can, explain your plan, showing that it will work and what the profit will be. If you cannot, explain why not.

2. Your company, The Cup and Cone, makes ice cream in three flavors—vanilla, chocolate, and strawberry. It can make no more than 3000 quarts a day. In addition, the sales people inform you that they can sell no more than 2000 quarts of vanilla, 1200 quarts of chocolate, and 900

Optimization: Math Does It Better

5.2 Introduction to Linear Programming: You Think You Have a Problem?

quarts of strawberry each day. The company makes a profit of 30 cents on each quart of vanilla, 40 cents on each quart of chocolate, and 35 cents on each quart of strawberry.

(a) Set up a schedule for this company by indicating the number of quarts of vanilla, chocolate, and strawberry to be made each day. Make sure that your schedule meets the given requirements.

(b) What profit does the company make each day from your schedule in (a)?

(c) Can you find a schedule, different from that in (a), which yields a higher profit? Explain your answer.

3. Your company continues to make ice cream in three flavors—vanilla, chocolate, and strawberry. However, due to a shutdown of one machine for maintenance, it can make no more than 2000 quarts a day. In addition, the sales people inform you that they can sell no more than 1000 quarts of vanilla, 1200 quarts of chocolate, and 800 quarts of strawberry each day. Due to other factors, the total amount of vanilla and strawberry produced must be at least as great as the amount of chocolate produced (it can be more). The company makes a profit of 30 cents on each quart of vanilla, 40 cents on each quart of chocolate, and 35 cents on each quart of strawberry.

(a) Set up a schedule for your company by indicating the number of quarts of vanilla, chocolate, and strawberry to be made each day. Check that your schedule meets the given requirements.

(b) What profit does your company make each day from your schedule in (a)?

(c) Can you find a feasible schedule, different from that in (a), which yields a higher profit? Explain your answer.

5.3 Linear Programming: A Graphical Approach

Learning Outcomes

After studying this section, you will be able to:

Explain what is meant by *decision variables*, *feasible solutions*, *optimal feasible solutions*, and *objective functions*

Explain what is meant by a *Linear Programming model*

Use the graphs of *feasible regions* and *profit lines* to solve Linear Programming problems with two variables.

In the previous section we mentioned problems facing the San Francisco police department and an oil company. Such problems are big and complex. An excellent problem-solving idea is to look at simpler problems, solve them, and try to see how your ideas can be extended to more difficult problems. We shall take a detailed look at some simpler problems and then try to show how these ideas can be extended to bigger and more complex problems.

Situation 1 A company makes ice cream in two flavors, vanilla and chocolate. The company can make no more than 2000 quarts a day. In addition, the sales people inform you that they can sell 1500 quarts of vanilla ice cream a day, but no more. They also tell you that they can sell 800 quarts of chocolate ice cream each day, but no more. The company makes a profit of 30 cents on each quart of vanilla and 50 cents on each quart of chocolate. The company wants to make as large a profit as possible.

5.6

1. How many quarts of the two types of ice cream should they make each day so that the total profit is as large as possible? Why do you think your solution is the correct one?

2. What would your solution be if the profit on vanilla ice cream was 50 cents a quart and the profit on chocolate ice cream was 30 cents a quart?

The manager of the company would like to know how many quarts of vanilla and how many quarts of chocolate should be made each day to make as much profit as possible. At the outset, these amounts are unknown and so variables are introduced to represent the unknown amounts. Let's use v to denote the number of quarts of vanilla made each day and c

the number of quarts of chocolate made each day. We normally write something like the following:
Let

v = Number of quarts of vanilla made each day

c = Number of quarts of chocolate made each day

The variables v and c are called *decision variables* because they enable the manager of the company to make decisions about scheduling the production of ice cream.

In **Situation 1** you are told that the company can sell no more than 1500 quarts of vanilla ice cream each day. Also, one cannot produce a negative amount of vanilla ice cream. Using mathematical symbols, one could write

$$0 \le v \le 1500 \qquad (1)$$

which says "v cannot be negative and is less than or equal to 1500" or simply translates to "the number of quarts of vanilla ice cream produced each day is less than or equal to 1500."

1. **For Situation 1, if someone wrote**

   $$0 \le v \le 1250$$

   5.7

   how would you translate this inequality into words?

2. **Suppose that the company could not sell more than 1200 quarts of vanilla ice cream each day. How would you write this fact in mathematical symbols?**

3. **Suppose that the company could not sell more than 1000 quarts of vanilla ice cream each day. How would you write this fact in mathematical symbols?**

4. **Write an inequality for the decision variable c.**

There is one more inequality that must be satisfied. Remember, the total amount of ice cream made by the company in one day cannot be more than 2000 quarts. This leads us to the inequality

$$v + c \le 2000$$

Do you think is it necessary to include

5.8

$$0 \le v + c$$

Explain.

We now have three inequalities which must be satisfied. They are summarized by

$$0 \le v \le 1500$$

$$0 \le c \le 800$$

$$v \le c \le 2000$$

These inequalities are called **constraints**.

About Words

A *constraint* is something that restricts your actions.

In this example we are restricted by the amount of ice cream that can be made and also by the amount of ice cream that can be sold. The above inequalities show these restrictions.

It might help to put these constraints into word form as well as symbolic form.

$$0 \le v \le 1500$$

"We cannot sell more than 1500 quarts of vanilla ice cream."

$$0 \le c \le 800$$

"We cannot sell more than 800 quarts of chocolate ice cream."

$$v + c \le 2000$$

How would you put this constraint into word form?

5.9   A pair of values for v and c which satisfy the constraints is known as a **feasible solution** to the problem.

A Word to Know: The word **feasible** is an adjective used to describe an action that is capable of being done or carried out. That is, an action that can be done successfully.

A feasible solution is not necessarily a final solution to the problem. Remember, a final solution to our problem is one which makes the total profit as large as possible. That is, our ultimate goal is to find a feasible solution which makes the total profit as large as possible. Such a feasible solution is called an *optimal feasible solution*.

1. Which of the following pairs of values for v and c will satisfy all of the constraints given by the three inequalities?

5.10

$$0 \leq v \leq 1500$$

$$0 \leq c \leq 800$$

$$v + c \leq 2000$$

That is, which of the following pairs of values of v and c are feasible solutions?

(a) $v = 300$ and $c = 1700$

(b) $v = 1000$ and $c = 400$

(c) $v = 1200$ and $c = 500$

2. In each part of 1 above where the constraints are satisfied, what is the total profit of each?

Again, our ultimate goal is to make the total profit as large as possible. If we let P denote the profit, in cents, then

$$P = 30v + 50c \qquad (2)$$

The expression in (2) represents our **objective function.** This phrase is used since (2) is related to the goal, or objective, of making the profit P as large as possible. That is, we want to *maximize* P. The word maximize is sometimes abbreviated as max.

Our mathematical model is now

objective function max $P = 30v + 50c$

subject to the constraints

$$0 \leq v \leq 1500$$

$$0 \leq c \leq 800$$

$$v + c \leq 2000$$

Although this is an acceptable model, a *standard* or *conventional* way of presenting such a model is

objective function max $P = 30v + 50c$

subject to the constraints

$$v \leq 1500$$

$$c \leq 800$$

$$v + c \leq 2000$$

$$v \geq 0, c \geq 0$$

Such a model is called a **Linear Programming model** since the objective function is a linear function and the constraints represent linear inequalities.

5.11

1. How would the model change if the profit on a quart of vanilla ice cream was 25 cents and the profit on a quart of chocolate ice cream was 75 cents?

2. An ice cream plant makes two flavors, vanilla and chocolate. The plant capacity is 1200 quarts per day, and the sales department says that it can sell any amount of vanilla—the maximum being 900 quarts—and any amount of chocolate—the maximum being 600 quarts. The profit per quart is 35 cents for vanilla and 50 cents for chocolate. Set up a Linear Programming model for maximizing the total profit. Find at least three different feasible solutions.

Let's return to **Situation 1** and the model:

objective function max $P = 30v + 50c$

subject to the constraints

$$v \leq 1500$$

$$c \leq 800$$

$$v + c \leq 2000$$

$$v \geq 0, c \geq 0$$

There are several ways of attacking this problem. First, it should be clear that making more ice cream results in higher profits. Thus, the company should make as much ice cream as possible. It follows that for an optimal feasible solution, the inequality (constraint)

$$v + c \leq 2000$$

should be an equality

$$v + c = 2000$$

which gives

$$c = 2000 - v \qquad (3)$$

However, $c \leq 800$ and it follows from (3) that the value of v must be at least 1200. That is, $v \geq 1200$. Now, substituting (3) into the objective function we have

$$P = 30v + 50\,(2000 - v)$$

or

$$P = 100{,}000 - 20v$$

1. Why will your profit get smaller as v gets larger?

2. From the previous question it follows that you want to make v as small as possible. What is such a value of v?

5.12

As a result, an optimal feasible solution occurs when $v = 1200$ and $c = 800$, yielding a total profit of 76,000 cents or \$760.

1. What would the optimal feasible solution be if the profit on a quart of vanilla ice cream was 50 cents and the profit on a quart of chocolate ice cream was 30 cents?

5.13

2. An ice cream plant makes two flavors, vanilla and chocolate. The plant capacity is 1200 quarts per day, and the sales department says that it can sell any amount of vanilla—the maximum being 900 quarts—and any amount of chocolate—the maximum being 600 quarts. The profit per quart is 35 cents for vanilla and 50 cents for chocolate. The company wants to maximize the total profit. Find an optimal feasible solution for the company using an algebraic approach.

A second attack on the problem of **Situation 1** involves using graphs. If you wish to review graphing, ask your teacher for a copy of the *Graphing Review*. Recall the Linear Programming model

$$\text{objective function max} \quad P = 30v + 50c$$

subject to the constraints

$$v \leq 1500$$

$$c \leq 800$$

$$v + c \leq 2000$$

$$v \geq 0, c \geq 0$$

A first step is to set up a graph of the constraints. For this purpose we use a *cv* coordinate plane instead of the usual *xy* coordinate plane as shown in Display 5.26.

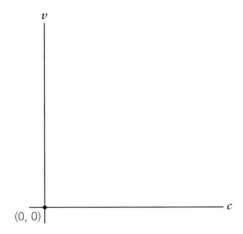

Display 5.26

Since $v \geq 0$ and $c \geq 0$ are constraints, which include the boundaries $v = 0$ and $c = 0$, we are interested only in points of the first quadrant of this plane. A graph of the set of points in the first quadrant satisfying the first constraint $v \leq 1500$ is given by the shaded region of Display 5.27. Note that this region includes points on the lines $v = 1500$, $v = 0$ and $c = 0$.

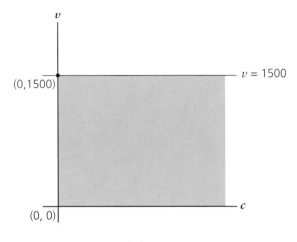

Display 5.27

A graph of the set of points in the first quadrant satisfying the second constraint $c \leq 800$, which includes the boundaries $v = 0$ and $c = 0$, is given by the shaded region in Display 5.28. Note that this region includes points on the lines $c = 800$, $v = 0$ and $c = 0$.

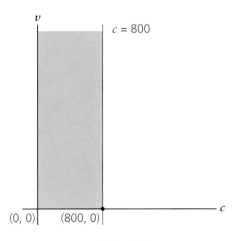

Display 5.28

The next step involves sketching a graph of the third constraint. The equation

$$v + c = 2000$$

divides the plane into two parts. On one side of this line the inequality $v + c < 2000$ is satisfied; on the other side, it is not satisfied.

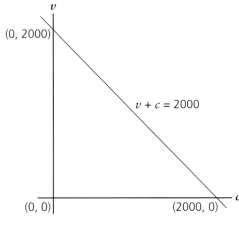

Display 5.29

To determine which side of the line satisfies the inequality, one need take only one specific point (c, v) on either side and test the values of c and v in the inequality. For example, the origin (c and v both zero) does satisfy the inequality. Thus, all points on the same side of this line as the origin will satisfy the inequality. This set of points in the first quadrant is shaded in Display 5.30.

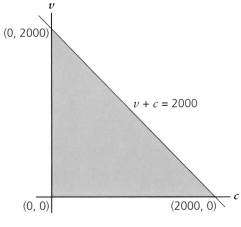

Display 5.30

All of the constraints of point (c, v) are satisfied in the shaded area of Display 5.31 which includes the boundary lines.

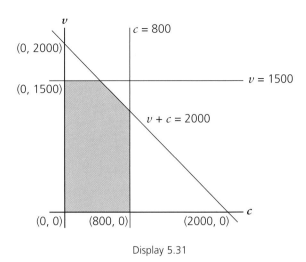

Display 5.31

The shaded region including the boundaries of Display 5.31 is known as the **feasible region** for this problem: because it satisfies all five constraints.

1. How would the feasible region change if the profit on a quart of vanilla ice cream was 50 cents, and the profit on a quart of chocolate ice cream was 30?

    5.14

2. Sketch the feasible region for the following problem:

   An ice cream plant makes two flavors, vanilla and chocolate. The plant capacity is 1200 quarts per day, and the sales department says that it can sell any amount of vanilla—the maximum being 900 quarts—and any amount of chocolate—the maximum being 600 quarts. The profit per quart is 35 cents for vanilla and 50 cents for chocolate. The company wants to maximize the total profit.

Observe that the feasible region is obtained from the constraints and has nothing to do with the objective function. We now return to the objective function in our situation.

$$P = 50c + 30v$$

For a fixed value of P, this is the equation of a straight line. Earlier in **MATH** *Connections*, such lines were called *contour lines*. In Linear Programming, such lines are called **profit lines**.

A Phrase to Know: A profit line is a straight line in a coordinate plane along which profit is a constant.

Since v was our choice for the vertical axis, we solve for v, obtaining

$$v = -\frac{5}{3}c + \frac{P}{30}$$

5.15

1. **What is the slope of a profit line?**

2. **What is the intercept of the v-axis if $P = 300$?**

3. **What is the intercept on the v-axis if $P = 600$?**

4. **Your teacher will give you a copy of the feasible region. Draw 5 profit lines corresponding to 5 different values of P.**

Observe that as P increases, the profit line moves parallel to itself upward to the right. Also note that all of these profit lines have a slope of $-\frac{5}{3}$ while the slope of $v + c = 2000$ has a slope of -1. It follows that the profit lines are steeper in the negative direction than the line $v + c = 2000$. These ideas are illustrated in Display 5.32.

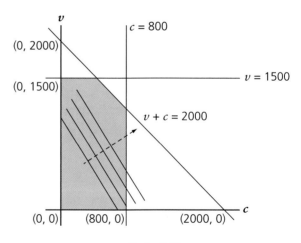

Display 5.32

The arrow in Display 5.32 indicates the direction of increasing profit. It is to our benefit to move these profit lines up and to the right as far as possible, remembering that we cannot leave the feasible region. The dark profit line in Display 5.33 is the best line that can be drawn.

The only point in the feasible region touched by this line is the point of intersection of the line $v + c = 2000$ and the line $c = 800$. This point of intersection is the point $(800, 1200)$. It follows that the optimal feasible solution to our problem is given by $c = 800$ and $v = 1200$. These values give a profit of 76,000 cents or $760.

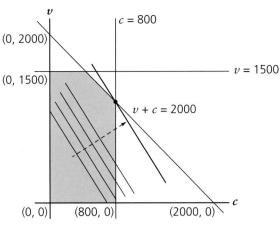

Display 5.33

1. **What would the optimal feasible solution be if the profit on a quart of vanilla ice cream is 50 cents and the profit on a quart of chocolate ice cream is 30 cents? Use a graph to solve this problem.**

5.16

2. **An ice cream plant makes two flavors, vanilla and chocolate. The plant capacity is 1200 quarts per day, and the sales department says that it can sell any amount of vanilla—the maximum being 900 quarts—and any amount of chocolate—the maximum being 600 quarts. The profit per quart is 35 cents for vanilla and 50 cents for chocolate. The company wants to maximize the total profit. Find an optimal feasible solution using the graphical approach.**

Let's look at another problem. Although this new problem is slightly more complicated than the vanilla-chocolate problem, a pattern begins to appear in the solution of such problems.

Situation 2 A new housing development is being built near Bart's house. Bart has noticed that the construction workers often leave the site to buy lunch. Always on the lookout to earn money, Bart figures that he can make lunches for the workers and sell them at a profit. We will assume that there are enough workers, and Bart can sell all of the sandwiches that he can make.

Bart decides to make two types of lunches. The first lunch will have two sodas and one sandwich, and will be called the Thirsty Worker Lunch. The second type of lunch will have two sandwiches and one soda, and will be called the Hungry Worker Lunch. Bart plans to buy the fixings for the sandwiches

from a local deli for $3.00 per sandwich and sodas for $0.50 per can. He will sell the Thirsty Worker Lunches for $5.00 and the Hungry Worker Lunches for $8.00.

1. What is Bart's profit on each Thirsty Worker Lunch?

2. What is Bart's profit on each Hungry Worker Lunch?

5.17

But Bart has two problems. One, the deli doesn't open until 11:30 A.M., which is too late to make the lunches and have them ready for the workers. He figures he needs to buy his supplies the night before, but that means he needs to keep sandwiches and sodas cool all night. Bart's mother will let him store up to 24 sodas in the family refrigerator. Bart finds a cooler in the basement which will hold up to 21 sandwiches.

Bart's second problem is to decide how many Hungry Worker Lunches and how many Thirsty Worker Lunches he should prepare in order to make the most money.

1. Show that 3 Thirsty Worker Lunches and 5 Hungry Worker Lunches form a feasible solution to Bart's problem. What is the profit from this feasible solution?

5.18

2. Find another feasible solution to Bart's problem. What is the profit from your feasible solution? How does this profit compare with that of other students in the class? Do you think that your feasible solution is an optimal feasible solution? Explain.

In order to take a careful look at this problem, let x represent the number of Thirsty Worker Lunches and y the number of Hungry Worker Lunches that Bart prepares. Let P denote the associated profit. Bart's objective function is given by

$$P = 1.00x + 1.50y$$

Since Bart can store no more than 24 cans of soda, he has the constraint

$$2x + y \le 24$$

Also, Bart can store no more than 21 sandwiches, so he has the constraint

$$x + 2y \le 21$$

As always, in such problems, x and y cannot be negative, so

$$x, y \ge 0$$

Note that we abbreviate $x \ge 0$, $y \ge 0$ by $x, y \ge 0$.

A Linear Programming model for Bart's problem is thus given by

$$\text{maximize } P = 1.00x + 1.50y$$

$$\text{subject to}$$

$$2x + y \leq 24$$

$$x + 2y \leq 21$$

$$x, y \geq 0$$

1. In a coordinate plane, sketch a graph of the inequality $2x + y \leq 24$ clearly indicating the x and y intercepts.

2. In a coordinate plane, sketch a graph of the inequality $x + 2y \leq 21$ clearly indicating the x and y intercepts.

5.19

Remember that the inequalities $x, y \geq 0$ indicate that we are working in the 1st quadrant. A graph of the set of points (x, y) satisfying the constraints in Bart's model (that is, the feasible region) is given in Display 5.34.

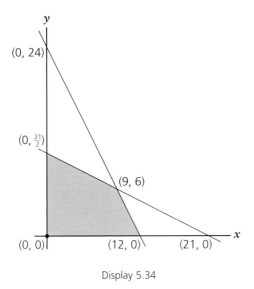

Display 5.34

How was the point $(9, 6)$ obtained in Display 5.34?

From our discussion of the vanilla-chocolate problem in Section 2, Bart is aware that the slopes of the boundary lines will be important.

1. **What is the slope of the straight line $2x + y = 24$?**

2. **What is the slope of the straight line $x + 2y = 21$?**

5.20

Information on the slopes of the boundary lines is included in Display 5.35. Slopes are designated with the letter m.

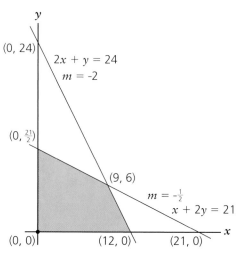

Display 5.35

We now return to Bart's objective function

$$P = 1.00x + 1.50y$$

or, solving for y,

$$y = -\frac{2}{3}x + \frac{2}{3}P$$

For a fixed value of P this is the equation of a straight line, which we call a *profit line*. The slope is $-\frac{2}{3}$ and the intercept on the y-axis is $\frac{2}{3}P$. Each different value of P gives a different profit line. For example, if $P = 6$, the line is

$$y = -\frac{2}{3}x + 4$$

If we change P to 9, the line is

$$y = -\frac{2}{3}x + 6$$

Observe that as P increases, the profit line moves parallel to itself upward to the right. Also note that all of these profit lines have a slope of $-\frac{2}{3}$. The boundary lines $2x + y = 24$ and $x + 2y = 21$ have slopes of -2 and $-\frac{1}{2}$, respectively. Thus, the profit lines are steeper, in the negative sense, than the line

$2x + y = 24$, but not as steep as the line $x + 2y = 21$. These ideas are illustrated in Display 5.36.

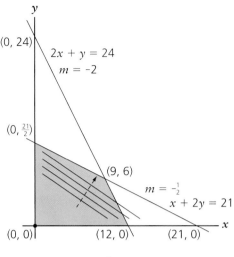

Display 5.36

The arrow in Display 5.36 indicates the direction of increasing profit. It is to Bart's benefit to move these profit lines up and to the right as far as possible, remembering that we cannot leave the feasible region. The dark profit line in Display 5.37 is the best line that can be drawn.

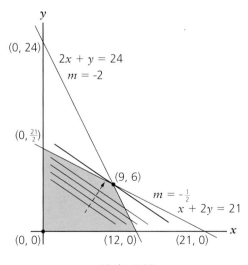

Display 5.37

The only point in the feasible region touched by this line is the point of intersection of the line $2x + y = 24$ and $x + 2y = 21$. This point of intersection is the point $(9, 6)$. It follows that the optimal feasible solution to Bart's problem is given by $x = 9$ and $y = 6$. These values give a profit of $18. That is, a maximum profit of $18 is obtained if Bart prepares and sells 9 Thirsty Worker Lunches and 6 Hungry Worker Lunches.

5.21

1. What would be the optimal feasible solution to Bart's problem if he made $3 profit on each Thirsty Worker Lunch and $1 profit on each Hungry Worker Lunch? (*Hint.* Look carefully at the slope of the profit lines.)

2. What would be the optimal feasible solution to Bart's problem if he made $1 profit on each Thirsty Worker Lunch and $3 profit on each Hungry Worker Lunch? (*Hint.* Look carefully at the slope of the profit lines. Does this optimal solution present any new difficulties for Bart?) Explain.

Problem Set: 5.3

1. Your teacher will give you a list of questions to answer about equations and inequalities. This list should help you review ideas about the graphs of inequalities.

2. The Pike Bike Company, a small manufacturing company, makes two types of bikes—regular 10-speed and deluxe 18-speed. The company can sell no more than 30 regular bikes and no more than 15 deluxe bikes per day. Frames for the bikes are made by machine. Each regular bike requires 1 hour of machine time while each deluxe bike requires 2 hours. The company has 5 machines, each of which can be operated for 8 hours a day. The profit on a regular 10-speed is $60 while the profit on a deluxe 18-speed is $80. The president of the Pike Bike Co. wants to know how many bikes of each type should be made each day in order to make the total profits as large as possible.

(a) Explain why the following model represents this problem:
Let R denote the number of regular bikes produced each day.
Let D denote the number of deluxe bikes produced each day.

$$\text{maximize } P = 60R + 80D$$

$$\text{subject to}$$

$$R \leq 30$$

$$D \leq 15$$

$$R + 2D \leq 40$$

$$R, D \geq 0$$

(b) Solve this problem graphically.

3. In order to improve the safety of their product, the Pike Bike Company has redesigned the regular 10-speed bike using a heavier metal. This redesign has caused the company's profit to decrease to $30 for each regular bike sold. The number of bikes the company is able to produce and all other information detailed in problem 2 remains the same.

Now that the redesign has been completed, the president of the company wants to know how many bikes of each type should be made each day in order to make the total profits as large as possible.

Your job is to write a report to the president showing:

(a) A model for this problem
(b) A graphical solution to the problem
(c) An explanation as to what happens to the solution of the problem as the profit changes.

4. The Hike-N-Bike Company, a small manufacturing company, makes two types of bikes—regular 10-speed and deluxe 18-speed. The company can sell no more than 40 regular bikes and no more than 20 deluxe bikes per day. Frames for the bikes are made by machine. Each regular bike requires 1 hour of machine time while each deluxe bike requires 2 hours. The company has 5 machines, each of which can be operated for 10 hours a day. The profit on a regular 10-speed is $60 while the profit on a deluxe 18-speed is $70. The president of the company wants to know how many bikes of each type should be made each day in order to make the total profits as large as possible.

(a) Set up a model for this problem
(b) Solve this problem graphically.

5.4 Linear Programming: An Algebraic Approach

Learning Outcomes

After studying this section, you will be able to:

Explain the meaning of *slack* in Linear Programming problems

Use dictionaries, instead of graphs, to solve Linear Programming problems

Solve Linear Programming problems with more than two variables.

About Words

One meaning of *slack* is "a part that is available but not used." For example, a rope is slack if it is not pulled tight; that is, if there is more rope than is needed.

In the previous section we looked at graphical methods of solving Linear Programming problems. In all cases, only two variables were involved so that graphs were a practical tool for solving such problems. However, it is seldom that one encounters a real problem with only two variables. In 1945, a mathematician, George Dantzig, developed a method for solving "big" Linear Programming problems. This method became known as the "simplex method" and in 1975, President Gerald Ford gave Dr. Dantzig a Presidential Award for his development of the simplex method. In this section we look at the basic ideas of this technique.

Let's return to Bart's problem in the previous section. Recall that the Linear Programming model for Bart's problem is

maximize $P = 1.00x + 1.50y$

subject to

$$2x + y \le 24$$

$$x + 2y \le 21$$

$$x, y \ge 0$$

In order to apply Dantzig's method we need to alter the model slightly. Consider the constraint

$$2x + y \le 24 \qquad \textbf{(1)}$$

Bart can store no more than 24 sodas. However, it is possible for him to purchase fewer than 24 sodas. For example, if Bart buys only 20 sodas, then there is room for 4 more and we say that there is a *slack* of 4 in constraint (1).

If Bart buys only 15 sodas, then there is a slack of 9 in constraint (1).

5.22

1. If Bart buys 14 sodas, what is the slack in constraint (1)?

2. If Bart buys 24 sodas, what is the slack in constraint (1)?

In general, if s_1 denotes the slack in constraint (1), then

$$2x + y + s_1 = 24$$

One can apply the same ideas to the constraint

$$x + 2y \leq 21 \qquad (2)$$

5.23

1. If Bart buys 15 sandwiches, what is the slack in constraint (2)?

2. If Bart buys 20 sandwiches, what is the slack in constraint (2)?

In general, if s_2 denotes the slack in constraint (2), then

$$x + 2y + s_2 = 21$$

Note that s_1 and s_2 cannot be negative, so s_1, $s_2 \geq 0$.

Our model now becomes

$$\text{maximize } P = 1.00x + 1.50y + 0s_1 + 0s_2$$

$$\text{subject to}$$

$$2x + y + s_1 = 24$$

$$x + 2y + s_2 = 21$$

$$x, y, s_1, s_2 \geq 0$$

The variables s_1 and s_2 are called *slack variables*. Note that in the objective function the coefficients of s_1 and s_2 are 0 since there is no profit from slack items.

Dantzig's idea was to begin by solving the constraint equations for the slack variables, leaving the objective or profit function unchanged. The result is called the *initial dictionary* and appears below

$$P = 1x + 1.5y$$

$$s_1 = 24 - 2x - y \qquad (3)$$

$$s_2 = 21 - x - 2y \qquad (4)$$

It is assumed that all variables are nonnegative. Variables on the left side of the constraint equations are called *basic variables*, while the variables on the right are called *nonbasic variables*. In other words, s_1 and s_2 are basic variables in the initial dictionary while x and y are nonbasic variables.

There is a feasible solution which can be seen from the initial dictionary. That solution is obtained by taking the nonbasic variables x and y to be 0. The complete solution is then given by $x = 0$, $y = 0$, $s_1 = 24$, and $s_2 = 21$ which yields $P = 0$. In other words, Bart does not make much profit by doing nothing.

Looking at the objective function, we see that we can increase the profit by producing whatever items x or y represent. However, each x item gives a profit of \$1 while each y item gives a larger profit of \$1.50. So let's start producing y items. It would be great if we could make $y = 1{,}000{,}000$ and make a profit of \$1,500,000.

5.24

1. **Why is it impossible for y to equal 1,000,000 in the initial dictionary?**

2. **Could y equal 15 in the initial dictionary?**

3. **What is the largest value of y that can occur in the initial dictionary?**

Our strategy depends on keeping x equal to 0 while we start producing y items. From equation (3) in the initial dictionary it is clear that y cannot get any larger than 24. Otherwise s_1 would be negative. Also, from equation (4) it is clear that y cannot get any larger than $\frac{21}{2}$, otherwise s_2 would be negative. The strongest restriction on y comes from equation (4) and Dantzig's method suggests that we solve equation (4) for y getting

$$y = \frac{21}{2} - \frac{1}{2}x - \frac{1}{2}s_2 \qquad (5)$$

Equation (5) now replaces equation (4) in the initial dictionary. Moreover, we must substitute the expression for y given in (5) into the objective function and into constraint equation (3). The result, given below, is called the *first dictionary.*

$$P = \frac{63}{4} + \frac{1}{4}x - \frac{3}{4}s_2$$

$$s_1 = \frac{27}{2} - \frac{3}{2}x + \frac{1}{2}s_2 \qquad (6)$$

$$y = \frac{21}{2} - \frac{1}{2}x - \frac{1}{2}s_2 \qquad (7)$$

first dictionary

1. Show the algebra used to obtained the first two lines of the first dictionary.

2. What are the basic variables in the first dictionary? Note that y and s_2 have changed positions in the constraint equation.

3. What are the nonbasic variables in the first dictionary?

5.25

By taking the nonbasic variables equal to 0, the first dictionary gives a feasible solution of $x=0$, $y=\frac{21}{2}$, $s_1=\frac{27}{2}$, $s_2=0$, and a corresponding $P=\frac{63}{4}$.

Looking at the objective function in the first dictionary, the coefficient of x is positive, thus it appears we can still increase the profit by producing some of the x items.

1. Is it possible for x to equal 1000 in the first dictionary? Why?

2. Is it possible for x to equal 20 in the first dictionary? Why?

5.26

By keeping $s_2=0$, equation (6) indicates that x cannot get any larger than 9, otherwise s_1 would be negative. Equation (7) indicates that x cannot get any larger than 21, otherwise s_2 would be negative. Thus, the strongest restriction on x comes from equation (6) and Dantzig's method suggests that we solve equation (6) for x getting

$$x = 9 - \frac{2}{3}s_1 + \frac{1}{3}s_2 \qquad (8)$$

Equation (8) replaces equation (6) in the first dictionary. Moreover, we must substitute the expression for x given in (8) into the objective function and into constraint equation (7). The result is called the *second dictionary* which appears below.

$$P = 18 - \frac{1}{6}s_1 - \frac{2}{3}s_2$$

$$x = 9 - \frac{2}{3}s_1 + \frac{1}{3}s_2$$

$$y = 6 + \frac{1}{3}s_1 - \frac{2}{3}s_2$$

second dictionary

5.27

1. Show the algebra used to obtain the first and third lines of the second dictionary.

2. What are the basic variables in the second dictionary?

3. What are the nonbasic variables in the second dictionary?

4. By taking the nonbasic variables equal to 0, what is the feasible solution obtained from the second dictionary?

There are no positive coefficients in the objective function, so it would appear that no further increase in the profit is possible. The theory developed by Dantzig indicates that the solution obtained in the second dictionary of this problem is indeed an optimal feasible solution. This method, using dictionaries, can be applied to problems which involve many more than two variables. However, the computation is tedious and is usually not an enjoyable activity, so computer programs have been written to solve these problems. One such program appears in Appendix D which is titled Linear Programming With Excel.

Although the dictionary method described above does not make use of graphs, it can be instructive to see how the dictionaries relate to a graph. From Section 3, the feasible region for Bart's problem is shown by Display 5.38.

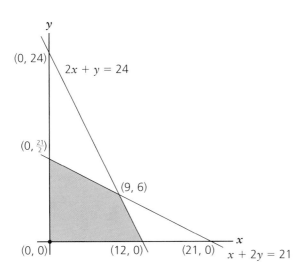

Display 5.38

Our initial dictionary gave the feasible solution $x = 0$, $y = 0$. The first dictionary gave the feasible solution $x = 0$, $y = \dfrac{21}{2}$ and the second (final) dictionary gave the optimal feasible solution $x = 9$, $y = 6$. Display 5.39 illustrates the path dictated by the dictionaries.

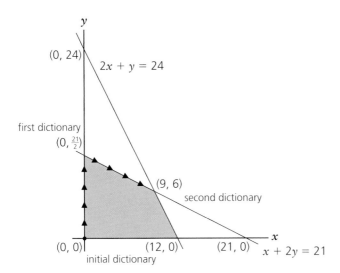

Display 5.39

In order to become more familiar with the language and ideas of Linear Programming, consider the following:

$$\text{maximize } P = 1x + 5y$$

subject to the constraints

$$3x + 7y \leq 420$$

$$2x + 8y \leq 400$$

$$x, y \geq 0$$

When slack variables are introduced, the problem becomes

$$\text{maximize } P = 1x + 5y$$

such that

$$3x + 7y + s_1 = 420$$

$$2x + 8y + s_2 = 400$$

The initial dictionary is given by

$$P = 1x + 5y$$

$$s_1 = 420 - 3x - 7y$$

$$s_2 = 400 - 2x - 8y$$

5.28

1. What are the basic variables in the initial dictionary?

2. What are the nonbasic variables in the initial dictionary?

3. What is the feasible solution obtained from the initial dictionary?

4. How can we tell that we should go on to the next dictionary?

5. By looking at the objective function in the initial dictionary, which variable do you want to become a basic variable? Explain.

6. Explain, algebraically, why the following dictionary is the (next) first dictionary:

$$P = 250 - \frac{1}{4}x - \frac{5}{8}s_2$$

$$s_1 = 70 - \frac{5}{4}x + \frac{7}{8}s_2$$

$$y = 50 - \frac{1}{4}x - \frac{1}{8}s_2$$

7. What are the nonbasic variables in the first dictionary?

8. What feasible solution is obtained from the first dictionary?

9. What does it mean to have $s_1 = 70$ in a feasible solution?

10. Explain why there is no need to go on to another (second) dictionary.

11. What is an optimal feasible solution?

Now that you're familiar with the language and ideas of Linear Programming, here are two examples for you to put the process to work:

5.29

1. The Nycon Camera Co. produces two well-known 35 millimeter cameras—the F1 and the F2. The production process involves two assembly lines. The production time requirements in the two assembly lines for each camera, the weekly production capacities in the assembly lines, and the profit on each type of camera are given in Display 5.40.

	Time Requirements		Production Capacity
	Nycon F1	Nycon F2	
Assembly Line 1	3 hours	3 hours	90 hours
Assembly Line 2	2 hours	4 hours	80 hours
Profit per camera	$400	$500	

Display 5.40

Use the graphical method to find how many of each type of camera should be produced each week in order to maximize the total profit.

2. Solve the preceding problem using dictionaries instead of graphs.

It should be clear that the dictionary method is a tedious process. Many real-world problems have hundreds, or even thousands, of variables. This is why computers are used to solve big Linear Programming problems. Proving that the dictionary method, and extensions of it, will always work with big problems, required a deep understanding of the mathematics involved. This is what earned Dr. Dantzig a Presidential Award.

Problem Set: 5.4

1. Bart's business is growing. He now decides to make a third type of lunch with 2 sandwiches and 2 sodas, called a Super Lunch. The Super Lunch will sell for $8.75 so that Bart's profit on each Super Lunch is $1.75. Let z represent the number of Super Lunches, with x and y being used to represent the number of other types of lunches as before. Set up a model for this problem. Find an optimal feasible solution using dictionaries.

2. The Pike Bike Company, a small manufacturing company, makes two types of bikes—regular 10-speed and deluxe 18-speed. The company can sell no more than 30 regular bikes and no more than 15 deluxe bikes per day. Frames for the bikes are made by machine. Each regular bike requires 1 hour of machine time, while each deluxe bike requires 2 hours. The company has 5 machines, each of which can be operated for 8 hours a day. The profit on a regular 10-speed is $30 while the profit on a deluxe 18-speed is $80. The president of the Pike Bike Co. wants to know how many bikes of each type should be made each day in order to make the total profits as large as possible.

    (a) Use dictionaries to solve this problem.
    (b) Find the solution to the problem using a graphical approach.
    (c) Does your solution using dictionaries agree with your solution using graphical methods? Explain.

5.5 Transportation Problems

In 1988, North American Van Lines (a moving company) began using mathematics to assign loads and routes to drivers. As a result, the company was able to provide better service to customers and reduced costs by 2.5 million dollars per year. Roadnet, a company that works with United Parcel Service (UPS), also uses mathematics to assign routes to drivers that are delivering packages. In this section, we shall look at situations which involve many of the same ingredients. You will see that many ideas from Linear Programming are blended into the mathematics.

Situation A dealer owns 70 carloads (cars on a train) of grain in Kansas City and 40 carloads in Chicago. The dealer has orders for 30 carloads from a baking company in Hartford, Connecticut, 46 carloads from a customer in Baltimore, Maryland, and 34 carloads from a customer in Atlanta, Georgia. The freight rates, in dollars per carload, to the various cities are given in Display 5.41.

From↓ To→	Hartford	Baltimore	Atlanta
Kansas City	84	65	74
Chicago	78	60	83

Display 5.41

Learning Outcomes

After studying this section you will be able to:

Find feasible solutions to transportation problems

Use ideas from Linear Programming to solve transportation problems

Solve small transportation problems with the aid of graphs and *cost lines*.

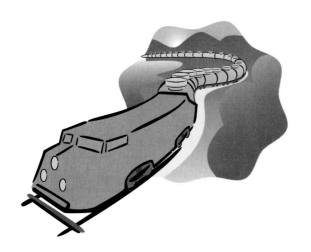

We can also model this situation in terms of a graph similar to that in Display 5.42.

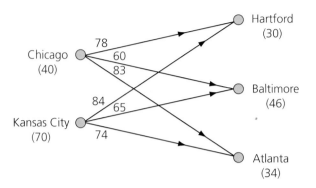

Display 5.42

For example, it costs $65 to ship a carload of grain for a shipment from Kansas City to Baltimore. Different train connections lead to rates which are not proportional to the distance between the cities. Note that the number of carloads of grain which has been ordered (110) is exactly the same as the number of carloads of grain in storage (110). In practice, this is not necessarily the case, but the ideas which we shall pursue are similar to both types of problems.

In order to begin finding feasible solutions and the associated costs, it helps to formulate a table similar to that in Display 5.43.

Quantity in ↓ Storage	To → From ↓	Quantity Needed → 30 Hartford	46 Baltimore	34 Atlanta
40	Kansas City	84	65	74
70	Chicago	78	60	83

Display 5.43

A feasible solution is obtained by substituting appropriate numbers for x, y, z, u, v, and w in Display 5.44. Note that x denotes the number of carloads shipped from Kansas City to Hartford, y the number of carloads shipped from Kansas City to Baltimore, etc.

Quantity in ↓ Storage	Quantity Needed → To → From	30 Hartford		46 Baltimore		34 Atlanta	
40	Kansas City	x	84	y	65	z	74
70	Chicago	u	78	v	60	w	83

Display 5.44

The set of numbers in Display 5.45 is appropriate and does form a feasible solution.

Quantity in ↓ Storage	Quantity Needed → To → From	30 Hartford		46 Baltimore		34 Atlanta	
40	Kansas City	10	84	10	65	20	74
70	Chicago	20	78	36	60	14	83

Display 5.45

The cost associated with this feasible solution is obtained from the following calculations:

$$10(84) + 10(65) + 20(74) + 20(78) + 36(60) + 14(83) = 7{,}852.00 \text{ (dollars)}$$

5.5 Transportation Problems

The set of numbers in Display 5.46 does not form a feasible solution. Why?

5.30

Quantity Needed →		30	46	34
Quantity in ↓ Storage	To → From ↓	Hartford	Baltimore	Atlanta
40	Kansas City	20 · 84	20 · 65	10 · 74
70	Chicago	10 · 78	26 · 60	24 · 83

Display 5.46

5.31

1. Write a set of rules for forming feasible solutions to the Situation at the beginning of this section.

2. Using your set of rules, find three different feasible solutions and calculate the cost of each. Which of your feasible solutions is the best? Do you think your best feasible solution is an optimal feasible solution? Why?

Quantity Needed →		30	46	34
Quantity in ↓ Storage	To → From ↓	Hartford	Baltimore	Atlanta
40	Kansas City	x · 84	y · 65	z · 74
70	Chicago	u · 78	v · 60	w · 83

Display 5.47

We can now describe our problem in the following way. Given the information in Display 5.47, find the number of carloads x, y, z, u, v, and w to fit into the six boxes so that three conditions are met.

Condition 1 The amounts in the first row add up to 40 and the amounts in the second row add up to 70. That is,

$$x + y + z = 40 \qquad (1)$$

and

$$u + v + w = 70 \qquad (2)$$

Condition 2 The amounts in the first, second, and third columns add up to 30, 46, and 34, respectively. That is,

$$x + u = 30 \qquad (3)$$

$$y + v = 46 \qquad (4)$$

and

$$z + w = 34 \qquad (5)$$

Condition 3 The total transportation cost is a minimum.

Conditions 1 and 2 ensure a feasible solution. It is Condition 3 that produces an optimal feasible solution. We might try guessing and come up with a solution. However, a systematic approach is more powerful since problems with more shipping points and more destinations require an immense number of calculations. A computer would be needed and a set of rules (algorithm) must be given to the computer to do the calculations (see Appendix D—Linear Programming With Excel).

Begin by observing that the number of carloads shipped from Chicago to Hartford, designated u, must be $30 - x$. That is $u = 30 - x$. This also follows directly from equation (3). Similarly, from equation (4), $v = 46 - y$.

The amount from Kansas City to Atlanta, denoted z, must be $40 - x - y$ if the total out of Kansas City is to be 40. That is, $z = 40 - x - y$. This result also follows from equation (1). Display 5.48 summarizes our results at this point.

	Quantity Needed →	30	46	34
Quantity in ↓ Storage	To → From ↓	Hartford	Baltimore	Atlanta
40	Kansas City	x 84	y 65	$40 - x - y$ 74
70	Chicago	$30 - x$ 78	$46 - y$ 60	w 83

Display 5.48

Now, the number of carloads from Chicago to Atlanta, designated w, must then be $34 - (40 - x - y) = x + y - 6$. Display 5.49 includes this information.

	Quantity Needed →	30	46	34
Quantity in ↓ Storage	To → From ↓	Hartford	Baltimore	Atlanta
40	Kansas City	x 84	y 65	$40 - x - y$ 74
70	Chicago	$30 - x$ 78	$46 - y$ 60	$x + y - 6$ 83

Display 5.49

There are constraints which will become part of our model. Each of the entries in Display 5.49 must be positive or zero. One cannot ship negative carloads of grain. Thus, we have the following constraints:

$$x \geq 0$$

$$y \geq 0$$

$$40 - x - y \geq 0$$

$$30 - x \geq 0$$

$$46 - y \geq 0$$

$$x + y - 6 \geq 0$$

Our objective is to minimize the total cost C. In this case

$$C = 84x + 65y + 74(40 - x - y) + 78$$
$$(30 - x) + 60(46 - y) + 83(x + y - 6)$$

or be able to explain how the following is obtained:

$$C = 15x + 14y + 7562$$

Our model for this transportation problem, in terms of x and y, can be written

$$\text{minimize } C = 15x + 14y + 7562$$

such that

$$x \geq 0$$

$$y \geq 0$$

$$x + y \leq 40$$

$$x \leq 30$$

$$y \leq 46$$

$$x + y \geq 6$$

1. **Set up a model for the transportation problem in Display 5.50.**

5.32

Quantity in ↓ Storage	To ——→ From ↓	Quantity Needed ——→		
		35	65	30
		Hartford	Baltimore	Atlanta
90	Kansas City	84	65	74
40	Chicago	78	60	83

Display 5.50

2. **Set up a model for the transportation problem in Display 5.51.**

Quantity Needed →		72		28	
Quantity in ↓ Storage	To → From ↓	Hartford		Baltimore	
30	Kansas City		84		65
50	Chicago		78		60
20	St. Louis		92		55

Display 5.51

Return to the model representing our original **Situation** (first page of this section).

$$\text{minimize } C = 15x + 14y + 7562$$

such that

$$x \geq 0$$

$$y \geq 0$$

$$x + y \leq 40$$

$$x \leq 30$$

$$y \leq 46$$

$$x + y \geq 6$$

Our goal is to solve this problem graphically. We begin by noting that the first two constraints inform us that we are only interested in the first quadrant of a coordinate plane. The shaded region (including points on the boundary) in Display 5.52 represents the intersection of the set of points (x, y) satisfying the remaining inequalities. This shaded region is the feasible region for this problem.

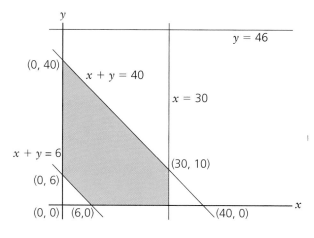

Display 5.52

The objective function

$$C = 15x + 14y + 7562$$

can be written

$$y = -\frac{15}{14}x + \frac{(C - 7562)}{14} \qquad (6)$$

For a fixed value of C, this equation represents a straight line, called a **cost line** with a slope $-\frac{15}{14}$ and a y-intercept of $\frac{(C - 7562)}{14}$.

> **A Phrase to Know:** A **cost line** is a straight line in a coordinate plane along which cost is a constant.

For example, if $C = 7590$, equation (6) becomes

$$y = -\frac{15}{14}x + 2 \qquad (7)$$

Similarly, if $C = 7576$, equation (6) becomes

$$y = -\frac{15}{14}x + 1 \qquad (8)$$

Graphs of equations (7) and (8) appear in Display 5.53.

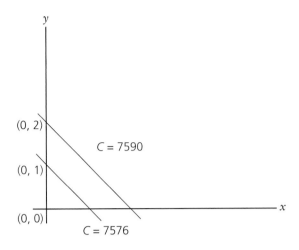

Display 5.53

Observe that as C gets smaller (decreases), the cost lines move down and to the left as illustrated in Display 5.54.

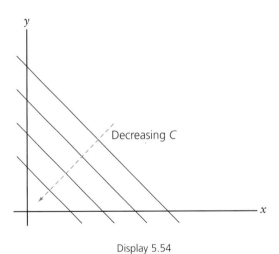

Display 5.54

In the feasible region, Display 5.55, the lines $x + y = 6$ and $x + y = 40$ both have a slope of -1. Since the cost lines all have a slope of $-\frac{15}{14}$, the cost lines will be steeper than either of these two boundary lines in the feasible region. Hence, if we add cost lines to our feasible region, the result would be similar to that of Display 5.55.

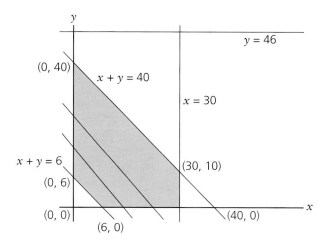

Display 5.55

Remember that we want to minimize C which means we want to move these cost lines down and to the left as far as possible without leaving the feasible region. It should be clear that the last point in the feasible region which is on a cost line is the point $(0, 6)$. This information is illustrated in Display 5.56.

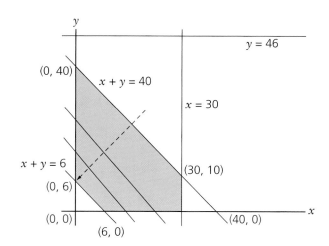

Display 5.56

An optimal feasible solution is obtained by taking $x = 0$ and $y = 6$. It is now easy to fill in the transportation schedule

Display 5.57 with the numbers representing the optimal feasible solution obtaining Display 5.58.

	Quantity Needed →	30	46	34
Quantity in ↓ Storage	To → From ↓	Hartford	Baltimore	Atlanta
40	Kansas City	x · 84	y · 65	$40 - x - y$ · 74
70	Chicago	$30 - x$ · 78	$46 - y$ · 60	$x + y - 6$ · 83

Display 5.57

	Quantity Needed →	30	46	34
Quantity in ↓ Storage	To → From ↓	Hartford	Baltimore	Atlanta
40	Kansas City	0 · 84	6 · 65	34 · 74
70	Chicago	30 · 78	40 · 60	0 · 83

Display 5.58

The cost of this schedule is given by

$$C = 0(84) + 6(65) + 34(74) + 30(78) + 40(60) + 0(83)$$

or

$$C = 7{,}646 \text{ dollars}$$

Problem Set: 5.5

1. Solve the transportation problem in Display 5.59 using a graphical approach.

Quantity in ↓ Storage	To → From ↓	Quantity Needed →	35	65	30
			Hartford	Baltimore	Atlanta
90	Kansas City		84	65	74
40	Chicago		78	60	83

Display 5.59

2. Solve the transportation problem in Display 5.60 using a graphical approach.

Quantity in ↓ Storage	To → From ↓	Quantity Needed →	72	28
			Hartford	Baltimore
30	Kansas City		84	65
50	Chicago		78	60
20	St. Louis		92	55

Display 5.60

3. Seldon Oil Company has 200,000 barrels of oil stored in Kuwait (on the Persian Gulf), 150,000 barrels stored in Galveston, Texas, and 100,000 barrels stored in Caracas, Venezuela. A customer in New York would like to buy 250,000 barrels and a customer in London would like to buy the remaining 200,000 barrels. The shipping cost, in cents per barrel, are shown in Display 5.61. Find the shipment schedule with the minimum cost using a graphical approach.

From ↓ To →	Kuwait	Galveston	Caracas
New York	48	20	28
London	44	32	35

Display 5.61

4. Mr. Kawi, president of the Seldon Oil Company asks his new manager whether he has a better way to solve transportation problems without using a graph. The manager thinks he does have a better way and uses the following example to illustrate his method:

	Quantity Needed →	15	5	5
Quantity in ↓ Storage	To → From ↓	Hartford	Baltimore	Atlanta
10	Kansas City	6	7	8
15	Chicago	15	80	78

Display 5.62

(a) Look for the lowest shipment cost. In this case, the lowest cost is $6 for one carload from Kansas City to Hartford. The manager says to put the largest number possible into that slot. In this case that number is 10. See Display 5.63.

	Quantity Needed →	15	5	5
Quantity in ↓ Storage	To → From ↓	Hartford	Baltimore	Atlanta
10	Kansas City	10	6	7	8
15	Chicago		15	80	78

Display 5.63

This means that the other two slots in the first row must be 0 since there are no more items left in storage at Kansas City. See Display 5.64.

	Quantity Needed →	15	5	5
Quantity in ↓ Storage	To → From ↓	Hartford	Baltimore	Atlanta
10	Kansas City	10	6	0	7	0	8
15	Chicago		15	80	78

Display 5.64

(b) Continue looking for the lowest shipment costs until the schedule is complete.

What is the final schedule using the manager's method? What is the cost of this schedule?

Do you think that the manager's method gives an optimal feasible solution? Explain.

What is an optimal feasible solution to this problem?

5.6 Introduction to Graph Theory: Trees That Bear Fruit

Learning Outcomes

After studying this section, you will be able to:

Explain what is meant by a *graph* with *vertices* and *edges*

Explain the importance of *weighted graphs, connected graphs, cycles,* and *minimal spanning trees* in solving real-world problems

Use graphs as a tool to solve real-world problems.

In previous sections of this chapter you have seen many ways of doing something better and, in some cases, how to do something the best way. The techniques discussed, such as Dynamic Programming and Linear Programming, are called *optimization techniques*. Optimization techniques form a foundation for a great deal of the interest and research in contemporary mathematics.

Much mathematics, discovered since World War II, was stimulated by computers and the needs of society. Problems in communication, manufacturing, ecology, energy conservation, and medicine extended mathematics known at that time and led to new areas of mathematics. One such area is *Graph Theory.* In this section we will look at a small, but important, piece of this topic.

Consider the following situation:

Situation The United Nations is helping a developing country build roads connecting eight cities. The result should enable people in any city to travel to any other city either directly or through other cities. The director wishes to minimize the total cost involved. The cities will be designated A, B, C, D, E, F, G and H. The cost, in millions of dollars, of constructing roads between certain pairs of cities is given in the following list.

A and B:	7	D and E:	1
A and C:	9	D and F:	2
B and D:	14	E and G:	5
C and D:	5	F and G:	4
C and F:	3	G and H:	5

For example, a road joining city B and city D would cost $14,000,000. Some direct roads, such as A and D, are missing because they are too expensive.

1. Why could costs be so variable?

2. Why might some roads be too expensive?

5.33

Solving problems like this from such a list can be difficult and confusing, especially if the problem involves many more cities and a much larger list. When thinking about joining cities, one might think of taking a trip and using maps. On a map, cities are usually represented by dots. Roads between the cities are normally illustrated with lines. In the spirit of a map, one might use dots to represent the cities, A, B, C, D, E, F, G and H, as in Display 5.65.

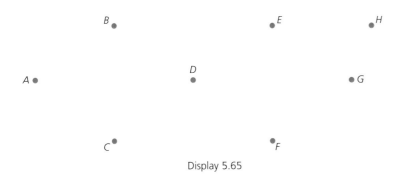

Display 5.65

In addition, the possible direct roads from our list could be represented by line segments connecting the appropriate dots, as in Display 5.66.

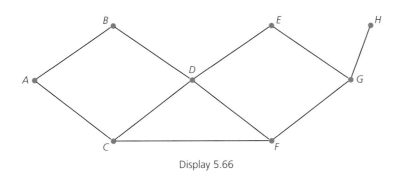

Display 5.66

Note that not all pairs of cities are connected with line segments. For example, D and G are not connected with a line segment since this pair of cities does not appear in our list.

The diagram in Display 5.66 is an example of a **graph**. The points A, B, C, D, E, F, G, and H are called **vertices** of the graph. Line segments which connect vertices, such as AB and BD, are called **edges**.

1. **List two other edges of the graph in Display 5.66**
2. **Why is the segment AD not an edge of the graph in Display 5.66?**

5.34

It is useful to go one step further and indicate the costs of each connection, a connection now being an edge on the graph. The resulting diagram is called a *weighted graph* and appears in Display 5.67.

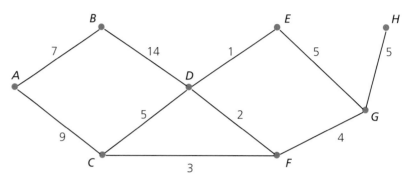

Display 5.67

One way of constructing the roads for this problem could be the connections shown in Display 5.68.

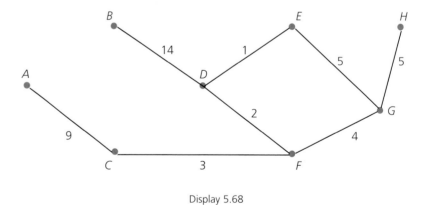

Display 5.68

Note that all of the cities are connected. That is, from any city there is a way to travel to any other city.

1. What is the total cost of constructing the lines in Display 5.68?

5.35

2. Can you remove one edge from the graph in Display 5.68 and still have a system of roads that connects all the cities? If so, what is the total cost of constructing the roads that remain in the graph? Is there more than one way to accomplish this task?

Another way of constructing the roads for this problem could be the connections shown in Display 5.69.

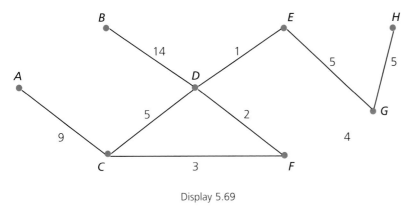

Display 5.69

Again note that all of the cities are connected. From any city there is a way to travel to any other city.

1. What is the total cost of constructing the roads in Display 5.69?

5.36

2. Can you remove one edge from the graph in Display 5.69 and still have a system of roads that connects all the cities? If so, what is the total cost of constructing the roads that remain in the graph? Is there more than one way to accomplish this task?

3. How can one tell, by looking at a graph, when an edge can be removed so that the remaining roads will enable one to travel from any city to every other city?

4. Make a graph for this problem which enables one to travel from any city to every other city, and for which you think the cost is as low as possible. A graph for the problem is repeated in Display 5.70.

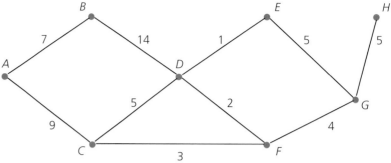

Display 5.70

What is the cost of constructing the roads represented in your graph? How does your cost compare with that of other students in the class? How would you explain to another student the method you used in constructing your graph?

It can be useful to formalize some of the ideas we have been discussing. First, a **graph** consists of the following: a set of points called **vertices** and a set of lines called **edges** that connect pairs (not necessarily all pairs) of vertices. The edges need not be straight line segments. Several graphs are shown in Display 5.71.

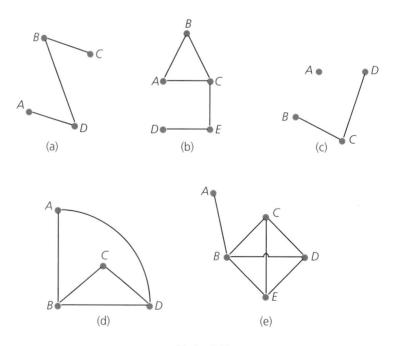

Display 5.71

Note that the half circle on the edge connecting vertices B and D in graph (e) indicates that there is no vertex at the crossing of edges CE and BD. This convention is frequently used in electrical circuit diagrams.

Describe any similarities and any differences that you observe in the five graphs of Display 5.71.

5.37

In the situation discussed at the beginning of this section, we wanted our solution to be a graph that connected the cities A, B, C, D, E, F, G and H in Display 5.72 in such a way that one could travel from any city to every other city.

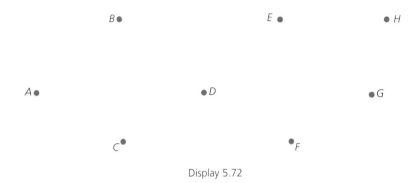

Display 5.72

In this spirit, a graph is said to be **connected** if we can reach any vertex from any other by traveling along the edges. For example, in Display 5.73, graph (a) is connected while graph (b) is not connected.

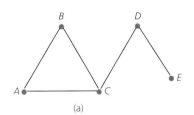 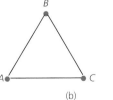 

Display 5.73

1. **Which of the graphs in Display 5.71 are connected?**

2. **Draw two graphs, each having 8 vertices, such that one is connected and the other is not connected.**

5.38

Suppose one wanted to connect three cities, A, B, and C, with roads (the costs in millions of dollars) as given in Display 5.74.

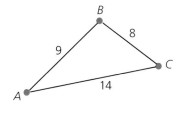

Display 5.74

Our objective is to be able to travel from any city to every other city.

5.39

1. Do we need all three roads, AB, BC, and CA which appear in Display 5.74? Why or why not?

2. What is the least costly way to connect the cities in Display 5.74?

The previous example suggests the following definition: A **cycle** is a path of edges in a graph that starts and ends at the same vertex but does not pass through any edge or vertex, other than the starting point, more than once. Note that a cycle need not include every vertex of the graph. The graph in Display 5.75 has a cycle.

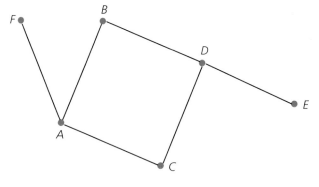

Display 5.75

In particular, by starting at A and then proceeding consecutively to C, D, B, and back to A, one obtains a cycle.

1. Draw a graph with 8 vertices that contains a cycle.

2. Draw a graph with 5 vertices that does not contain a cycle.

5.40

3. Which of the graphs in Display 5.71 contain a cycle?

Mathematicians have combined two of the concepts introduced in this section into the following definition: A **tree** is a connected graph with no cycles.

1. Which of the graphs in Display 5.76 are trees?

5.41

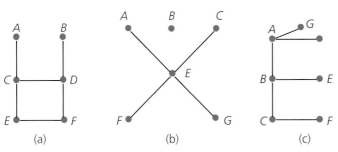

Display 5.76

2. Draw trees with 2, 3, 4, 5, and 6 vertices.

3. Is the graph in Display 5.77 a tree? Be careful.

Display 5.77

Finally, we return to our problem (the **Situation**). We want to find a connected graph containing the vertices A, B, C, D, E, F, G and H in Display 5.78.

Display 5.78

Moreover, the graph we seek can only contain edges from the weighted graph given in Display 5.79.

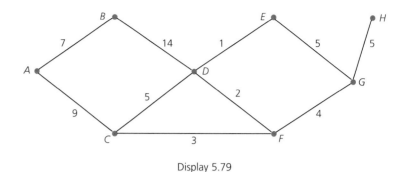

Display 5.79

The previous discussion and problems suggest that our final graph should contain no cycles, otherwise an edge (which costs money) can be removed and the remaining edges still connect the cities. For example, in the graph of Display 5.80, the road system DCF forms a cycle, and we could eliminate one of the sides, say DF, with the remaining sides still connecting the cities.

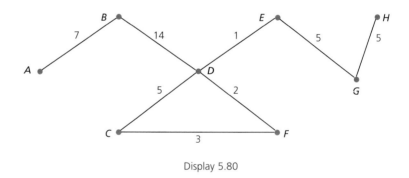

Display 5.80

Thus we are looking for a graph with vertices A, B, C, D, E, F, G, and H, using the edges of Display 5.80, which is a tree for which the cost is minimum.

5.42

1. Find a tree with vertices A, B, C, D, E, F, G and H, using the edges of Display 5.80. What would be the cost of constructing the roads in your tree?

2. How does the cost of your tree compare with that of the trees of other students in the class? Do you think that your tree provides a minimum cost for constructing the roads? Why?

In 1956, mathematician Joseph Kruskal developed a set of rules (an algorithm) for solving such problems and proved that it will always work. You may have already discovered such a set of rules. Kruskal's process involves the following steps, which refer to Display 5.81:

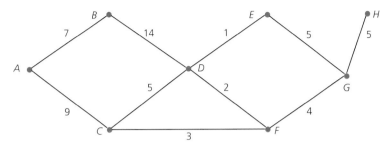

Display 5.81

Step 1 In Display 5.81, the smallest number on an edge is 1. This number is road DE, so DE is going to appear in our final graph (Display 5.82).

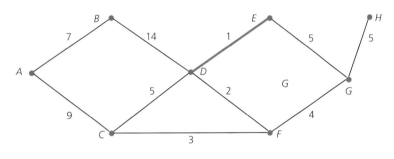

Display 5.82

Step 2 Of the remaining numbers on edges, 2 is the smallest. Thus, include DF in the final graph (Display 5.83).

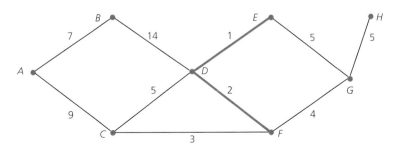

Display 5.83

Step 3 Of the remaining numbers on the edges, 3 is the smallest, so include CF in the final graph (Display 5.84).

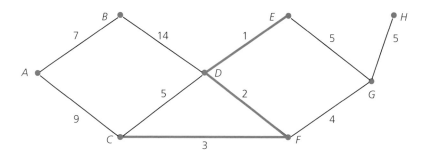

Display 5.84

Step 4 Of the remaining numbers on the edges, 4 is the smallest. The number 4 appears on the edge FG. Thus, FG will appear in the final graph (Display 5.85).

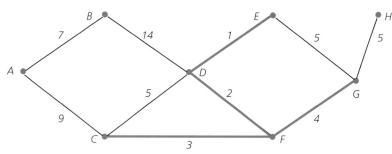

Display 5.85

Step 5 Of the remaining numbers on the edges (not already considered) the smallest is 5 which appear on the edges CD, EG, and GH. However, CD and EG will create cycles. Thus, we include GH for our final graph (Display 5.86).

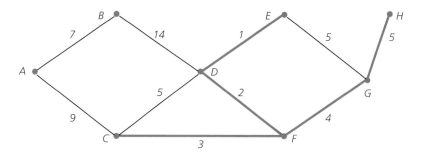

Display 5.86

Final Steps Of the numbers on edges not previously considered, the smallest number is 7 which appears on the side AB. Thus AB should be included in our final graph. Finally, we take the next smaller number, which is 9, and include AC (Display 5.87).

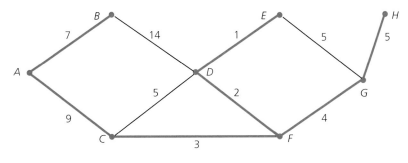

Display 5.87

STOP All the cities are connected by roads. It is possible to travel from any city to every other city. The final graph with the chosen edges appears in Display 5.88.

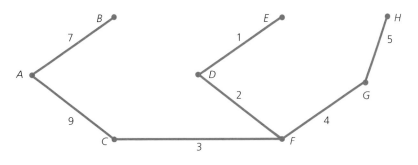

Display 5.88

The total cost to construct this set of roads is $31,000,000. According to Kruskal's algorithm, this cost is the minimum cost of building the roads. The graph in Display 5.88 is called a *minimal spanning tree*, since it is a tree that minimizes the sum of the weights on the edges and "spans" (includes) all of the vertices.

Problem Set: 5.6

1. A telephone company intends to establish communications for the first time in 7 villages (designated A, B, C, D, E, F, and G) in a developing area of South America. Each village must be able to communicate with any other village, either directly or through other villages. The weighted graph in Display 5.89 represents the problem. The numbers on the edges are estimates of the costs, in millions of dollars, of

constructing links between villages. Some links are missing because they are excessively expensive. The company wants to establish the communications at the smallest construction cost. Find a minimal spanning tree for solving this problem. What is the minimum cost?

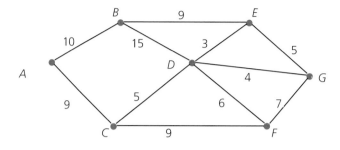

Display 5.89

2. Find a minimal spanning tree for the weighted graph in Display 5.90.

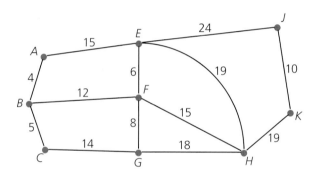

Display 5.90

3. Show that the weighted graph in Display 5.91 has two distinct minimal spanning trees.

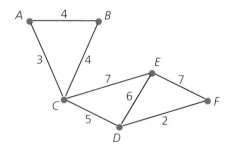

Display 5.91

4. List at least three uses, other than roads or telephone lines, where graphs and minimal spanning trees might be used to solve real-world problems.

5.7 Introduction to Geometric Programming: A Quality Inequality

Learning Outcomes

After studying this section, you will be able to:

Derive the basic arithmetic-geometric mean inequality using geometric methods

Derive the basic arithmetic-geometric mean inequality using algebraic methods

Use arithmetic-geometric mean inequalities to solve optimization problems.

People who work in the field of optimization have many different tools available for solving problems. You have seen several of these tools in the previous sections of this chapter. Some of the tools are relatively new and some are old. Geometric Programming is a relatively new area based on mathematics that is quite old. The purpose of this section is to examine classic inequalities basic to this area and demonstrate how they are used.

Let's begin with some questions involving the rectangle of Display 5.93.

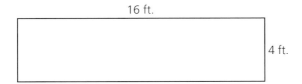

Display 5.93

5.43

1. What is the area of this rectangle?

2. What is the length of the side of a square which has the same area?

3. Which figure, the rectangle in question 1 or the square in question 2, has the smaller perimeter?

Now let's do the same thing for the rectangle in Display 5.94.

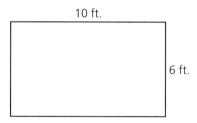

10 ft.

6 ft.

Display 5.94

5.44

1. What is the area of this rectangle?

2. What is the length of the side of a square which has the same area? Use a calculator and give your answer rounded to two decimal places.

3. Which figure, the rectangle in 1 or the square in 2, has the smaller perimeter?

Suppose one follows this procedure for the general rectangle given in Display 5.95.

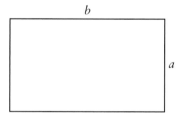

b

a

Display 5.95

5.45

1. What is the area of this rectangle?

2. What is the length of the side of a square which has the same area?

3. Which figure, the rectangle in 1 or the square in 2, do you think has the smaller perimeter? Why?

The correct answer to question 2 above is known as the **geometric mean** of the two nonnegative numbers a and b.

In order to answer question 3, it appears one needs to be able to compare

$$2a + 2b \quad \text{and} \quad 4\sqrt{ab}$$

or equivalently, compare

$$a + b \quad \text{and} \quad 2\sqrt{ab}$$

or equivalently, compare

$$\frac{a + b}{2} \quad \text{and} \quad \sqrt{ab}$$

1. Using a calculator, with at least five choices for a and b as nonnegative numbers, compare $\frac{a + b}{2}$ and $\sqrt{ab}$. What conjecture would you make from this comparison?

5.46

2. What happens if $a = b$?

3. What geometric interpretation, in terms of rectangles and squares, is given by your conjecture from question 1?

Consider the following geometric display, Display 5.96:

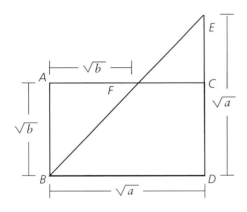

Display 5.96

1. What is the area of rectangle $ABDC$?

2. What is the area of triangle ABF?

5.47

3. What is the area of triangle BDE?

4. Looking at the sum of the areas of triangles ABF and BDE, compared to the area of rectangle $ABDC$, what inequality is suggested?

5. What happens if $a = b$?

Now we can come to the conclusion that for any nonnegative numbers a and b,

$$\frac{a + b}{2} \geq \sqrt{ab} \qquad (1)$$

We have encountered the number $\frac{a + b}{2}$ before as the arithmetic mean of the two numbers a and b. The number $\sqrt{ab}$ has been introduced as the geometric mean of the two numbers a and b. We have been led to conclude that the arithmetic mean of two nonnegative numbers is always greater than or equal to the geometric mean of those two numbers. This inequality, expressed in (1) above, is known as the *basic arithmetic-geometric mean inequality*.

a

5.48

From the geometric displays that we have worked with in comparing the two means, when does equality hold in (1)? That is, under what conditions does

$$\frac{a + b}{2} = \sqrt{ab}$$

We can also show how to arrive at the inequality in (1) by using algebra. We know that the square of any number can never be negative. Thus, for any numbers a and b,

$$(a - b)^2 \geq 0$$

By expanding the left side,

$$a^2 - 2ab + b^2 \geq 0$$

Now add $4ab$ to both sides to get

$$a^2 + 2ab + b^2 \geq 4ab$$

so that

$$(a + b)^2 \geq 4ab$$

If a and b are numbers which are nonnegative, then put in the steps needed to show that

$$\frac{a + b}{2} \geq \sqrt{ab}$$

b

5.49

From the algebra above can you see when equality holds? That is, when do we have

$$\frac{a + b}{2} = \sqrt{ab}$$

As an idea of how the basic arithmetic-geometric mean inequality is used in applications, let's look at the following problem.

A farmer has 600 feet of fence and wishes to enclose a rectangular plot of land. The plot is located along a river, and no fencing is needed along the river. This farmer wishes to enclose as much area as possible. What dimensions should be used?

This problem can be solved with the basic arithmetic-geometric mean inequality. First we need to introduce some symbols. For a rectangle, let L denote the length and W denote the width, in feet, as in Display 5.97.

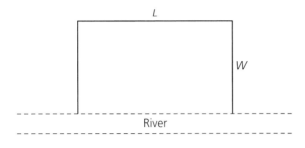

Display 5.97

Let A denote the area of the rectangle so that

$$A = LW$$

We know that the total length of fence must be 600 feet so

$$L + 2W = 600$$

Our job is to make

$$A = LW$$

as large as possible where

$$L + 2W = 600$$

Now, from the basic arithmetic-geometric mean inequality, $\frac{a+b}{2} \geq \sqrt{ab}$, by substitution

$$\frac{(L) + (2W)}{2} \geq \sqrt{(L)(2W)} \qquad \textbf{(2)}$$

or

$$\frac{600}{2} \geq \sqrt{2A}$$

or

$$A \leq 45{,}000 \qquad \textbf{(3)}$$

That is, *no matter how* this farmer uses 600 feet of fence to enclose a rectangular plot of land along a river, the area can be no more than 45,000 square feet. In order to have this largest area, the two sides of inequality (3) must be equal. But this can only happen if the two sides of inequality (2) are equal. However, we know that the two sides of (2) are equal if and only if

$$L = 2W$$

Since $L + 2W = 600$ and $L = 2W$, we must have

$$2L = 600$$

or

$$L = 300 \text{ feet}$$

It also follows that $W = 150$ feet. The largest area, as mentioned above, is 45,000 square feet.

Here are some practice problems, to see if you are on the right track.

5.50

1. A farmer has 1200 feet of fence and wishes to enclose the largest possible area of a rectangular plot of land along a river. No fence is needed along the river. Use the basic arithmetic-geometric mean inequality to determine the dimensions of the plot. What is the maximum area?

2. The manager of a lumber yard wishes to enclose a rectangular plot of land. Fence for the front and back sides cost $2 a foot while stronger fence from the other two sides costs $8 a foot. The manager has $1,000 to spend on fence and wishes to enclose the largest possible area. Use the basic arithmetic-geometric mean inequality to determine the dimensions of the plot. What is the maximum area?

We might also consider a related problem as follows. A farmer wishes to fence in a rectangular plot of land containing an area of 28,800 square feet. One side of the plot will be along a river, so no fence is needed there. What are the dimensions of such a piece of land that uses the smallest length of fencing?

Again, we use L for the length and W for the width, in feet, as in Display 5.98.

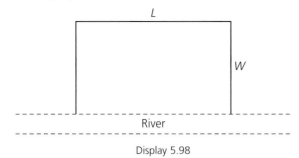

River

Display 5.98

Let F denote the length of fence needed so that

$$F = L + 2W$$

We know that the area must be 28,800 sq. ft., so

$$LW = 28{,}800$$

Our job is to make

$$F = L + 2W$$

as small as possible, where

$$LW = 28{,}800$$

From the arithmetic-geometric mean inequality $\dfrac{a + b}{2} \geq \sqrt{ab}$ it follows that

$$\frac{(L) + (2W)}{2} \geq \sqrt{(L)(2W)} \qquad (4)$$

Explain how this leads to

$$\frac{F}{2} \geq \sqrt{2 \cdot 28{,}800}$$

or finally

$$F \geq 480 \qquad (5)$$

That is, *no matter what dimensions* are used for a rectangular plot with an area of 28,800 sq. ft., we need at least 480 feet of fence to enclose the plot. In order to have this shortest length of fence, the two sides of inequality (5) must be equal. But this can only happen if the two sides of inequality (4) are equal, which means

$$L = 2W$$

Since

$$LW = 28{,}800$$

it follows by substitution that

$$2W^2 = 28{,}800$$

and

$$W = 120 \text{ feet.}$$

Thus $L = 240$ feet and $W = 120$ feet give the dimensions wanted. The total length of fence needed is 480 feet.

Here are some more practice problems to see if you are on track.

5.51

1. A farmer wishes to fence a rectangular plot of land containing an area of 45,000 square feet. One side of the plot will be along a river, so no fence is needed there. Use the basic arithmetic-geometric mean inequality to find the dimensions of such a field that uses the shortest length of fencing. What is the shortest length of fence needed?

2. The manager of a lumber yard wishes to enclose a rectangular plot of land containing 9800 square feet. Fence for the front and back sides costs $6 a foot while stronger fence for the other two parallel sides costs $12 a foot. The manager wants the total cost to be as small as possible. Use the basic arithmetic-geometric mean inequality to determine the dimensions that should be used. What is the minimum cost?

Let's move up in dimensions by answering several questions about the rectangular box in Display 5.99.

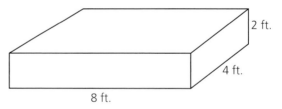

Display 5.99

5.52

1. What is the volume of the box?

2. What is the arithmetic mean (average) s of the lengths of the three sides of this box?

3. What is the length l of the side of a cube which has the same volume as this box?

4. Which is larger, s or l?

Let's try the same procedure with another rectangular box (Display 5.100).

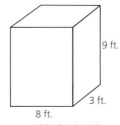

Display 5.100

1. What is the volume of the box?

2. What is the arithmetic mean (average) s of the lengths of the three sides of this box?

3. What is the length l of the side of a cube which has the same volume as this box?

4. Which is larger, s or l?

5.53

Now consider a general rectangular box with sides of length a, b, and c (Display 5.101).

Display 5.101

1. What is the volume of the box?

2. What is the arithmetic mean (average) s of the lengths of the three sides of this box?

5.54

3. What is the length l of the side of a cube which has the same volume as this box?

4. Conjecture—which is larger, s or l?

5. Under what conditions will s and l be equal?

The number l obtained in question 3 is known as the **geometric mean** of the three numbers a, b, and c.

The basic arithmetic-geometric mean inequality $\frac{a+b}{2} \geq \sqrt{ab}$ (given in (1)) was known over two thousand years ago. It was several hundred years ago, however, that people became convinced that this inequality could be generalized. Indeed, mathematicians have now proved that

$$\frac{a+b+c}{3} \geq \sqrt[3]{abc} \tag{6}$$

$$\frac{a+b+c+d}{4} \geq \sqrt[4]{abcd} \tag{7}$$

etc. Moreover, equality holds in (6) if and only if $a = b = c$ and in (7) if and only if $a = b = c = d$.

The inequalities in (6) and (7) are also called *arithmetic-geometric mean inequalities*.

As an example of how inequality (6) can be used in an application, consider the following problems:

The U.S. Postal Service limits the size of boxes that can be sent through the mail. The length of a box plus the *girth* can not exceed 84 inches (this number has varied with time and location). The length of a box is taken to be the *length* of its longest side. The **girth** of a box is the perimeter of a cross section.

For example, in Display 5.102, the length of the dashed line is the girth. We have used L, W, and H to denote the length, width, and height, in inches, of such a box.

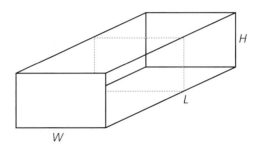

Display 5.102

Remember, the length plus the girth can be less than 84 inches but not more than 84 inches. The problem is the following: What are the dimensions of a box that can be sent through the mail which has a volume that is as large as possible?

Since we want the volume to be as large as possible, it makes sense to use the full limit of 84 inches, otherwise one could increase one of the dimensions to produce a greater volume. Hence, we want to find the maximum value of the volume V given by

$$V = LWH$$

subject to the constraint

$$L + 2W + 2H = 84$$

Using the arithmetic-geometric mean inequality $\frac{a + b + c}{3} \geq \sqrt[3]{abc}$, by substitution

$$\frac{L + 2W + 2H}{3} \geq \sqrt[3]{(L) + (2W) + (2H)} \qquad (8)$$

Explain how this leads to $\frac{84}{3} \geq \sqrt[3]{4V}$

or finally

$$\frac{(28)^3}{4} \geq V \qquad (9)$$

That is, a box sent through the mail cannot have a volume larger than $\frac{(28)^3}{4} = 5488$ cubic inches. In order to obtain this largest volume, we must have equality in (9) and hence in (8). But this is possible if and only if $L = 2W = 2H$ which means that $3L = 84$. So, $L = 28$ inches, $W = 14$ inches, and $H = 14$ inches.

Note how this method gives not only the dimensions of the largest box, in terms of volume, but also gives the numerical value of the greatest volume.

When you go on to study calculus you will see other ways of solving problems like the ones in this section. There are many real-world problems, however, where the use of inequalities, such as the arithmetic-geometric mean inequality, is much easier than other methods. Indeed, the ideas of this section form the basis for a new area of mathematics called Geometric Programming which was developed in 1964.

REFLECT

In this chapter we have seen a number of mathematical techniques for doing something in a better way. In some cases, we were able to do something in the best way. It should be clear that real-world activities require efficient methods for solving problems.

Dynamic Programming, Linear Programming, Geometric Programming, and Graph Theory are only a few of the optimization tools presently available. New methods can be expected. Mathematics is a dynamic subject that will never be called finished.

Problem Set: 5.7

1. Mr. Velez has a rectangular plot of land along a stream that he uses as a garden. He has 600 feet of fence to enclose the garden. No fence is needed along the stream, but double fencing must be used on each of the two sides perpendicular to the stream. Use the basic arithmetic-geometric mean inequality to determine the dimensions that should be used to maximize the area enclosed. What is the maximum area?

2. Best Buy Auto Sales in Tulsa wishes to fence in its car lot to protect its vehicles. BBAS has money for 900 feet of fence. The rectangular lot abuts a building. No fence is needed along the building, but a fence will be used to provide a partition of the rectangle. See Display 5.103.

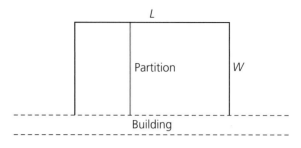

Display 5.103

BBAS wishes to enclose as much area as possible. Use the basic arithmetic-geometric mean inequality to determine what dimensions should be used. What is the maximum total area?

3. The city of Washington let a neighborhood use a rectangular piece of land containing 1000 square feet for a community garden. Fencing is needed only on three sides. The cost of the fence on the two parallel sides is $4 a foot, while the cost for the remaining side is $5 a foot Use a basic arithmetic-geometric mean inequality to determine the dimensions that should be used if one wishes to minimize the cost of the fence. What is the minimum cost?

4. At a certain location, the U.S. Postal Service limits the size of boxes that can be sent through the mail by the following restriction: The length plus the girth cannot exceed 100 inches. Use an arithmetic-geometric mean inequality to determine the dimensions that should be used if one wishes to maximize the volume of a box to be sent through the mail.

Regina Darby
Building a Case

"There is not an area of law that doesn't involve mathematical thinking and calculations," states Regina Darby who is known as one of the top litigators in New York City. "It doesn't matter if you are talking about entertainment law and royalty percentages, negotiating divorces, or building criminal defenses you must always use deductive reasoning and think structurally as a mathematician. Legal arguments are basically points that you need to make in the most logical sequence using the best previously established legal precedence. In other words, they are like a well-constructed mathematical solution to a problem."

Regina first became interested in law as a young girl while watching Perry Mason on television. "I didn't have the opportunity to see lawyers or other professionals in my neighborhood as I was growing up, but I was fascinated by what I saw on TV. I was drawn to the court room and how attorneys would question witnesses and create a logical sequence that could put the pieces of a puzzle together." She has a keen interest in justice. "I see the legal profession as a way to help establish fairness in this world."

As another example on how logic and mathematics is used in the legal profession Regina continues, "Every lawyer that puts an expert witness on the stand in a scientific or technical field has to learn that field. We have to demonstrate to the court and to the jury that the methodology used is scientifically sound. If we don't understand and are not able to explain the logic of the expert's opinion we are at a significant disadvantage."

"Young people who want to become attorneys often ask me what I think they should major in. Conventional wisdom would be to tell them political science, but I always suggest math and English. Those are the two most important skills that they will need to develop to become successful attorneys."

Playing by the Rules: Logic and Axiomatic Systems

CHAPTER 6

6.1 Every Game Has Its Own Rules: Axiomatic Systems

Learning Outcomes

After studying this section you will be able to:

Explain what axioms and theorems are, and how they are different

Identify and describe the main components of an axiomatic system

Describe what an instance of an axiomatic system is, and explain how one axiomatic system can have many different instances.

This chapter is about systems based on rules. Here are the rules of a game called Quick Six. Play it.

6.1

These are the rules of Quick Six:

1. There are two players.

2. There are six cards, numbered 1, 2, 3, 4, 5, 6.

3. Each player is dealt three cards from the shuffled pack.

4. Each player chooses one card and places it face (number side) down on the table.

5. Then both players turn their cards over.

6. If the sum of the numbers showing is even, the player who put down the higher numbered card takes both cards.

7. If the sum of the numbers showing is odd, the player who put down the lower numbered card takes both cards.

8. The play of Rules 4–7 is repeated until one player has all six cards; that player wins.

Now that you've had a chance to play a few games of Quick Six, let's use some tools from earlier chapters and a little common sense to analyze what the rules say. What you find out may improve your chances of winning.

6.2

1. How many different possible hands are there? Justify your answer.

2. Call the distribution of all the cards a *deal*. How many different possible deals are there? Justify your answer.

3. Is the number of possible deals the same as the number of possible games? Why or why not?

4. If your opponent is left with only one card, can you *always* win on the next play? Will you? Explain.

5. Suppose that in the course of a game you have the hand 1–2–4–6 and your opponent has 3–5. Which card should you play to guarantee that you will win the game? Explain.

6. Suppose that you are dealt 2–3–5 and your opponent is dealt 1–4–6. How can you win the game in three plays, regardless of what your opponent plays? Explain.

7. Suppose that you are dealt 1–3–4 and your opponent is dealt 2–5–6. Will any of your three cards be a guaranteed winner on the first play? Explain.

Play a few more games and see if you are better at winning now.

Thinking Tip

Understand and rephrase the question. Many interesting questions are not precise enough to be answered without some refinement. You may need to give a precise meaning to a vague word.

Let's take a closer look at the hands of question 7. Neither one is good enough to *guarantee* a win, even if it is played carefully. Which is the better hand? What should "better" mean here? One way to look at this question is to list all possible first plays for this deal (How many are there?) and to count how many of them each hand wins. Then the hand with more winning plays is the better hand, right? That seems reasonable. Let's try it. The possible first plays appear in Display 6.1.

Display 6.1 shows that hand *A* (1–3–4) wins five of the nine possible first plays, whereas hand *B* (2–5–6) only wins four. Thus, it seems sensible to call *A* the better hand.

Hand *A* (1-3-4)	Hand *B* (2-5-6)	Winner
1	2	A
1	5	B
1	6	A
3	2	B
3	5	B
3	6	A
4	2	A
4	5	A
4	6	B

The possible first plays for two hands of Quick Six

Display 6.1

Now you try it. Decide which of the hands (2–4–5) and (1–3–6) is better by making a table to see which one wins more of the possible first plays.

6.3

Take a careful look at your results for the previous question. Which of those two hands would you rather get? Something should bother you. What is it? Can you explain what's wrong?

6.4

Using the probability language you studied earlier, we could say from Display 6.1 that the probability of winning with hand *A* is $\frac{5}{9}$ and the probability of winning with hand *B* is $\frac{4}{9}$. In symbols,

$$P(A) = \frac{5}{9} \quad \text{and} \quad P(B) = \frac{4}{9}$$

We *could* say this, but if we did, we would be assuming something that may not be true. When we state the probability of an event as the ratio of desirable outcomes over total outcomes, *we are assuming that all the outcomes are equally likely*. But are they? Look at the hands (2–4–5) and (1–3–6) that you just analyzed; call them *C* and *D*, respectively. The probabilities for these hands are

$$P(C) = \frac{4}{9} \quad \text{and} \quad P(D) = \frac{5}{9}$$

This says that the better hand is *D* because it will win the first play 5 times out of 9, on the average. That's true—*if the cards are played randomly*. The hidden assumption here is that all first plays are equally likely, that neither player is using any strategy. But that assumption doesn't make sense in this case. If you were dealt hand C (2–4–5), would you just play a card at random? We hope not. We hope you would think about the hand long enough to realize that 5 beats every card in hand D (1–3–6), and then play 5. Thus, assuming that the players are using some commonsense strategy for winning, the probabilities for these hands become

$$P(C) = 1 \quad \text{and} \quad P(D) = 0$$

The lesson to be learned from this is

> *When your mathematical results conflict with your common sense, look for hidden assumptions.*

6.5 In analyzing hands of Quick Six, do you think it would ever make sense to assume that the plays are equally likely? If so, in what circumstances? If not, why not? Give some examples to illustrate your explanation.

Quick Six is a simple example of a very important kind of mathematical structure. It is called an **axiomatic system** and it has four essential components—*axioms, undefined terms, defined terms,* and *theorems*. As we describe each of these, you should observe how they fit together.

- An **axiom** is a statement that is accepted as a starting point for the system. If you think of an axiomatic system as a game (such as Quick Six), then the axioms are the rules.

- An **undefined term** is a basic word or phrase of the axiomatic system. The undefined terms are starting point words of the system. Their meanings are inferred from their use in the axioms, but they are not formally defined within the system. In Quick Six, for example, *player, card,* and *take* are undefined terms. Even though they are not defined, we can tell from the rules what they mean.

- A **defined term** is a word that is defined within the system, using the undefined terms and/or words defined previously. In Quick Six, for example, the last part of Rule 8 suggests the following definition:

  A *winner* is a player who has all six cards.

This definition uses the undefined terms *player* and *card*.

A **theorem** is a statement that can be proved from the axioms. It is a statement that *must* be true whenever the axioms are true. A simple theorem of Quick Six is: A player with five cards can win the game on the next play.

Which of the following five statements are theorems of Quick Six?

6.6

For each theorem, give a logical argument to prove that it must be true in *every* game of Quick Six.

For each statement that is not a theorem, explain how there could be a game for which it is not true.

1. At all times, each player knows exactly what cards the other player has.

2. A player who wins the first two plays can always win the game on the next play.

3. A player who wins the first two plays will win the game on the next play.

4. The 1 card beats every other card.

5. Every card loses to some other card.

Sometimes a situation becomes clearer if its essential features are treated as axioms. Here is a simple example.

Some of the students at Sasquatch School in Anydale, Minnesota, are related as follows:

Axioms
   (a) Exactly three students are named Janovic.
   (b) Every Janovic is related to at least two Masryks.
   (c) No Masryk is related to more than two Janovics.

1. Draw a diagram to represent the relationships described by these three axioms.

6.7

2. In your diagram, what represents the Janovics? What represents the Masryks? What represents the relationships?

3. What are the undefined terms of this axiomatic system? Justify your answer.

The diagrams that you and your classmates drew are examples of an important general idea.

6.8 **A Word to Know:** An **instance** of an axiomatic system is the assignment of meanings to the undefined terms in such a way that all the axioms become true statements about those meanings.

About Words

The everyday expression *for instance* means "here is a particular case of what we're talking about."

Note that the word "instance" is not the standard mathematical term for this idea. Most mathematicians call such things "models" of an axiomatic system. However, as you have seen already, model also has a more common, very different meaning in mathematics. This is one of those few unfortunate times in which a standard mathematical term has different meanings in different contexts. To avoid confusion, we use "instance" for this meaning. If you read about axiomatic systems in other books, you probably will find instances of axiomatic systems called models.

6.9 **Another instance of the Janovic–Masryk axiomatic system is given by the diagram in Display 6.2.**

1. What meaning has been assigned to *Janovic*? What meaning has been assigned to *Masryk*? What meaning has been assigned to *related to*?

2. Make up another instance of this axiomatic system, one that is different from those you have already seen.

3. In your new instance, what meanings have you assigned to the undefined terms?

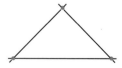

An instance of the Janovic–Masryk axiomatic system

Display 6.2

This idea that the words in axioms can have many different meanings is not new to us. Think about Quick Six as an axiomatic system. Because the term player doesn't refer to any particular person, the rules about players apply to *anyone* who plays the game. The rules containing the term card apply to *any* cards in the game. When two particular people are dealt two hands and play the game correctly, that's one instance where the rules are satisfied. Two other people playing out two other hands form another instance of the game. The game can be played by many different people with many different hands, but it's still Quick Six because the same rules are satisfied each time. Each particular game is an instance of the rules.

The most important fact about axiomatic systems is that

Any statement that can be proved from the axioms of a system *must be true in every instance* **of the system.**

That is, any time you can show that a statement about the terms of an axiomatic system follows logically from the axioms, then you have *guaranteed* the truth of that statement as it is interpreted in every instance of that axiomatic system, no matter how different those instances appear to be! Thus, the more theorems an axiomatic system has, the more powerful it is, because all its theorems are *automatically* true in any situation for which the axioms are true.

Problem Set: 6.1

1. For each of the following deals of Quick Six, decide which hand is better by making a table (like Display 6.1) to see which one wins more of the possible first plays. If the result of your table conflicts with your common sense of how the game should be played, explain why.

   (a) 1–2–3 and 4–5–6
   (b) 2–3–4 and 1–5–6
   (c) 1–3–5 and 2–4–6

2. Which of the following statements are theorems of Quick Six? For each one that is, prove it; that is, give a logical argument to show that the statement must be true in *every* game of Quick Six. For each one that is not, describe a game for which the statement is not true.

   (a) The player who wins the first play can always win the game in two more plays.
   (b) The player who wins the first play will win the game.
   (c) Every card loses to two other cards.
   (d) The 1 card beats every even card.
   (e) Every card beats some other card.
   (f) There is an even card that beats every odd card.

3. Find or make an instance of this axiomatic system.

   Undefined terms: gizmo, widget, attracts
   Axioms
   (a) There are exactly three gizmos.
   (b) All gizmos attract the same widget.
   (c) There is exactly one widget that no gizmo attracts.

4. Find or make two different instances of this axiomatic system.

   Undefined terms: point, line, on
   Axioms
   (a) There are at least four points.
   (b) Every point is on exactly two lines.
   (c) Some line is not on any point.

5. Find or make two different instances of this axiomatic system.

   Undefined terms: X, Y, related
   Axioms
   (a) There are exactly five Xs.
   (b) At least one Y is related to each X.
   (c) No X is related to every Y.
   (d) Every X is related to at least two Ys.

PROJECT

The following axiomatic system, which we shall call System **A,** describes some familiar properties of plane geometry:

Undefined terms: point, line, on

Axioms

A1 There is at least one point.
A2 Every point is on at least two lines.
A3 Every line is on at least two points.
A4 Given any two points, there is exactly one
      line on both of them.

Here are four different instances of System **A.**

Instance 1 Any plane in 3-space is an instance of this system
          if we give the undefined terms their usual geometric
          meanings. That is, let points and lines be the *points*
          and *lines* of that plane, and say that a point is *on*
          a line if the line contains it.

Instance 2 Let *point* mean "one of the numbers 1, 2, or 3";
          let *line* mean "one of the sets {1, 2}, {1, 3}, or
          {2, 3}"; let *on* mean "contains" or "is contained
          in," as appropriate.

Instance 3 Think of the three vertices of triangle ABC in
          Display 6.3 as the *points*, the three sides of the
          triangle as the *lines*, and let *on* have its usual
          geometric meaning.

Instance 4 The *points* in this case are the four small circles D,
          E, F, and G in Display 6.3. The *lines* are the six
          segments connecting these circles. A circle (*point*) is
          on a segment (*line*), and vice versa, if the circle is at
          one end or the other of the segment. Thus, the
          segment DF is on circles D and F and no others.

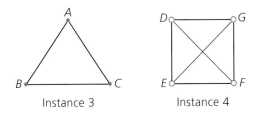

Instance 3   Instance 4

Two instances of System **A**

Display 6.3

1. Here is an example of a simple theorem in System **A**.

   Theorem For any given line, there is at least one point not on that line.

   Prove it.

2. In System **A**, let us define two *lines* to be *parallel* if there is no point that is *on* both of them. This definition agrees with our usual idea of parallel lines in Instance 1.

   (a) List all possible pairs of parallel lines in Instance 2, if there are any. If there are none, explain how you know.
   (b) List all possible pairs of parallel lines in Instance 3, if there are any. If there are none, explain how you know.
   (c) List all possible pairs of parallel lines in Instance 4, if there are any. If there are none, explain how you know.

3. Prove this theorem for System **A**.

   There are at least three lines.

4. Consider this statement about System **A**.

   Every line is on at least three points.

   (a) Is this statement true in Instance 4?
   (b) Is this statement true in Instance 3?
   (c) Is this statement a theorem of System **A**? Explain.
   (d) In general, how can you show that a statement is *not* a theorem of a particular axiomatic system?

6.2 Say What You Mean: Writing Good Definitions

Understanding just about anything—a contract, an insurance policy, a tax form, a scientific theory, or a mathematical system—begins with knowing what the words mean. That's what the definitions tell you. But you have to use words to define words, so you can't expect to define *everything*. You have to accept some words as the starting point of your technical vocabulary. In an axiomatic system, these are the undefined terms. Once this starting point has been chosen, every other term of the system must be logically linked with those basic terms by precise definitions. That's how the logical thread connecting the axioms to the theorems is protected.

Designing a good definition can be trickier than you might think.

Describe in your own words what you think is wrong with each of these "definitions" of *addition*.

6.10

1. *Addition* is a way of combining numbers.

2. *Addition* is adding numbers.

3. *Addition* is like 2 + 3 = 5.

4. When you combine 2 and 3 to get 5, you are doing *addition*.

Defining a word or phrase is a labeling process. A definition states a condition that something must satisfy in order to be labeled with the word being defined. A good definition must have two key properties.

1. It must be **characteristic**; that is, it must state a condition clearly enough for us to decide whether or not any given object satisfies it. The word being defined will become a label for *every* object that satisfies this condition and will not label anything else.

2. It must be **noncircular**; that is, the defining condition cannot be described by using words whose meanings depend on the word we are defining.

Learning Outcomes

After studying this section, you will be able to:

Explain the application of characteristic to definition

Distinguish between circular and noncircular definitions

Write good definitions.

Here are some samples of what can go wrong if you ignore these two key properties.

"An *odd* number is a number that is not even."

is a true statement, but it's not a good definition of *odd*. At least one of the two key properties is missing, maybe both. First of all, it's not characteristic. The numbers $\frac{1}{3}$ and $\sqrt{2}$ are not even, but they shouldn't be called odd, either. We could fix this problem by saying

"An *odd* number is an integer that is not even."

Now the statement is characteristic, but it may be circular. It depends on how we define *even*. If we say

"An *even* number is an integer that is not odd."

we're in trouble! This statement is true, too, but it's not very helpful. These two statements, taken together, put us into a circular loop—knowing what an odd number is depends on knowing what an even number is, which depends on knowing what an odd number is, ... If, instead, we say

"An *even* number is an integer that has 2 as a factor."

then we have a good definition of *even* that allows us to define *odd* by saying

"An *odd* number is an integer that is not even."

6.11

Look back at the four incorrect definitions of *addition* **in the previous discussion question. Explain what is wrong with each one by referring to the two key properties of good definitions.**

Remembering that a definition must be characteristic will help you avoid such definition errors as

"A *square* is when all four sides are equal."

There are many things wrong with this definition. To begin with, the proposed definition doesn't say what *kind* of thing a square is. The phrase "is when" implies that a square is a *time*, which is false. Remember: Do not use "when" in a definition unless you are referring to time, and never use the grammatical disaster "is when." One might guess that the writer of this definition really means to say that a square is some kind of planar figure, but the definition does not supply this information. It is far better to begin by saying

"A *square* is a rectangle..."

assuming, of course, that *rectangle* has already been defined. To distinguish the rectangles we want to call squares from the rest, we can add

"...such that all four sides have the same length."

This makes the definition characteristic.

Suppose you begin the definition of *square* by saying

"A square is a quadrilateral..."

6.12

1. If you end it the same way as above, by saying "... such that all four sides have the same length," do you have a true statement? Explain why it is not a good definition of *square*.

2. How would you complete this definition? Justify your answer.

Problem Set: 6.2

1. Only one of these proposed definitions of familiar mathematical objects is correct. Identify the correct one and explain what is wrong with each of the others.

   (a) A *circle* is a planar figure with no vertices.
   (b) An *equation* is when two algebraic expressions are equal.
   (c) The number π is the ratio of the circumference of a circle to its diameter.
   (d) A function is *periodic* if its values repeat.
   (e) A *definition* is when something is defined.
   (f) A *regular polygon* is like a square or an equilateral triangle.

2. Which of the following "definitions" of visible light best fits the requirements for a good definition, as described in this section? Explain why you didn't choose each of the others.

Visible light is...

(a) ... something bright and shiny

(b) ... a sensation aroused by stimulation of the visual receptors

(c) ... something that makes vision possible

(d) ... part of the electromagnetic spectrum that triggers the visual receptors in human eyes

(e) ... damaging to our eyes.

3. In your own words, write a definition for each of the following words. They are terms from natural science, but they can also have many other meanings.

(a) star

(b) rock

(c) cell

6.3 Some Rules About Rules: Basic Logic

In Section 6.1 you learned about the four essential components of an axiomatic system: axioms, undefined terms, defined terms, and theorems. The axioms are the rules of the mathematical "game" being played. The undefined terms provide a way to apply the power of that game to the real world, through instances. Section 6.2 explained how to form good definitions, so that the vocabulary of a system can be made more precise and efficient. All of these pieces have a single purpose—constructing and proving theorems.

Explain this statement: "The more theorems an axiomatic system has, the more powerful it is."

6.13

Proving theorems is the process of getting the truth of some statements to guarantee the truth of others. We begin by thinking of the words *true* and *false* as labels that are applied somehow to some sentences. These two words are called **truth values**. Formally, a **statement** is a sentence that has a truth value—that is, a sentence that can be labeled either *true* or *false*. Often we rely on our common sense view of reality to tell us whether a statement is true or false. Sometimes we simply assume a statement to be true (or false) "for the sake of argument," to see the consequences of that assumption. In any case, a sentence *must* have a truth value in order for it to be called a statement.

To see how the idea of truth value applies to mathematics, look at this simple algebraic sentence:

$$x^2 = 9$$

Is this a *statement*? No. Why not? Because we have no way of knowing whether it is true or false! That depends on the value of x, and at the moment x is just a symbol waiting for a specific meaning.

Learning Outcomes

After studying this section you will be able to:

Describe the two basic laws that govern the truth values of standard logic

Identify and construct negations of statements, including negations of quantified statements

Explain how *and* and *or* determine the truth values of statements they are in

Apply De Morgan's Laws to statements involving *and*, *or*, and *not*

State the hypothesis, the conclusion, and the converse of a conditional statement.

6.14

1. Is $x^2 = 9$ true for *some* number x?
   Justify your answer.

2. Is $x^2 = 9$ true for *every* number x?
   Justify your answer.

3. Which of the following two sentences is a statement? Are both of them statements? Explain.

   (a) For some number x, $x^2 = 9$.

   (b) For every number x, $x^2 = 9$.

About Words

In English, a *quantity* is an amount or a number of something. A *quantifier* tells you something about how many things are being considered.

The universe commonly means everything. A *universal statement* is about everything in some set (a universal set).

Existentialism is a modern philosophy based on analyzing human existence.

Terms such as *every, all, some, one, there exists, there are,* etc., are called **quantifiers**. A statement containing such a word or phrase is said to be **quantified**. The two main types of quantified statements are *universal* and *existential*.

A Word to Know: A **universal** statement asserts that all things of a certain kind satisfy some condition.

"All rabbits are animals" and "For every number x, $2x = x + x$" are universal statements.

A Word to Know: An **existential** statement asserts the existence of at least one thing that satisfies some condition.

"There's a fly in my soup" and "For some number x, $x^2 = 9$" are existential statements.

Note that the word *some* in mathematics is an existential quantifier. It is a short form of "there is at least one." It does not mean that there must be more than one thing that fits the conditions of the statement (though there may be), nor does it rule out the possibility that *all* things might fit the statement.

Some statements are not quantified because they are about specific things. They are called **particular** statements. "The Clintons have a cat named Socks" and "$3^2 = 9$" are particular statements.

Classify each statement as *universal*, *existential*, or *particular*. Justify your answers.

6.15

1. Some parallelograms are rectangles.

2. All integers that are divisible by 6 are even.

3. There is an even prime number.

4. The smallest prime number is even.

5. There is an $x < 0$ such that $x^2 > 0$.

6. For every $x < 0$, $x^2 > 0$.

7. $(-3)^2 > 0$.

Standard logic rests on two basic, reasonable assumptions about truth values.

> **The Law of Contradiction** No statement may be both true and false at the same time (in the same context).

> **The Law of the Excluded Middle** There are only two truth values, *true* and *false*. That is, every statement must be either true or false.

These laws may seem almost too obvious to mention, but they have far reaching effects on what we can say and what we can prove. For instance, the sentence

"This sentence is false."

is *not* a statement in standard logic because it cannot have either truth value.

- If we consider it true, then we must accept what it says, which makes it also false, violating the Law of Contradiction.

- If we consider it false, then we must deny what it says. By the Law of the Excluded Middle, then, the sentence must be true, which again violates the Law of Contradiction.

6.16 Simone the Space Explorer was captured by a band of aliens from a distant galaxy. These aliens, for whom logic and truth were valued above all else, brought Simone before their leader. By tradition, a captive was required to make a single statement. The leader, acting as judge of good and evil, would determine whether this statement was true or false. If it was true, then the captive would be carried off to their galaxy to be studied as a specimen of goodness in the universe. If it was false, then the captive would be judged as evil and instantly atomized. Simone didn't like either alternative. Recalling her Space Academy training in logic, she stated: "I will be atomized." Explain why the aliens let her go.

By the Law of Contradiction and the Law of the Excluded Middle, *true* and *false* are "logical opposites." In this sense, every statement has a logical opposite, called its *negation*.

> **A Word to Know:** The **negation** of a statement is a statement whose truth value is always opposite to the truth value of the original statement.

The word "always," as used here, means "in every circumstance." That is, *whenever* a statement is true, its negation *must* be false; and *whenever* the statement is false, its negation *must* be true. For example, "Today is Tuesday" and "Today is Wednesday" are *not* negations of each other. Although they cannot both be true at the same time, they *can* both be false at the same time (every Thursday, Friday, Saturday, Sunday, or Monday). The negation of "Today is Tuesday" is "Today is not Tuesday"; these statements always have opposite truth values.

As in algebra, symbols and other abbreviations make writing about logical statements more efficient. Letters such as s, p, and q are used to stand for statements. We abbreviate the negation of a statement s as "$\sim s$." For instance, if s is "Sam likes racing bikes," then $\sim s$ is "Sam does not like racing bikes."

Sometimes forming the negation of a statement can be tricky. A little common sense usually is enough to keep you out of trouble. However, when quantifiers are involved the situation may call for careful thought. Here's an example.

For all natural numbers n, $n^2 - 1 > 0$.

The negation of this statement is

For some natural number n, $n^2 - 1 \leq 0$.

Notice that the logical opposite of "greater than" is "less than *or equal to*."

Exactly one of the foregoing two statements about natural numbers is true. Which is it?

6.17

The previous example illustrates how a quantified statement is related to its negation. The following two principles should help you to untangle the often confusing ways of negating quantified statements.

- The negation of a universal statement is an existential statement.

- The negation of an existential statement is a universal statement.

Of course, you must remember to negate the property or condition in the statement.

Negate each statement.

1. Every prime number is odd.

6.18

2. For some real number x, $x^2 - 3x = 5$.

3. Some right triangles are isosceles.

4. Every quadratic equation has at least one real root.

If you negate the negation of a statement, the logical result is the original statement. For instance,

s: The whole number n is even.

$\sim s$: The whole number n is not even.

$\sim(\sim s)$: It is not true that the whole number n is not even.

This last statement is just a roundabout way of saying, "The whole number n is even," which is the original statement s. Even though s and $\sim(\sim s)$ are grammatically different, they are logically "the same." That is, they always have the same truth value; when either one is true, so is the other.

A Phrase to Know: Two statements that always have the same truth values are called **logically equivalent** (or simply **equivalent**) statements.

Because they have identical truth values, equivalent statements are logically interchangeable. They are just different ways to say the same thing. To keep the wording in this book simple, we usually treat two different ways of saying the same thing as the same statement. For instance,

>Some animals do not have fur.

and

>Not all animals have fur.

say the same thing. They are the same statement, expressed in two different ways. That's why we can talk about *the* negation of a statement, even though there is more than one way to phrase the negation in most cases.

The power of logic stems from the fact that complicated sentences can be rewritten as logically equivalent combinations of simpler ones. We seldom speak or write in simple sentences. Even in everyday conversation, most people use fairly complex sentences that string together several interconnected thoughts. The bad news from the viewpoint of logical analysis is that there are *lots* of ways to do this in English. Many different English words and phrases serve as connectives that allow us to build complex sentences out of simpler ones. Here's the good news.

When we model reasoning by formal logic, all these different ways of linking statements together are described in terms of just three connectives,

>*and   or   if... then*

These three, together with the idea of negation discussed in the previous section, are all we need to analyze any statement or combination of statements. Remember: Abstraction is a *simplifying* process!

Rewrite each of these sentences as two or three simpler clauses connected by *and*, *or*, or *if... then*. Keep as much of the original meaning as you can. The first two are done for you.

6.19

1. All that glitters is not gold.

   An answer: Something glitters <u>and</u> it is not gold.

2. We can't go to the beach because it's raining.

   An answer: <u>If</u> it's raining, <u>then</u> we can't go to the beach; <u>and</u> it's raining.

3. The package will be sent either today or tomorrow.

4. Neither Alice nor Zeke has arrived yet.

5. Cats always purr when they're happy.

6. Since x is a positive integer, $x + 1 \geq 2$.

7. Those who cannot remember the past are condemned to repeat it. [*Santayana*]

The three basic connectives—*and*, *or*, *if... then*—are all we need to build even the most complicated statements, step by step, by combining simpler statements two at a time. The rules for finding the truth value of each connected pair of statements from the truth values of its two parts are natural extensions of our common sense about what the connective words mean. Using p and q to represent the statements being combined, the truth-value rules for *and* and *or* can be stated as follows:

An ***and*-statement** is a statement of the form "p and q." It is true if p and q are both true; it is false otherwise.

An ***or*-statement** is a statement of the form "p or q." It is false if p and q are both false; it is true otherwise.

About Words

In English, a *junction* is a place where two roads or railroad lines or electric wires are connected to each other.

6.20   In formal logic, *and*-statements are called **conjunctions** and *or*-statements are called **disjunctions.** We avoid this terminology because some people have a hard time remembering which is which. However, if you refer to other books about logic, these are the terms you'll probably see.

Each rule covers the four truth-value possibilities for two statements,

- both are true

- first is true, second is false

- first is false, second is true

- both are false.

Do these rules agree with your common sense? They should. For example, if

p: Today is Friday.   and q: The sun is shining.

the rules tell us that "p and q" is true only on sunny Fridays, but "p or q" is true every Friday, regardless of the weather, and also on every sunny day. Isn't that what your common sense would say?

We have defined *or* as it is used in mathematics. This is one of two slightly different ways in which the word is used in everyday English. Some other languages have different words for these two different meanings. The mathematical usage is called the *inclusive or* because it allows both parts of the statement to be true at the same time. Sometimes it is written as "and/or." The usage in which both parts cannot be true at the same time is called the *exclusive or*. For instance

inclusive: "To qualify for financial aid, a student must demonstrate financial need or high scholastic ability."

exclusive: "Jaime's pet is either a dog or a cat."

The exclusive *or* is not treated as a separate connective because it can be described in terms of *and*, negation, and the inclusive *or*.

For each of the following statements, determine from the context whether *or* is being used in the inclusive sense or the exclusive sense.

6.21

1. The first prize for the contest is a trip to Hawaii or the cash equivalent.

2. To receive a passing grade you either must have an average of 75% or better before the final, or you must score at least 80% on the final exam. (Interpret both *or*'s.)

3. To be exempt from the tax, you must be a senior citizen or have an annual income less than $10,000.

4. Terry intends to join the Army or the Navy next week.

At this point, it is natural to wonder how negation affects *and*-statements and *or*-statements. That is, how are the negations of "*p* and *q*" and "*p* or *q*" related to the two separate statements ~*p* and ~*q*? Here are the four obvious combinations involving negation.

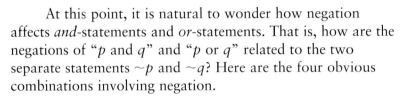

$$\sim(p \text{ and } q) \quad \sim(p \text{ or } q) \quad (\sim p) \text{ and } (\sim q) \quad (\sim p) \text{ or } (\sim q)$$

As usual, we first perform the operations within the parentheses. Thus, in "~(*p* and *q*)" we first consider "*p* and *q*" and then negate it. On the other hand, in "(~*p*) and (~*q*)" we first form the negations ~*p*, ~*q*; then we combine them using *and*.

These four combinations are actually two logically equivalent pairs of statements. For instance,

> Saying that you didn't win both first *and* second prize in a contest [~(*p* and *q*)] means that you didn't win first prize *or* you didn't win second prize [~*p* or ~*q*].

> Telling someone who wants you to take a message that you don't have paper or pen [~(*p* or *q*)] means that you don't have paper *and* you don't have a pen [~*p* and ~*q*].

The logical principles represented by these common-sense examples are called *De Morgan's Laws.*[†]

Facts to Know:
(1) "$\sim(p$ and $q)$" is logically equivalent to "$(\sim p)$ or $(\sim q)$"
(2) "$\sim(p$ or $q)$" is logically equivalent to "$(\sim p)$ and $(\sim q)$"

De Morgan's Laws show precisely how the negations of *and*-statements and *or*-statements must be treated, even in confusing situations. Sometimes common sense may not be enough to rely on. In such cases, De Morgan's Laws can help to clarify matters.

For instance, what is the negation of $3 \leq x \leq 7$? That is, what does it mean to say that $3 \leq x \leq 7$ is false? The expression $3 \leq x \leq 7$ is algebraic shorthand for "a number x is greater than or equal to 3 and less than or equal to 7." If it is false, then its negation

$$\sim(3 \leq x \leq 7)$$

is true. Just what does that negation say about the number x? De Morgan's Laws tell us, as follows.

- Rewrite $3 \leq x \leq 7$ as "$x \geq 3$ and $x \leq 7$." Then De Morgan's Law (1) tells us that the negation is "$x \ngeq 3$ or $x \nleq 7$."

- Now, $x \geq 3$ means "$x > 3$ or $x = 3$" so, by De Morgan's Law (2), $x \ngeq 3$ means "$x \ngtr 3$ and $x \neq 3$." That is, $x < 3$.

- Similarly, $x \nleq 7$ means "$x \nless 7$ and $x \neq 7$" so, $x > 7$.

- Thus, $\sim(3 \leq x \leq 7)$ must be "$x < 3$ or $x > 7$." Display 6.4 illustrates this with number-line diagrams.

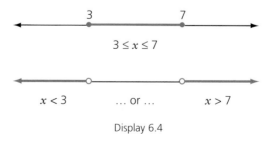

Display 6.4

[†]They are named after the 19th century British mathematician Augustus De Morgan.

Write the negation of each of the following expressions in terms of inequalities without using the *not* symbol $\sim$. In each case, explain how De Morgan's Laws apply.

6.22

1. $x \leq 5$

2. $x \geq 0$

3. $0 \leq x \leq 5$

The most subtle of the basic connectives is *if... then*. As with the other connectives, its truth-value rules reflect everyday English usage *if we think of such statements in just the right way*. A good way to think of an *if... then* statement is as an agreement between two people. For instance, suppose that your rich uncle makes you this promise.

> "If you get a perfect score on your next math test, then I'll give you $10."

When is this statement true (the promise kept), and when is it false (the promise broken)? The promise is made up of two simple statements.

p: You get a perfect score on your next math test.

q: I'll give you $10.

Each of these statements might be either true or false, so there are four cases to consider:

(1) p and q might both be true.

You get a perfect score and your uncle gives you $10.

(2) p might be true and q false.

You get a perfect score, but your uncle doesn't give you $10.

(3) p might be false and q true.

You don't get a perfect score, but your uncle gives you $10 anyway.

(4) p and q might both be false.

You don't get a perfect score and your uncle doesn't give you $10.

Obviously, the promise is kept in Case (1) and is broken in Case (2). But what about the other two cases? Since the condition of getting a perfect score on the test is not fulfilled in those cases, your uncle can give you $10 or not, as he sees fit, without breaking his promise. Thus, the promise is kept *in all cases except* (2).

This example illustrates the truth-value rule in the following definition of the *if... then* statement form.

> **Words to Know:** A **conditional statement** (or a **conditional**) is a statement that can be put into the form "if p, then q," where p and q are statements. It is false if p is true and q is false; it is true otherwise. The statement p is called the **hypothesis**; the statement q is called the **conclusion.**

A conditional statement says that, whenever some condition (the hypothesis) is fulfilled, some consequence (the conclusion) must necessarily follow. The conditional "if p, then q" is symbolized by

$$p \to q$$

which can also be read "p implies q."

6.23

Rules 6 and 7 of the game Quick Six are conditionals.

Rule 6: If the sum of the numbers showing is even, the player who put down the higher numbered card takes both cards.

Rule 7: If the sum of the numbers showing is odd, the player who put down the lower numbered card takes both cards.

1. What is the hypothesis of Rule 6? What is its conclusion?

2. What is the hypothesis of Rule 7? What is its conclusion?

3. Satoshi and Normee are playing Quick Six. Satoshi plays the 4 card and Normee plays the 5 card; then Normee takes both cards. One, but not both, of the rules has been broken. Which one? Explain.

4. Describe a situation that violates the other rule, the one that was not your answer to question 3.

5. Can you describe a situation in which both of these rules are broken at the same time? If so, do it. If not, explain why not.

Here are three helpful things to remember about conditional statements.

- The hypothesis and the conclusion of a conditional, when considered separately, must be statements themselves. The word "if" is *not* part of the hypothesis, and the word "then" is *not* part of the conclusion. These words are connectives, like *and*, *or*, etc.

    Example: The hypothesis of "If it is spring, then the grass is green" is "It is spring." Its conclusion is "The grass is green."

- The word "if" *always* labels the hypothesis. Any statement of the form "*q* if *p*" is logically equivalent to "if *p*, then *q*."

    Example: The hypothesis of "A number is not prime if it is divisible by 4" is "It [a number] is d visible by 4." Its conclusion is "The number is not prime."

- Any universal statement of the form "All [-*xxx*-] are [-*yyy*-]" or "Every [-*xxx*-] is [-*yyy*-]" can be restated in conditional form as

    "If something is [-*xxx*-], then it is [-*yyy*-]."

    Example: "Every rectangle is a parallelogram" can be rephrased as

    "If something is a rectangle, then it is a parallelogram."

6.24

1. State the hypothesis and the conclusion of each of these conditionals.

    (a) If this is Thanksgiving Day, then it's Thursday.
    (b) If all its angles are equal, the triangle is equilateral.
    (c) The line is horizontal if its slope is 0.

2. Rephrase each of these statements as a conditional; then state its hypothesis and its conclusion.

    (a) All turkeys are birds.
    (b) Every multiple of 6 is an even number.
    (c) Every first degree equation can be graphed as a straight line.

The distinction between the hypothesis and the conclusion of a conditional is very important. In fact, $p \to q$ usually says something quite different from $q \to p$. For instance,

> If *ABCD* is a square, then it is a rectangle.

is not at all the same thing as

> If *ABCD* is a rectangle, then it is a square.

What are p and q in this example?

> **A Word to Know:** The **converse** of a conditional statement $p \to q$ is the statement $q \to p$, formed by interchanging the hypothesis and the conclusion.

6.25

1. What is the converse of "If a triangle is equilateral, then it contains a 60° angle"?

2. What is the converse of "All prime numbers greater than 2 are odd"?

6.26

Overheard at the Mad Hatter's Tea Party,

"...You should say what you mean," the March Hare went on.

"I do," Alice hastily replied; "at least—at least, I mean what I say—that's the same thing, you know."

"Not the same thing a bit!" said the Hatter. "Why, you might just as well say that 'I see what I eat' is the same thing as 'I eat what I see'!"

"You might just as well say," added the March Hare, "that 'I like what I get' is the same thing as 'I get what I like'!"

"You might just as well say," added the Dormouse, which seemed to be talking in its sleep, "that 'I breathe when I sleep' is the same thing as 'I sleep when I breathe'!"

"It *is* the same thing with you," said the Hatter, and here the conversation dropped, and the party sat silent for a minute....

[From the Tea Party scene in Lewis Carroll's *Alice in Wonderland*.]

1. There are four pairs of conditional statements in this conversation. In each pair, the second conditional is the converse of the first one. Restate each pair in "*if... then...*" form, and identify clearly the two statements that form the hypothesis and the conclusion.

2. If you were at this party, what example would you add to the conversation?

As you can see, a true conditional may not have a true converse. However, sometimes both a conditional $p \rightarrow q$ and its converse $q \rightarrow p$ have the same truth value. In such a case, the truth of either the hypothesis, p, or the conclusion, q, guarantees the truth of the other. The short way to say this is

p is true *if and only if* q is true

which is abbreviated as "p iff q" or as "$p \leftrightarrow q$." Such statements are called *biconditional statements*. For example,

A polygon has three sides if and only if it is a triangle.

Thus, a biconditional statement asserts the logical equivalence of its two parts.

For each of the following statements,

6.27

(a) State its converse.

(b) Combine the statement and its converse into a biconditional.

(c) State whether the biconditional is true or false. If it is false, explain why.

1. If all three angles of a triangle are equal, then all three of its sides are equal.

2. If a quadrilateral is a square, then it is a rectangle.

3. If a whole number is odd, then it is not divisible by 2.

4. If $a + b = 12$, then $a = 8$ and $b = 4$.

5. If the last digit of a number is 5 or 0, then the number is divisible by 5.

Problem Set: 6.3

1. Classify each of the following statements as *universal* or *existential*. Then say whether it is true or false, and justify your answer.

   (a) All squares are regular polygons.
   (b) Some polygons are circles.
   (c) No polygons are circles.
   (d) Not all polygons are circles.
   (e) For every real number x, $|x| = -x$
   (f) For some real number x, $|x| = -x$
   (g) Some positive real number is less than or equal to every positive real number.
   (h) Every positive real number is less than or equal to some positive real number.

2. For each part, write two true statements that begin with the given phrase.

   (a) All triangles...
   (b) Some triangles...
   (c) No triangles...
   (d) Every circle...
   (e) There exists a circle...
   (f) Not all circles...

3. Write a negation for each of these statements.
   (a) All roses are red.
   (b) Some apples are red.
   (c) Not all snakes are poisonous.
   (d) No man is an island.
   (e) Nothing in the room escaped Sherlock Holmes' notice.
   (f) $8 + 3 = 11$
   (g) For some number x, $8 + x = 11$
   (h) For every number x, $8 + x = 11$

4. Henry Hero and his one person submarine stray too close to the lost undersea kingdom of Atlantis. Brought before the Supreme Shark, Henry tries in vain to explain that he just made a simple navigational error.

   "Lies, all lies!" shouts the skeptical Supreme Shark. "People always lie to me. Tell me just one thing that's clearly not a lie and I'll free you. But I warn you: No one has ever convinced me that they're not lying!"

   What can Henry say to win his release?

5. Write each of the following four statements in symbolic form as combinations of p, q, and r, using these meanings

$$p: x > -1 \qquad q: x = -1 \qquad r: x \leq 4$$

   For each statement, also make a number line sketch of the region described.

   (a) $-1 \leq x$
   (b) $x \leq -1$
   (c) $-1 \leq x \leq 4$
   (d) $x < -1$ or $x > 4$

6. Each of the following expressions is a particular statement in which the variable is a specific, but unknown number. Use De Morgan's Laws, rules for quantifiers, and common sense to rewrite each one as a combination of two simpler, negative statements.

   (a) x is not less than or equal to 12.
   (b) y is not positive and less than 1.
   (c) k is not an integer greater than 100.
   (d) z is neither even nor a multiple of 3.

7. Denote by $p \rightarrow q$ the conditional statement,

   "If Lopez pitches well, then the team wins."

   Write each of these statements in symbolic form, using the notation of this section.

   (a) If the team wins, then Lopez pitches well.
   (b) If Lopez doesn't pitch well, then the team doesn't win.
   (c) If the team doesn't win, then Lopez doesn't pitch well.
   (d) The team wins and Lopez pitches well.
   (e) Either Lopez doesn't pitch well or the team wins.
   (f) Lopez pitches well and the team doesn't win.

8. State the hypothesis, the conclusion, and the converse of each statement.

   (a) If there is snow on the ground, then this is winter.
   (b) The game is official if we complete the fifth inning.
   (c) If $x = 5$, then $x^2 = 25$
   (d) $3x = 3y$ implies $x = y$
   (e) $|x| > 0$ if $x \neq 0$
   (f) $\dfrac{5}{x}$ is a well defined number unless $x = 0$. Be careful!
   (g) All elephants have trunks. *Convert to conditional form first.*
   (h) No man is an island. *Convert to conditional form first.*

9. Two political slogans from George Orwell's famous novel, *1984*, are

   "War is peace"   and   "Freedom is slavery"

   Assume that both of these statements are false. What is the truth value of each of the following statements? Justify your answers.

   (a) War is not peace.
   (b) War is not peace and freedom is slavery.
   (c) Either freedom is slavery or war is peace.
   (d) Either freedom is slavery or war is not peace.
   (e) If war is not peace, then freedom is not slavery.
   (f) If war is not peace, then freedom is slavery.

6.4 Coming to Conclusions: Direct and Indirect Proofs

Deductive reasoning is the process of using logic to prove statements from other statements that are known or assumed to be true. Conditional statements provide the key to this process. You might think of a *proof* as one long conditional statement. It may have a single statement or more likely several statements as its hypotheses. The purpose of a proof is to guarantee that its conclusion is true whenever all of its hypotheses are true. If it does this, the proof is said to be **valid.** In this section you will see how the guarantee supplied by a valid argument is used both forwards and backwards.

A *direct proof* starts with hypotheses that are known or presumed to be true. By using conditional statements, this known truth is extended step by step to reach the statement to be proved, which is the final conclusion. The arguments are not usually written out exactly that way, so the conditional form is sometimes hard to recognize. But it's always there.

Here is an example.

Theorem If 3 is a divisor of both a and b, then 3 is a divisor of $a + b$.

Proof We know (by the hypothesis) that 3 is a divisor of a and also of b. This means that $a = 3x$ and $b = 3y$ for some integers x and y. Therefore,

$$a + b = 3x + 3y$$

Now, the Distributive Law is true, so it can be used as the hypothesis.

$$3x + 3y = 3(x + y)$$

Since x and y are integers, so is their sum. Putting these facts together, we have

$$a + b = 3(x + y)$$

That is, 3 is a divisor of $a + b$.

Learning Outcomes

After studying this section you will be able to:

Distinguish between direct and indirect proofs

Explain the role of counterexamples in the proof process

Use direct and indirect proofs to justify statements

Form the contrapositive and the inverse of a conditional statement.

417

Summary Starting with the hypothesis that 3 is a divisor of both a and b and the known truth of the Distributive Law, the proof proceeds through a chain of conditional statements to reach the final conclusion that 3 is a divisor of $a + b$.

6.28 Give a direct proof of the following geometric statement:

> In an isosceles triangle, the bisector of the angle between the two equal sides also bisects the side opposite that angle.

Here are some steps to help you organize your thoughts.

1. Begin by rephrasing the statement as a conditional. What is its hypothesis? What is its conclusion?

2. Use the diagram in Display 6.5 to visualize the situation. Restate what you know and what you must prove in terms of the lettering of that diagram.

3. Plan a strategy for this proof. What is the main idea of an argument you think will work?

4. Now finish the proof. Give a reason to justify every statement you make.

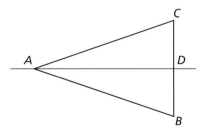

Display 6.5

A conditional statement guarantees that, whenever its hypothesis is true, then its conclusion *must* be true. Thus, the claim that a conditional statement is *false* says that there are times when the hypothesis is true and the conclusion is false. For example, to say that the statement

"If a number ends in 3, then it is divisible by 3"

is false means that *there exists* a number that satisfies the hypothesis (ends in 3) but not the conclusion (is not divisible by 3). Thus, to prove the conditional false, all we have to do is find one such number. Recall that an example that proves a statement false is called a **counterexample**.

These questions refer to our usual base ten numeration system.

6.29

1. Find a counterexample for: "If a number ends in 3, then it is divisible by 3." Then find an example for which both the hypothesis and the conclusion are true.

2. Is the statement, "If a number ends in 2, then it is divisible by 2," true or false? How do you know?

3. Is the statement, "If a number ends in 4, then it is divisible by 4," true or false? How do you know?

Sometimes it is not obvious whether a statement is true or false. Maybe it appears to be true, but you can't prove it directly. In such cases, the next step is to try to find a counterexample. But sometimes that doesn't work, either. In such cases, a backwards approach, called *indirect proof,* often works.

An indirect proof, also known as a *proof by contradiction*, is based on the Law of Contradiction and the Law of the Excluded Middle. A statement *must* be either true or false, and it can't be both at the same time. Therefore, we may prove that a statement is true *by assuming that it is false* and showing that this assumption leads to some kind of impossible situation. Here is an example from geometry.

Draw two circles of any sizes that intersect. Call their two intersecting points P and Q. From P, draw a diameter of each circle. Label the other ends of these diameters A and B. Now draw segment AB. Your picture should look something like Display 6.6(a). Does AB go through Q (the other intersection point), or does it just come close? Are you sure?

6.30

In Display 6.6(a), the dot at Q is very large to emphasize the fact that drawings, no matter how carefully they are done, are not good enough to determine whether Q is exactly on AB or is just very close to it. In fact, Q might be on one side or the other of *AB* in some of the figures you and your classmates drew, but always pretty close to it. This makes it tempting to believe the following conjecture:

> If two circles intersect at two points, *P* and *Q*, and if *PA* and *PB* are diameters of the two circles, then *Q* is on line *AB*.

Is it true? Does it hold for any two intersecting circles of any size? We'll settle this question by indirect proof.

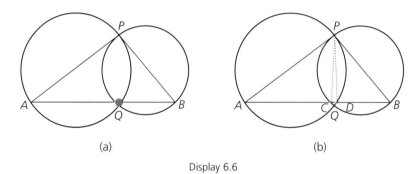

(a)   (b)

Display 6.6

Proof Assume that the conjecture is false. Then there are two circles (somewhere) for which the hypothesis is true, but the conclusion is false. That is, the other intersection point of the circles, *Q*, is not on line *AB*. This means that *AB* intersects the two circles in two different points; call them *C* and *D*. Draw *PC* and *PD*, as in Display 6.6(b).

Now, *PB* is a diameter of a circle, so $\angle PCB$ is an angle inscribed in a semicircle. This means that $\angle PCB$ is a right angle. Similarly $\angle PDB$ is a right angle because *PA* is a diameter of the other circle. But that means that both *PC* and *PD* are perpendicular to *AB* from the same point, which cannot be! Do you see why it cannot be? Think about the angle sum of $\triangle PCD$.

The *assumption* that the conjecture is false has led to a contradiction. This means that the conjecture is not false, so it must be true! There's no other choice. Thus, we have proved the following theorem.

Theorem If two circles intersect at two points and if a diameter of each circle is drawn from one of these intersection points, then the line connecting the other ends of these diameters passes through the other intersection point.

Prove this statement indirectly.

6.31

If $\frac{6}{x}$ is a rational number in lowest terms,

then x is an odd integer.

What is the first step you should take?

Proof by contradiction is a powerful thinking tool. If you don't understand why (or if) some statement must be true, think about what would happen if it were false. See if the assumption that it's false leads to some contradiction or nonsense. If it does, then the original statement can't be false, so it *must* be true because there's no other choice.

A Theorem in Quick Six is:

6.32

A player with five cards can win the game on the next play.

1. Prove this theorem.

2. Is your proof direct or indirect? Explain.

3. Now prove it the other way.

4. Which way was easier for you, direct or indirect? Why?

The two different approaches to proof can be summarized by two principles.

Direct proof A valid argument with a true hypothesis must have a true conclusion.

Indirect proof A valid argument with a false conclusion must have a false hypothesis.

The idea of reversing both the direction of the argument and the truth values of the hypothesis and conclusion is mirrored in the formal logic of conditional statements. Interchanging the hypothesis and the conclusion of a conditional and negating them results in a new statement, called the *contrapositive* of the original conditional. In symbols, the contrapositive of $p \rightarrow q$ is

6.33

$$(\sim q) \rightarrow (\sim p)$$

The value of the contrapositive is that *it is logically equivalent to the original conditional statement*. That is, it can be used in place of the original conditional in any logical argument.

6.34

1. What is the contrapositive of "If $x = 3$, then $x^2 = 9$"?

2. What is the contrapositive of "All athletes eat Wheaties"?

3. Make up another example of a conditional statement and its contrapositive.

The *inverse* of a conditional statement is formed by negating the hypothesis and the conclusion of the original conditional. In symbols, the inverse of $p \rightarrow q$ is

$$(\sim p) \rightarrow (\sim q)$$

6.35

1. What is the inverse of "If $x = 3$, then $x^2 = 9$"?

2. What is the inverse of "All athletes eat Wheaties"?

Problem Set: 6.4

1. (a) Prove directly the following useful fact.
   If a and b are positive numbers and $a < b$, then $a^2 < b^2$.
   Give a reason to justify each step you take.

   (b) Show by counterexample that the hypothesis that a and b be positive is a necessary condition for part (a).

2. (a) Use the fact established in problem 1 to prove directly that, if the square root of a positive number is less than half the number, then the number is greater than 4.
   In symbols,
   $$\text{If } x > 0 \text{ and } \sqrt{x} < \frac{x}{2}, \text{ then } x > 4$$

   Give a reason to justify each step you take.
   (b) Make a conjecture analogous to part (a) for the case $x < 4$. Then prove it.

3. Many students run into algebraic trouble by forgetting the following fact:
   $$\text{If } a \neq 0 \text{ and } b \neq 0, \text{ then } \sqrt{a^2 + b^2} \neq a + b$$

   (a) Give an example to illustrate this statement.
   (b) Prove this statement indirectly.

4. Two friends claim that you can simplify the expression $\frac{4x - 1}{4}$ by cancelling the 4s to get $x - 1$. You say that this is not correct, but they do not believe you. Use indirect proof to show that

$$\frac{4x - 1}{4} \neq x - 1$$

5. Prove: If $a \neq 0$ and $b \neq 0$, then $\frac{1}{a} + \frac{1}{b} \neq \frac{2}{a + b}$.

6.5 How Are Axioms Chosen? Mathematical Modeling

Learning Outcomes

After studying this section you will be able to:

Explain what a mathematical model is

Explain the difference between inductive and deductive reasoning

Describe some advantages and some disadvantages of using mathematical models

State and apply the Law of the Lever

Recognize the axioms for a group.

About Words

Some other words with the same root are *ex-tract, dis-tract, sub-tract, at-tract, con-tract.*

The history of science is the story of us humans trying to master the complex world we live in. To master our world, we must understand it. To understand something complex, we must simplify it. We must weed out confusing details that get in the way of seeing how it works. A key to simplifying is *modeling*.

6.36

Think of three or four kinds of things outside of mathematics that are called models and the ways in which they are used. For each one, describe how the model is simpler than the real thing it represents. Then explain how that simplification leads to better mastery or control of the real situation.

6.37   Making a model is a form of abstraction. The word *abstract* is discomforting for some people. They think it means vague or hard to understand. In fact, its meaning is quite different. The literal meaning of the verb *abstract* is "pull away from." It has the same root as tractor. The adjective *abstract* just says that some properties of a thing are being considered apart from the thing's other characteristics. Thus, abstraction is a way to *simplify* something by stripping it down to its essential features, like the Cheshire Cat of Wonderland, which faded away slowly before Alice's eyes, until only the grin remained.

Mathematical modeling is this kind of simplifying process. As you learned earlier in **MATH** *Connections*, a mathematical object that is used to describe a situation outside of mathematics is called a **mathematical model** of that situation. A mathematical model can be as small as a single equation or figure, or as large as an entire theory, such as probability or plane geometry. You have already seen many mathematical models this year. For instance,

- The growth of compound interest was modeled by an exponential function.

- The cycle of daylight hours in a year was modeled by a periodic function.

- The commonsense reasoning we do every day was modeled by the logical principles of Section 6.4.

Recall at least three more mathematical models from your work in MATH *Connections* Year 3 besides the ones mentioned in the previous paragraph. In each case, identify both the model and the real-world object or situation that is being modeled.

6.38

For all these models, there's good news and bad news.

- The good news is that a model is relatively simple. We can use mathematics to understand how it works, and then apply that understanding to the corresponding real-world object.

- The bad news is the same as the good news: a model is relatively simple. When we identify certain properties as "the" important ones and abstract them to form the model, we may leave behind some properties that are more important than we think. This means that sometimes what we learn about the model might not fit exactly the reality from which it came.

Plane geometry, for example, is a mathematical model of how flat maps work. This geometry and the maps themselves are models of the Earth's surface. They are accurate enough for surveying fields or taking trips of a few hundred miles. However, they do not describe the Earth's surface accurately because the Earth is not flat, so they are not very good for charting long ocean voyages or airline routes.

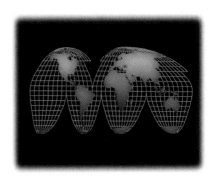

Despite the bad news, the power of abstraction depends on separating essential ideas from unnecessary details. For example, think about *levers*. Levers are everywhere—as tools, as parts of machines, even in playgrounds. Usually, a lever is pictured as a long beam being used to move a large rock. But we use levers in many, many other ways, too. Every time you pry open a paint can with a screwdriver you're using a lever. If you play the piano, you're using lots of levers. When you drive a car, the gas and brake pedals work by levers. Even a playground seesaw is a lever. See Display 6.7.

Bar moving sack adapted from Hogben's *Science for the Citizen*, Allen & Unwin (1956); hammer and pry bar based on drawings from the NEW COMPLETE DO-IT-YOURSELF MANUAL, copyright © 1991 The Reader's Digest Association, Inc. Used by permission of The Reader's Digest Association, Inc.

Some simple uses of levers

Display 6.7

6.39

1. **Describe the essential idea of a lever in your own words. What are its characteristic features?**

2. **How many times did you use some kind of lever this week? Describe at least two of these situations. In each case, say what is being moved by the lever and where the force is being applied to it.**

6.40   What basic ideas tell us that a lever is at work? Let us abstract the essential features of a lever from the examples we have seen.

   • First of all, a *lever* is something rigid. It might not be straight or flat, but it works just as if it were a solid bar of some sort. So we can think of it as a straight bar.

   • This bar pivots or balances on something. That thing is called the *fulcrum* of the lever.

   • Force is applied to the bar on one side of the fulcrum in order to move something on the other side.

Display 6.8, which illustrates these features, is also an abstraction. It doesn't represent any particular, real lever; it represents *all* levers by picturing the properties that every lever must have.

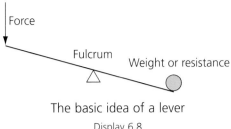

The basic idea of a lever

Display 6.8

Now combine this abstraction with experience. Farmers throughout history have known that they can move larger rocks by using longer levers. Mechanics apply extra force to a wrench by extending its handle with a piece of pipe. A child who weighs less than her brother knows that they can balance on a seesaw if her brother sits closer to the center. The underlying (abstract) idea is that the lifting power of a lever depends on

1. the force applied to it, and

2. the distance of that force from the fulcrum.

Picture the lever of Display 6.8 as a sort of seesaw, and think of the weight on one side as just another force pushing down, as in Display 6.9. How much force on one side is needed to balance (lift) the force on the other? It depends on their distances from the fulcrum, of course, but how? Is there some nice, neat relationship?

6.41

A powerful relationship between the forces and distances of a lever was discovered more than 2000 years ago. The lever will balance like a seesaw if the product of the force and distance on one side of the fulcrum equals the product of the force and distance on the other side.

We shall call this the Law of the Lever. Algebra allows us to state this law very simply, using the notation of Display 6.9:

The Law of the Lever Let F_1 be the force applied at distance d_1 on one side of the fulcrum, and let F_2 be the force applied at distance d_2 on the other side of the fulcrum. Then

$$F_1 \cdot d_1 = F_2 \cdot d_2$$

The Law of the Lever

Display 6.9

6.42

1. When you pry open a paint can with a screwdriver, the distance between the tip of the screwdriver and the rim of the can (the fulcrum) is about 5 mm (0.5 cm).

   (a) If you push down on the screwdriver 15 cm from the can rim with 10 lbs. of force, how much force is pushing up on the lid at the tip of the screwdriver?

   (b) If you get a longer screwdriver and push down on it 21 cm from the can rim with 10 lbs. of force, how much force is pushing up on the lid at the tip of the screwdriver?

2. Alma, who weighs 55 lbs., wants to ride on the seesaw with her older brother Julio, who weighs 85 lbs. If Alma sits at one end of the seesaw, 7 feet from the fulcrum, where must Julio sit to balance her? Round your answer to the nearest half foot.

The Law of the Lever is the basis for a mathematical model of any situation involving levers. The model helps us predict how real levers will work without actually making them or trying them out. The law itself is an abstraction, made up to fit many, many observations of levers. It is the result of **inductive reasoning,** the process of looking at particular examples and abstracting a general statement that appears to be true about all of them.

Unlike deductive reasoning, there are no formal rules to guarantee the truth of an inductive result. An inductive conclusion is considered to be true as long as it appears to be an accurate reflection of how things work in the real world.

6.43

A striking example of the truth and power of the Law of the Lever occurred in 212 B.C., when Archimedes used it to defend the city of Syracuse (in Sicily) from the Roman legions. The war machines he designed held off the invading Romans for many weeks!

Do some library research on Archimedes' defense of Syracuse. Then write a one or two page paper about it. Part of your paper should explain how Archimedes used levers to make his powerful war machines. Be sure to cite any references you use.

In more formal terms, the Law of the Lever is an **axiom.** That is, we assume it to be true and we use it as a basic

Playing by the Rules: Logic and Axiomatic Systems

6.5 How Are Axioms Chosen? Mathematical Modeling

building block for mechanical theory. Like any good axiom, it does two things well:

• it *unifies* many different examples under one principle

• it *simplifies* reality by bringing out the essential features.

The rest of this chapter explores a more modern, but equally important example of this unifying and simplifying process. It is a system of several axioms taken together. These axioms model the structure of many apparently different things, from molecules to music, from tiling patterns to computer codes, from the arithmetic of whole numbers to the arithmetic of functions.

6.44

1. Using addition or multiplication only, solve the following equations. You can use any rational numbers.
$$x + 4 = 12$$
$$x + 3486 = 5723$$
$$4x = 12$$
$$3486x = 5723$$

2. Suppose that a and b are nonzero rational numbers. Using addition or multiplication only, solve the equations
$$x + a = b \text{ and } ax = b$$

That is, write them in the form $x = [something]$.

Let's look carefully at how such equations are solved. Their solutions all follow the same pattern. This pattern is what we want to pull out (abstract) from the clutter of particular numbers and operations. Here, in painful detail, are the steps for solving $x + 3 = 5$ and $3x = 5$.

$$(x + 3) + (-3) = 5 + (-3) \qquad \frac{1}{3} \cdot (3 \cdot x) = \frac{1}{3} \cdot 5$$

$$x + (3 + (-3)) = 2 \qquad \left(\frac{1}{3} \cdot 3\right) \cdot x = \frac{5}{3}$$

$$x + 0 = 2 \qquad 1 \cdot x = \frac{5}{3}$$

$$x = 2 \qquad x = \frac{5}{3}$$

6.45 Write out, side by side, the steps for solving the equations $x + a = b$ and $a \cdot x = b$, where a and b can stand for any positive integers.

One of these equations uses addition and the other uses multiplication, but *their solutions follow the same pattern.* In both cases we choose a number to "cancel" the number paired with x. That is, after regrouping by associativity and combining the two numbers, the result is a number that leaves x unchanged.

- To solve $x + 3 = 5$, we choose -3 because $3 + (-3) = 0$, and 0 added to any number x leaves x unchanged.

- To solve $3 \cdot x = 5$, we choose $\frac{1}{3}$ because $\frac{1}{3} \cdot 3 = 1$, and 1 multiplied by any number x leaves x unchanged.

6.46 To abstract the common pattern, let "the operation" mean either addition or multiplication. Then, in both cases, the equation-solving recipe requires three things.

1. The operation must be associative. Why?

2. There must be a neutral number—a number that does not change anything with which it is combined. For addition, what is that number? For multiplication, what is that number?

3. For any number, a, that is combined with x in the equation, there must be a "neutralizing number"— a number that combines with a to form the neutral number. For addition, what is that number? For multiplication, what is that number?

Are you thinking, "Why do we need all this abstract language just to talk about adding and multiplying?"

We don't—not if we're going to talk *only* about adding and multiplying. The payoff to this abstraction is that it also applies to many other processes besides adding and multiplying, and to many other things besides numbers. We are making a model of how addition and multiplication work, but there are many other instances of this model.

The key step is defining what we mean by an operation. Think about the four common arithmetic operations: addition, subtraction, multiplication, and division. You have also seen a fifth one: exponentiation. What do these five different processes

Playing by the Rules: Logic and Axiomatic Systems

6.5 How Are Axioms Chosen? Mathematical Modeling

have in common? They are ways of combining two numbers to form another number. The definition of *operation* abstracts (pulls out) this idea of combining two things, allowing it to apply to things besides numbers.

A Word to Know: An **operation** on a set is any rule or process that assigns to each ordered pair of elements of the set exactly one element of that same set.[†]

The four common arithmetic operations are represented by familiar symbols: $+$, $-$, $\times$ (or $*$ or $\cdot$), $\div$. The $\wedge$ key on the calculator shows a common symbol for exponentiation. We shall use $\diamond$ to stand for an arbitrary operation. The element that an operation $\diamond$ assigns to the ordered pair (x, y) is usually written as $x \diamond y$. For example, "$3 + 4 = 7$" means that 7 is the number assigned to the ordered pair $(3, 4)$ by addition.

1. For each of the following operations, represent the number it assigns to the ordered pair $(5, 3)$ by using a familiar symbol for the operation. Also write the number it equals. The first one is done for you.

   6.47

   (a) Addition. $[\, 5 + 3 = 8 \,]$

   (b) Subtraction.

   (c) Multiplication.

   (d) Division.

   (e) Exponentiation.

2. The definition of operation requires the results of applying an operation to be back in the original set. With this in mind, explain why exponentiation is an operation on the set of all positive integers, but *not* on the set of all integers.

3. Give a reason for each *Yes* answer and a counterexample for each *No* answer.

   Is subtraction an operation on

   (a) the set of all integers?

[†]Such operations are usually called *binary operations* because they combine two elements at a time. There are other kinds of operations. However, this is the only kind we shall consider, so we omit the word *binary* for simplicity.

(b) the set of all positive integers?

(c) the set of all negative integers?

(d) the set of all odd integers?

(e) the set of all even integers?

So far, we have mentioned only operations on numbers. But there are others, too.

• Composition is an operation on functions.

• Union and intersection are operations on sets.

• The "followed by" process is an operation on symmetries of geometric figures.

Some of these operations, and others, appear in Sections 6.6 and 6.7 as instances of the axiomatic system we are building here.

Now it's time to finish the model. We want to choose a few axioms that form a system in which we can always answer the basic, natural question,

"What can we combine with a to get b?"

for any elements a and b in the system. In symbols, we want a system that contains a solution for every equation of the form

$$a \diamond x = b \quad \text{or} \quad x \diamond a = b$$

Now, every result proved within an axiomatic system applies to every instance of that system. Therefore, the more instances an axiomatic system has, the more powerful it is. This means that our axioms should be as general as we can make them. We want the axioms to apply to many different kinds of operations on many different kinds of sets, not just to numbers and arithmetic.

To do this, we begin with two undefined terms: a set G and an operation $\diamond$. Then, remembering how the equations $x + 3 = 5$ and $3 \cdot x = 5$ were solved, we choose axioms that allow us to take the same steps.

Axioms

(a) If a, b are elements of G, then $a \diamond b$ is also an element of G.

(b) The operation $\diamond$ is associative on G.

(c) There is a neutral element, z, in G. That is, for every element a in G,   6.48

$$z \diamondsuit a = a \quad \text{and} \quad a \diamondsuit z = a$$

(d) For each element a in G, there is a neutralizing element, a', in G. That is,

$$a \diamondsuit a' = z \quad \text{and} \quad a' \diamondsuit a = z$$

A set with an operation that satisfies these four axioms is called a **group.** That's why we called the set G, not S.

There are surprisingly many different instances of these axioms—groups of all shapes and sizes. Section 6.6 will show you some of them. The power of this seemingly simple axiomatic system will be explored further in Section 6.7.

Problem Set: 6.5

1. In the past 350 years, world population has increased dramatically. Here are the population figures, in millions, for a few of those years.

1650 — 550 million	1750 — 725 million
1850 — 1175 million	1900 — 1600 million
1950 — 2564 million	1980 — 4478 million
1990 — 5279 million	2000 — 6085 million

This growth pattern can be modeled approximately by the function

$$P_1(x) = 0.0085e^{0.0065x}$$

where $P_1(x)$ is the population for the year x.

Put these data into the first two lists of your graphing calculator. Use L1 for year and L2 for population. Size the graph Window so that $1500 < x < 2200$ and $-4000 < y < 6000$.

(a) Use the calculator's statistical plotting function to graph the data points. Also graph the function P_1.

(b) Does P_1 pass through any of the data points? Does it come close enough to be a good enough model for the world population? Good enough for what? Explain.

(c) What population does P_1 predict for the year 2010? For 2020? For 2050?

2. This problem depends on problem 1. Use the data and calculator instructions from problem 1.

   (a) Replace P_1 with the function

   $$P_2(x) = \frac{1}{.009828 - .000004854x}$$

   Then graph the function P_2 and the data points.

   (b) Does P_2 fit the data points better than P_1?

   (c) Is P_2 a better model of the world's population than P_1? Why or why not?

   (d) What population does P_2 predict for the year 2010? For 2020? For 2050?

   (e) What is the meaning of the vertical line in the graph of P_2?

3. One end of a 6-foot lever is placed under a large rock. A pivot stone (fulcrum) is placed 1 foot from that end. A force of 150 lbs. is applied at the other end.

   (a) Draw a sketch of this situation.

   (b) How much force is exerted on the rock? Ignore the weight of the lever. Use the Law of the Lever to justify your answer.

   (c) Moving the fulcrum can increase the effect of the 150 lb. force being applied. Where should the fulcrum be placed so that the same 150 lbs. of force exerts exactly twice as much pressure on the rock as it did in part (a)? Justify your answer.

   (d) Tyrone guessed that the answer to part (c) is to put the fulcrum exactly halfway between where it was originally and the rock end. That's a pretty good guess, but it's not quite right. If the fulcrum is placed there (exactly half a foot from the rock end), will the force on the rock be more than or less than twice as much as it was in part (a)? How can you tell? You should be able to answer this by looking back at your answer to part (c).

4. As an advertising stunt, a lightweight, fuel efficient car has been put on a small platform at one end of a 30-foot I-beam. A man is to stand on a small platform at the other end of the I-beam, as shown in Display 6.10. The car, together with its platform, weighs 2300 lbs. The man, together with his platform, weighs 260 lbs. The I-beam weighs 24 lbs. per foot. Where along the I-beam is the balance point? Justify your answer.

Display 6.10

5. There is another type of lever than the one described by Display 6.8. For this type, the load on the lever is between the fulcrum and the point where the force is applied. Wheelbarrows, bottle openers, and nutcrackers are common examples. Display 6.11 illustrates this second type of lever. Three distances are labeled in that diagram.

d_1 is the distance between the fulcrum and the force

d_2 is the distance between the fulcrum and the resistance

d_3 is the distance between the resistance and the force

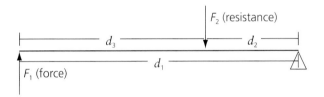

Another type of lever

Display 6.11

One of the following two equations is an appropriate mathematical model for this kind of lever; the other is not. Which is which? Justify your choice.

$$F_1 \cdot d_1 = F_2 \cdot d_2$$

$$F_1 \cdot d_3 = F_2 \cdot d_2$$

(*Hint:* Express d_3 in terms of d_1 and d_2. Then imagine moving F_2 closer and closer to F_1 and think about what each equation is saying.)

6. For each of the following questions, give a reason if you answer Yes, and give a counterexample if you answer No.

(a) Is multiplication an operation on

   (i)   the set of all integers?
   (ii) the set of all positive integers?
   (iii) the set of all negative integers?
   (iv) the set of all odd integers?
   (v)   the set of all even integers?

(b) Is division an operation on

   (i)   the set of all integers?
   (ii) the set of all positive integers?
   (iii) the set of all negative integers?
   (iv) the set of all odd integers?
   (v)   the set of all even integers?

7. (a) Group Axiom 2 says, "The operation $\diamond$ is associative on G." What does this mean? Write its meaning as a quantified statement.

   (b) Write the negation of the statement you wrote in part (a). In other words, write what it means to say that the operation $\diamond$ is *not* associative on G.

   (c) The other three group axioms are quantified statements, too. Write the negation of each one as clearly and as simply as you can. You might find it helpful to look back at Section 6.3.

6.6 Instances of the Group Axioms

In this section you will see many different instances of the group axioms. In the next section you will see how the axioms show us ways in which all these different instances are alike.

Here again are the axioms for a group, along with the standard names for the special elements they describe.

A group, $(G, \diamond)$, is a set G together with an operation $\diamond$ for which these four axioms are true:

Axioms

(a) For any elements a and b of G, the result $a \diamond b$ is also an element of G. This property is called **closure.**

(b) For any elements a, b, and c of G,

$$(a \diamond b) \diamond c = a \diamond (b \diamond c)$$

That is, the operation $\diamond$ is associative on G.

(c) There is an element z in G such that, for every element a of G,

$$z \diamond a = a \quad \text{and} \quad a \diamond z = a$$

This element z is called an **identity** element of the group.

(d) For each element a of G, there is an element a' in G such that

$$a \diamond a' = z \quad \text{and} \quad a' \diamond a = z$$

The element a' is called an **inverse** of the element a.

In the language of Section 6.5, the identity is the neutral element for the group, and an inverse of a is a neutralizing element for a.

Learning Outcomes

After studying this section you will be able to:

Explain the axioms for a group

Describe various properties of the integers and the rational numbers in terms of the group axioms

Describe and work with addition mod n for various integers $n > 1$.

6.49 The group axioms that guarantee that, for any of its elements *a* and *b*, the system always contains an answer for the question

"What can we combine with *a* to get *b*?"

Here are some systems in which that question doesn't always have an answer. For each one, find two numbers, *a* and *b*, for which the question *cannot* be answered. The first one is done for you. Then name at least one axiom that fails in the system.

1. The positive integers with addition.

   There is no solution in the system for $7 + x = 4$. That is, no positive integer added to 7 will give you 4.

2. The odd integers with addition.

3. The integers with multiplication.

Our first two instances of a group are the number systems that suggested them.

6.50 **The integers with addition:** To avoid rewriting this phrase over and over again, we'll use **I** for the set of integers and (**I, +**) for the integers together with usual addition. Now let's check the group axioms.

1. **Closure** You know from elementary arithmetic that the sum of two integers is always an integer, so this is OK.

2. **Associativity** You know this property of addition from earlier study in **MATH** *Connections*. For example,

$$32 + (15 + 27) = (32 + 15) + 27$$

3. **Identity** The integer 0 works as an identity because 0 added to anything (from either side) is that other thing. For instance,

$$0 + 5 = 5 \quad \text{and} \quad 5 + 0 = 5$$

4. **Inverses** The additive inverse of each integer is its negative. For instance, the inverse of 5 is -5 because

$$5 + (-5) = 0 \text{ and } (-5) + 5 = 0$$

   The inverse of -3 is 3 because

$$(-3) + 3 = 0 \text{ and } 3 + (-3) = 0$$

Thus, all four axioms are true in (**I, +**), so it is a group.

Notice that the definition of a group requires us to check the identity and inverse properties by combining the pairs of elements in both orders.

6.51

1. Is this really necessary for addition of integers? Why or why not?

2. Can you think of any operations that might give different results when the order of the elements being combined is reversed?

3. Some operations *never* give different results when the order of elements being combined is reversed. What are such operations called?

The nonzero rational numbers with multiplication: Again we start with some shorthand. The set of rational numbers is usually denoted by **Q**.[†] We'll use **Q*** for the nonzero rationals and (**Q***, ×) for the nonzero rationals together with usual multiplication. Now it's your turn to check the group axioms.

Show that (**Q***, ×) is a group by answering these questions. You may use anything you know about multiplication *of integers.*

6.52

1. How is multiplication of rational numbers defined? Work out $\frac{2}{3} \times \frac{4}{5}$ as an example. Then write a general definition by completing the equation

$$\frac{a}{b} \times \frac{c}{d} = \underline{\quad}$$

2. *Closure* Explain how your definition of multiplication guarantees that the product of two nonzero rational numbers is a nonzero rational number. What is a rational number? How can you recognize the rational number 0?

3. *Associativity* How does the fact that multiplication of integers is associative guarantee that multiplication of rational numbers is associative? Look back at your answer to question 1.

4. *Identity* What number is an identity for multiplication?

[†]The Q stands for "quotient." Rational numbers are quotients of integers. For instance, $\frac{2}{3}$ stands for $2 \div 3$, $\frac{-17}{5}$ stands for $-17 \div 5$, etc.

5. *Inverses* What is an inverse for $\frac{2}{3}$? For $\frac{73}{41}$? For $\frac{-7}{15}$? For $\frac{a}{b}$, where a and b are any nonzero integers? Justify your answers.

6. Why don't we include zero?

6.53   It's no surprise that $(\mathbf{I}, +)$ and $(\mathbf{Q}^*, \times)$ are groups. After all, that's where the axioms came from. We abstracted the properties needed to solve simple equations in those two systems. The surprise is that *many* other systems are groups! Example 1 below is a small, commonplace group that you run into practically every day. Examples 2 and 3 are different instances of it.

1.   A 3-way light has four switch positions—*low, medium, high,* and *off.* Each time the switch is turned, the light goes from one of these settings to the next, in order. Each click of the switch signals a movement from one brightness level to the next. With the fourth click the light is *off,* with the fifth it is at *low* again, and so on.

2.   The duty periods for crew members aboard ship are called *watches.* By a tradition dating back to the early days of sailing ships, each watch is four hours long and the passing of every hour is marked by pairs of bells—2 bells for the first hour, 4 for the second, 6 for the third, and 8 bells to signal the end of a watch and the beginning of another.

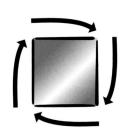

3.   A square tile works loose from its place in a bathroom floor. It can be put back in any of four ways: exactly as it was, or rotated (clockwise) 90°, or 180°, or 270°. A 360° rotation puts it back to its original position. Even if it has been kicked around for a while, whatever way it is put back *must* correspond to one of these four quarter turns relative to its original position.

Now we put abstraction to work. Some common features of these three very different situations are obvious.

- Each involves four things—brightness levels, watch hours, tile positions.
- We can go from each to the next in succession until we return to a starting point—*off*, beginning of watch, original position.

If we focus not on the things themselves but on the way of getting from one to another, a common structure emerges. In each case, we go from one thing to another by steps in a cyclic pattern. If we take more than 3 steps we will have gone around the cycle completely and will have started over. Thus, we might as well ignore all strings of 4 successive steps. For example,

- 5 switch clicks from *off* gets us to *low* again, so it's the same as 1 click
- 6 hours from the beginning of a watch is 2 hours into a watch (the next one, of course)
- 7 quarter turns of the tile puts it in the same position as 3 quarter turns

and so on.

The number of steps that take us to the different positions in each situation form the set {0, 1, 2, 3}. If we follow any of these numbers by any other, we get the same result as one of these four numbers. For instance, 2 steps following 3 steps is equivalent to 1 step. (In the light-switch instance, five clicks of the switch gives the same result as clicking it once.) If we let f mean "followed by," we can write this fact as

$$2 \, f \, 3 = 1$$

This shorthand notation makes it easy to tabulate all possible pairings of the four step numbers.

Display 6.12 shows the combinations of the four step numbers using "followed by," but many of the entries are missing.

6.54

1. Your teacher will give you a copy of Display 6.12. Complete the entries on your copy and keep it for reference. When the book refers to Display 6.12 later, it means your completed copy.

2. Does this table have a place for every possible pairing of the set {0, 1, 2, 3}? Explain.

$0 f 0 = 0$	$0 f 1 = 1$	$0 f 2 = 2$	$0 f 3 = 2$
$1 f 0 = 1$	$1 f 1 = \_\_$	$1 f 2 = \_\_$	$1 f 3 = \_\_$
$\_ f \_ = \_\_$	$\_ f \_ = \_\_$	$\_ f \_ = \_\_$	$2 f 3 = 1$
$\_ f \_ = \_\_$	$3 f 1 = 0$	$\_ f \_ = \_\_$	$\_ f \_ = \_\_$

Combinations of the four step numbers

Display 6.12

We have claimed that instances 1, 2, and 3 (above) all represent a group. Can you prove this? Where would you start? The following questions will guide you through the process of verifying that the four group axioms are satisfied.

6.55

Remember that the elements of each instance are represented by {0, 1, 2, 3}, and the process of combining these elements is represented by f (followed by). Use Display 6.12 to help you answer these questions.

1. How do you know that f is an operation on the set {0, 1, 2, 3}?

2. How do you know that closure holds?

3. Is f associative on this set?

4. Which number is an identity for this system? How can you tell this from Display 6.12?

5. Specify an inverse for each element. Justify your choices.

Did you have trouble showing that f is associative? We thought you might. Are you sure that it really is associative? Here is another way of thinking about f and {0, 1, 2, 3} that will make associativity obvious and also lead to an infinite family of important groups.

In each of the three instances above, the cycle of steps (for brightness settings, shipboard watches, tile rotations) starts over with every fourth step. That is, any bunch of four steps can be ignored or thrown away without affecting the final result. If you think of the *f* process as adding steps, this means that multiples of 4 don't affect the answer. In other words,

> *the answer in this kind of addition is just the remainder you get when you divide the ordinary sum by 4.*

For instance, 5 steps followed by 6 more steps is really the same as 3 steps

$$5 + 6 = 11, \text{ and } 11 \div 4 \text{ leaves a remainder of } 3.$$

Think of rotating the tile 11 quarter turns, or turning the light switch for 11 clicks.

You may already have seen this kind of addition in your earlier mathematical studies. In elementary school it's called *clock addition*. In this case, the clock has just 4 hours! Sometimes it's called *remainder addition*. Its formal name is **modular addition**, and the divisor (in this case, 4) is called the **modulus**. The usual symbol for modular addition is $\oplus$ (mod *n*), where the *n* stands for the divisor. Thus, the previous example is written

$$5 \oplus 6 = 3 \text{ (mod 4)}$$

When the modulus number is obvious in a situation (as in the instances above), the (mod *n*) part of the expression may be left out.

Here's some practice to get you used to the notation. Calculate each of these modular sums.

6.56

1. $7 \oplus 3$ (mod 4)
2. $7 \oplus 3$ (mod 5)
3. $7 \oplus 3$ (mod 6)
4. $7 \oplus 3$ (mod 8)
5. $7 \oplus 3$ (mod 12)
6. $2 \oplus 3$ (mod 4)
7. $5 \oplus 4$ (mod 7)
8. $8 \oplus 9$ (mod 12)
9. $6 \oplus 3$ (mod 2)
10. $7 \oplus 7$ (mod 11)

Now associativity is easy to handle. Modular addition is just the same as regular addition, except that it throws away all multiples of the modulus. Using $\oplus$ to represent addition mod *n*,

$(a \oplus b) \oplus c =$ the remainder of $(a + b) + c$ divided by n;

$a \oplus (b \oplus c) =$ the remainder of $a + (b + c)$ divided by n;

for any numbers a, b, and c. But $(a + b) + c = a + (b + c)$ because ordinary addition is associative. Therefore, the remainders must be the same. For example, using addition mod 4,

$$(1 \oplus 2) \oplus 3 = 3 \oplus 3 = 2$$

and,

$$1 \oplus (2 \oplus 3) = 1 \oplus 1 = 2$$

Display 6.12 (which you completed) fully describes the operation $\oplus$ (mod 4). It shows the result for each ordered pair, but it's cluttered and hard to read. The same information can be shown more clearly by making something called an *operation table*. An operation table works like a grid for reading a road map. The following steps explain how to make an operation table, using $\oplus$ (mod 4) as a typical example.

- List the elements of the set in a column down the left side and in a row across the top, as in Display 6.13. This creates a square array of boxes to be filled, indicated by the dotted lines.

- Each box corresponds to the ordered pair formed by the element to its left (first) and the element above it (second). Put into each box the element that the operation assigns to its ordered pair. Display 6.13 shows one instance of this.

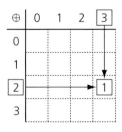

$$2 \oplus 3 = 1$$

Display 6.13

Display 6.14 shows the completed operation table for addition mod 4. The symbol for the operation is put in the upper left corner for reference.

⊕	0	1	2	3
0	0	1	2	3
1	1	2	3	0
2	2	3	0	1
3	3	0	1	2

Addition Mod 4

Display 6.14

Display 6.15 shows the form of an operation table for ⊕ (mod 6).

6.57

1. List the ordered pairs that correspond to each box. Then find their sums (mod 6).

2. Your teacher will give you an enlarged copy of Display 6.15. Fill in the boxed entries.

⊕	0	1	2	3	4	5
0			□			
1		□				
2	□					□
3			□		□	
4					□	□
5		□	□			

Display 6.15

Problem Set: 6.6

1. (a) Give an example to illustrate that ordinary addition of integers is associative. Work out the arithmetic.

(b) Give an example to illustrate that subtraction of integers is not associative. Work out the arithmetic.

(c) Does the example you gave for part (a) *prove* that addition of integers is associative? Why or why not?

(d) Does the example you gave for part (b) *prove* that subtraction of integers is not associative? Why or why not?

(e) Is 0 an identity element for subtraction? Why or why not?

2. This problem shows why modular arithmetic is sometimes called clock addition. Think about the *hour* display of a digital clock.

   (a) What numbers are used in this display?
   (b) If you add 5 hours to 10 o'clock, what hour is displayed?
   (c) What is the modulus for this clock addition?
   (d) What hour is an identity for this clock addition?
   (e) What is an inverse for 2? For 6? For 7?
       How do you know?
   (f) Solve the equation $5 \oplus x = 1$.

3. (a) Make an operation table for addition mod 5. Then verify that it is a group. Be sure to specify an identity element and an inverse for each number.
   (b) By analogy with addition, define multiplication mod 5, and denote it by $\otimes$ (mod 5). Is $\otimes$ (mod 5) an operation on the set {0, 1, 2, 3, 4}? Why or why not? Is it an operation on the set {1, 2, 3, 4}? Why or why not?
   (c) Is $\otimes$ (mod 5) associative? Justify your answer.
       (*Hint*: Look back at the discussion of associativity for $\oplus$ (mod 4) and argue by analogy.)
   (d) Make an operation table for $\otimes$ (mod 5) on the set {0, 1, 2, 3, 4}. Is this a group? Why or why not?
   (e) Does $\otimes$ (mod 5) make {1, 2, 3, 4} into a group? Why or why not?

4. Answer these questions by using the information in Display 6.16.

   (a) Is $\star$ an operation on the set {1, 2, 3, 4}?
       Why or why not?
   (b) $3 \star 4 = ?$
   (c) $1 \star (1 \star 4) = ?$
   (d) Work out a counterexample to show that $\star$ is not associative.
   (e) Which number, if any, is an identity element?
       Justify your answer.
   (f) Which number, if any, is an inverse of 4?
       Justify your answer.

★	1	2	3	4
1	1	2	1	3
2	2	2	2	2
3	1	2	3	4
4	3	2	4	1

Display 6.16

5. Recall that $\mathbf{Q}^*$ represents the set of nonzero rational numbers.

   (a) Does the averaging operation $\dfrac{a+b}{2}$ make $\mathbf{Q}^*$ a group? That is, if we define an operation $\diamond$ by

$$a \diamond b = \frac{a+b}{2}$$

   is $(\mathbf{Q}^*, \diamond)$ a group?

   (b) What about $\dfrac{a \cdot b}{2}$? If we define an operation $\diamond$ by

$$a \diamond b = \frac{a \cdot b}{2}$$

   is $(\mathbf{Q}^*, \diamond)$ a group?

   Justify your answers by checking the group axioms.

6. (a) If we define an operation ★ on the integers by $a \star b = (a + 2) - b$, is $(\mathbf{I}, \star)$ a group? Justify your answer by checking the group axioms.

   (b) If we define an operation on the integers by $a \star b = (a - 2) + b$, is $(\mathbf{I}, \star)$ a group? Justify your answer by checking the group axioms.

6.7 The Power of Proof

Learning Outcomes

After studying this section you will be able to:

Recognize the identity element, inverses, and the Cancellation Laws in operation tables

Explain the proofs of some theorems about groups

Work with symmetries of polygons as permutations

Combine symmetries by function composition;

Construct groups of symmetries.

6.58

Think about the groups that you saw in Section 6.6.

1. Do any of those groups have more than one identity element? If so, name one.

2. In any of those groups, is there an element with more than one inverse? If so, name one.

3. What does it mean to say that an operation is commutative? Are any of the group operations in Section 6.6 *not* commutative? If so, name one.

4. What is a theorem?

The preceding questions point out that the following three statements are true for all the groups we have seen so far.

1. Each of those groups has only one identity element.

2. Each element of each of those groups has only one inverse.

3. Each of those group operations is commutative.

Are these statements true for *all* groups everywhere, even ones we haven't thought of yet? If so, then they should be theorems. That is, it should be possible to prove them from the group axioms. If any one of them is not, then we ought to be able to find at least one counterexample, a group for which that statement is false. Let's examine these three questions one by one.

Question Does every group have only one identity?

Thoughts Suppose you rummage around in a group and find an identity element, which you call z. A little while later, I rummage around in the same group and find an identity element, which I call y. If the group has only one identity, then you and I must have found the same element; that is, $z = y$.

Now, turn this reasoning around: Suppose that *any time* two identity elements are found in a group they turn out to be the same. If that is *always* the case, then the group must have only one identity. This provides a strategy for proving a theorem. Remember: A proof must depend only on axioms and on theorems already proved. Do you recall the group axioms? If not, look them up now.

Proof Suppose y and z are two identity elements in a group $(G, \diamond)$. By closure, $y \diamond z$ is an element of G. Now, since y is an identity,

$$y \diamond z = z$$

But, since z is also an identity,

$$y \diamond z = y$$

That is, both y and z equal the same thing, so they must equal each other.

This argument depends only on the group axioms, so it holds for every group. Thus, we have a theorem.

Theorem 1 Every group has exactly one identity element.

This exercise illustrates Theorem 1 with operation tables. Any operation on the set $\{1, 2, 3, 4, 5\}$ can be defined by filling in the table of Display 6.17. Make three copies of that (empty) table. Then:

6.59

1. Fill in a row and a column of your first copy of the table to show that 2 is an identity element for this system.

2. Fill in a row and a column of your second copy of the table to show that 4 is an identity element for this system.

3. If possible, fill in rows and columns of your third copy of the table to show that *both* 2 and 4 are identity elements for this system. If you cannot do this, explain what goes wrong.

$\diamond$	1	2	3	4	5
1					
2					
3					
4					
5					

Display 6.17

Question Does every element of a group have only one inverse?

Thoughts This is an "only one" question, like the previous question, so the same approach might work. The idea is to be sure that there is no possible counterexample. Think of it this way: You and your friend Xavier find a dusty old group hidden away in a trunk up in the attic. Picking out an element at random, say a, you look for an inverse (which you know it must have). You find one and call it y (for "yours"). When your back is turned, Xavier finds an inverse for a, which he calls x (for Xavier's). *Must* Xavier have found the same inverse for a that you found or could he have found a different one? In other words, can we prove that x and y must be the same, without knowing anything specific about the element a or the group it's in?

Proof Suppose both x and y are inverses of an element a in a group $(G, \diamond)$ with identity z. Then, by the definition of inverse,

$$a \diamond y = z \quad \text{and} \quad a \diamond x = z$$

so

$$a \diamond y = a \diamond x$$

Now, inverses work from both sides, so we can use y (your inverse) to eliminate a from the equation. Combine y with both sides, keeping the equation in balance.

$$y \diamond (a \diamond y) = y \diamond (a \diamond x)$$

$$(y \diamond a) \diamond y = (y \diamond a) \diamond x$$

Which group axiom allows us to regroup in this way? Now, $y \diamond a$ is the identity z so the previous equation becomes

$$z \diamond y = z \diamond x$$

$$y = x$$

Why? That is, the two inverses for a must actually be the same element.

As before, this argument uses only the group axioms, so it holds for every group. That is, we have another theorem.

Theorem 2 Every element of a group has only one inverse.

6.60

The proof of Theorem 2 uses all four group axioms at least once. Each time the operation is applied, closure tells us that the result is an element of the group. Find at least one place in the proof where each of the other three axioms is used.

There is a bonus in the proof of Theorem 2. It begins by observing that

$$a \diamondsuit y = a \diamondsuit x$$

and ends with

$$y = x$$

Is this pattern familiar?

1. In ordinary arithmetic, if you know that $3 \cdot a = 3 \cdot b$, what can you say about the numbers a and b? How can you justify your answer?

6.61

2. Make up a question analogous to question 1, using addition instead of multiplication. Then answer it.

3. Is it true for any number k that $k \cdot a = k \cdot b$ implies $a = b$? Justify your answer.

4. Is it true for any number k that $a + k = b + k$ implies $a = b$? Justify your answer.

5. Exponentiation, which we'll denote by " $\wedge$ " is an operation on the integers.

   (a) Give an example to show that $a \wedge k = b \wedge k$ does *not* imply $a = b$.

   (b) Give an example to show that $k \wedge a = k \wedge b$ does *not* imply $a = b$.

The property that you just explored is called *cancellation*. It works for usual addition of numbers all the time and for usual multiplication almost all the time. There are some systems in which it doesn't work. Here's one.

Let $\odot$ stand for multiplication (mod 12) on the set $\{0, 1, ..., 11\}$. That is,

$a \odot b =$ the remainder when $a \cdot b$ is divided by 12

In this system, $8 \odot 4 = 8$ and $8 \odot 10 = 8$ (Do you see why?) so

$$8 \odot 4 = 8 \odot 10$$

But, of course, $4 \neq 10$, so cancellation doesn't work here.

Find two more counterexamples for cancellation using multiplication (mod 12). Do you notice anything interesting about the numbers in these counterexamples? If so, what?

6.62

The fact that cancellation doesn't always work for operations makes the next theorem more interesting. It's a theorem you already know how to prove.

Theorem 3 The Cancellation Laws. For any elements a, b, and c of a group $(G, \diamond)$:

(**1**) $a \diamond b = a \diamond c$ implies $b = c$

(**2**) $b \diamond a = c \diamond a$ implies $b = c$

Usually, Law 1 is called *left cancellation* and Law 2 is called *right cancellation*.

6.63

Write out a careful proof of both Cancellation Laws. (*Hint*: Look back at the proof of Theorem 2.)

Cancellation is a powerful tool. It is particularly powerful in dealing with operations that can be described by tables. Its power comes from this fact.

> **A Fact to Know:** For an operation described by a table, the Cancellation Laws hold if and only if no element appears more than once in each row or column.

6.64

Explain why this Fact to Know is true. What would it mean if there were a repetition in some row or column of a table, and why would this violate the Cancellation Laws?

Suggestion: Make up a table with a repetition in a row or a column; then write out an equation that describes this repetition. How is this related to cancellation? Turn what you discover into a convincing general explanation.

6.65

Here is a simple example of the power of cancellation. The form of a table for an operation on a four element set $\{a, b, c, d\}$ appears in Display 6.18. Copy this table and use it for the rest of these questions.

1. Suppose that a is the identity element. Fill in all the table entries determined by this fact.

2. Suppose that c is its own inverse and that b and d are inverses of each other. Fill in all the entries determined by these facts.

3. Your operation table so far specifies an identity element and an inverse for each element. Assuming that you want closure to hold, in how many different ways could you complete this table? Explain.

4. Now assume that you want the Cancellation Laws to hold. Complete the table. Can it be done in more than one way? Why or why not?

	a	b	c	d
a				
b				
c				
d				

Display 6.18

We began this section with three questions. Two of them have led to theorems. Now let's look at the third one.

Question Is every group operation commutative?

Thoughts Commutativity means that the order in which you put two elements together doesn't affect the result. This is true of every group we have seen so far, but we haven't seen very many groups. If a counterexample exists, where is it likely to be? The ordinary arithmetic operations are either both commutative and associative (+ and ×) or neither (− and ÷). A counterexample would have to be associative but not commutative.

Let us try to make an example out of some ideas from your earlier work with symmetries of figures in a plane. Recall that a **symmetry** is a movement of the figure that returns it to its original imprint (or outline) in the plane. You saw two kinds of symmetries of plane figures—rotations around a "center" point and reflections about an axis. Now, each symmetry is a motion that returns the figure to its original outline in the plane, so following one symmetry by another must do that, too. In other words, the combination of one symmetry followed by another must itself be a symmetry of the figure. This means that, for any figure, the *followed by* process is an operation on the set of all its symmetries.

The following exploration looks at the *followed by* operation on the set of all symmetries of an equilateral triangle. The question is,

Is this system a group, and, if so, does commutativity hold?

EXPLORATION

6.66 SETUP

- Cut an equilateral triangle out of cardboard. Make it about 10 cm on a side *and be sure that it is equilateral.*

- Mark the corners (the vertices) 1, 2, and 3 on both sides. Make sure that each vertex has the same number on both sides of the cardboard!

- Put your triangle on a blank sheet of paper, with the counterclockwise numbering facing up. Trace its outline around the outside. See Display 6.19(a).

- Leave your triangle on the paper. Number the corners of the traced triangle (outside of it) with the same numbers as those on the cardboard so that your result looks like Display 6.19(a).

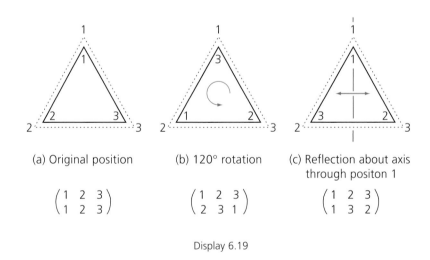

(a) Original position

$$\begin{pmatrix} 1 & 2 & 3 \\ 1 & 2 & 3 \end{pmatrix}$$

(b) 120° rotation

$$\begin{pmatrix} 1 & 2 & 3 \\ 2 & 3 & 1 \end{pmatrix}$$

(c) Reflection about axis through positon 1

$$\begin{pmatrix} 1 & 2 & 3 \\ 1 & 3 & 2 \end{pmatrix}$$

Display 6.19

QUESTIONS

1. Rotate your triangle 120° counterclockwise and put it back in its imprint. *From here on, "put it back in its imprint" should be understood as part of the directions for each movement of your triangle, and rotations are always counterclockwise unless we say differently.* Display 6.19(b) shows how your triangle should look now:

- corner 1 is now in imprint position 2

- corner 2 is in position 3

- corner 3 is in position 1.

   This rearrangement of the corners is shown by the two rows of numbers in the parentheses. What do the numbers in the top row represent? What do the numbers in the bottom row represent? What double row of numbers represents a 240° rotation?

2. How many symmetries of this triangle are there? Justify your answer.

   Dealing with the *followed by* operation requires some care. You must think of each axis of reflection in terms of the *imprint vertex position* that it goes through. For example, the reflection shown in Display 6.19(c) uses the axis through *position* 1, the vertical axis of symmetry. If we call this A1, then A1 is *always* the reflection about the vertical axis, regardless of how the triangle has been placed in the imprint.

3. Use your cardboard triangle to help you answer these questions:

   (a) When the 120° rotation is followed by A1 (the reflection about the vertical axis), what is the resulting symmetry? Describe your answer as a permutation and as a movement of the triangle.

   (b) When the vertical-axis reflection is followed by the 120° rotation, what is the resulting symmetry? Describe your answer as a permutation and as a movement of the triangle.

   (c) What do your answers to (a) and (b) tell you about the *followed by* operation?

Movement	Position	Symbol
Rotation of 0°	$\begin{pmatrix} 1 & 2 & 3 \\ 1 & 2 & 3 \end{pmatrix}$	0
Rotation of 120°	$\begin{pmatrix} 1 & 2 & 3 \\ 2 & 3 & 1 \end{pmatrix}$	120
Rotation of 240°	$\begin{pmatrix} 1 & 2 & 3 \\ 3 & 1 & 2 \end{pmatrix}$	240
Reflection about axis through position 1	$\begin{pmatrix} 1 & 2 & 3 \\ 1 & 3 & 2 \end{pmatrix}$	A1
Reflection about axis through position 2	$\begin{pmatrix} 1 & 2 & 3 \\ 3 & 2 & 1 \end{pmatrix}$	A2
Reflection about axis through position 3	$\begin{pmatrix} 1 & 2 & 3 \\ 2 & 1 & 3 \end{pmatrix}$	A3

The symmetries of an equilateral triangle

Display 6.20

4. Display 6.20 lists all the symmetries of the equilateral triangle. Each one is described as a movement and as a double row of vertex numbers, and then is assigned a shorthand symbol. This information is needed to complete the operation table shown in Display 6.21. Your teacher will give you a copy of this table. Fill it in, using your cardboard square and its numbered outline to help you.

For each table entry, first use the symmetry in the far left column and then apply the symmetry in the top row. For instance, the result of a 120° rotation followed by a reflection about the axis through position 2 should be in the 120 row and the A2 column. This answer, A3, has been put in for you. Use your triangle and outline to check this result.

The symbol "o" for *followed by* makes it easy to write down such combinations:

$$120 \; o \; A2 = A3$$

Here are two more results to help you get started:

$$A1 \; o \; 240 = A2 \qquad\qquad A3 \; o \; A1 = 240$$

Check each of them with your triangle and outline to see that you understand how the process works. Then fill in the rest of Display 6.21.

o	0	120	240	A1	A2	A3
0						
120					A3	
240						
A1		A2				
A2						
A3			240			

Operation Table for the symmetries of an equilateral triangle

Display 6.21

5. Does Display 6.21 represent a group? Check the group axioms by working through these questions:

   (a) Does closure hold? How can you tell?

   (b) Is o associative? How do you know?

   (c) Is there an identity element? If so, what is it? If not, how can you tell?

   (d) Find the inverse for each symmetry that has one. For each one that doesn't, explain how you know that it doesn't.

   (e) Do the Cancellation Laws hold? How can you tell?

   (f) Is this system a group? Justify your answer.

6. Is o a commutative operation? Use Display 6.21 to justify your answer.

   Has this Exploration settled the question, "Is every group commutative?" If not, what is left to be done? Explain.

6.67

It's time to tie off a loose end of the **Exploration.** In question 5, you should have been able to check all the group axioms *except associativity*. Surely you didn't find a counterexample. But how can you be *sure* that it is associative? The only way to be certain from the information in the table is to check all possible cases—and there are 216 of them! (Where does the number 216 come from?) However, by thinking a little differently about what's going on, we can use algebra to settle all 216 cases at once.

6.68

The key is to think of symmetries as functions. Each symmetry is determined by where the vertices of the triangle go. This means that each symmetry can be thought of as a function from the set {1, 2, 3} to itself. Each of these functions is one-to-one because two vertices can't end up in the same place.

Now, the *followed by* process is just function composition, which you may remember from earlier in **MATH** *Connections*. This provides another way to find the result of one symmetry followed by another. Instead of moving the triangle around, just keep track of what each function does to the vertices. For example, Display 6.22 illustrates how to calculate 120 o A2.

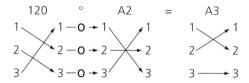

120 followed by A2 equals A3

Display 6.22

Once you see how the process works, you don't need to draw a picture, of course. Just follow what each function does to each number and write down the result. For instance, Display 6.22 shows that the 120° rotation function takes corner 2 to 3, and then the A2 reflection takes 3 to 1. Therefore, the composite function, 120 o A2, takes 2 to 1.

6.69

1. **Calculate A3 o 240 by drawing a diagram like Display 6.22. Does your result agree with what you got for Display 6.21? It should.**

2. **Calculate 240 o 120 by drawing a diagram like Display 6.22.**

Putting Algebra to Work

6.70 In this situation, abstraction and algebra actually make things very easy. They allow us to handle the 216 different associativity calculations of Display 6.21 all at once!

Abstraction Each symmetry of the triangle is a function, so each associativity case asks if

$$(f \text{ o } g) \text{ o } h = f \text{ o } (g \text{ o } h)$$

for some functions f, g, and h, where o is function composition. This equality will hold provided that the composite functions on each side of the equation take each domain element (each vertex) to the same image.

Algebra Let x represent any domain element (in this case, any vertex of the triangle). We want to know if $((f \circ g) \circ h)(x)$ and $(f \circ (g \circ h))(x)$ are always the same. Using the definition of function composition (carefully), we rewrite each expression, as follows:

$$((f \circ g) \circ h)(x) = h((f \circ g)(x)) = h(g(f(x)))$$

$$(f \circ (g \circ h))(x) = ((g \circ h)(f(x)) = h(g(f(x)))$$

Both expressions reduce to exactly the same form!

Result This means that these two different ways of combining functions *never* changes the outcome. Since we used an x instead of a particular number, we know that this is true for every domain element. AND—since f, g, and h can be *any* functions (not just symmetries of a triangle), not only have we taken care of all 216 cases for Display 6.21, but we have also proved an important general fact.

> **A Fact to Know:** Function composition is always associative.

Since the *followed by* operation is associative, Display 6.21 describes a group. That puts in place the last piece of the commutativity puzzle. This time we did not get a theorem. Instead, we have:

Counterexample The symmetries of an equilateral triangle form a group that is not commutative. Thus, *not every group is commutative.*

The symmetries of every regular polygon form a non-commutative group under function composition. Since there is a regular polygon for each natural number from 3 on, there are infinitely many of these groups, and every one of them is non-commutative. Some of these groups have become very useful in modern science, particularly for studying molecular structure.

The study of molecular structure is important in chemistry and other physical sciences. The shape of a molecule influences the way it behaves with respect to electromagnetic radiation. Because of this, a molecule's symmetric structure is closely related to its physical and chemical properties. That

6.7 The Power of Proof

symmetric structure can be described as a group, known as the *point group* of the molecule. This name comes from the fact that any symmetry that takes a molecule back into itself cannot move the point at its center of mass.

Here is an example. The methyl chloride molecule can be diagrammed as in Display 6.23, with three hydrogen atoms forming the equilateral base of a triangular pyramid that is topped by a carbon atom linked to a chlorine atom.

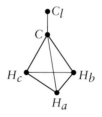

A methyl chloride molecule

Display 6.23

In this case, the fact that any symmetric operation must leave the center of mass fixed implies that both the carbon and chlorine atoms must stay where they are. This means that *all* the symmetries of this molecule are determined by the symmetries of the equilateral base triangle $H_a H_b H_c$. These symmetries form the group you just explored!

Problem Set: 6.7

1. Display 6.24 describes an operation $\heartsuit$ on the set $\{1, 2, 3, 4, 5\}$.

   (a) Does closure hold? Why or why not?
   (b) Does this system have an identity element? If so, what is it? If not, why not?
   (c) Identify the inverse of each number that has one. Is there any number that does not have an inverse? If so, which?
   (d) Do the Cancellation Laws hold in this system? Why or why not?
   (e) Prove that this system is *not* a group.

♡	1	2	3	4	5
1	3	4	1	5	2
2	5	3	2	1	4
3	1	2	3	4	5
4	2	5	4	3	1
5	4	1	5	2	3

Display 6.24

2. (a) Set up a table for an operation on the set {a, b, c, d, e} by listing the elements across and down, in that order.

   (b) Fill in all the entries that are determined by the following information:
   - The table describes a group.
   - The identity element is a.
   - e and c are inverses of each other.
   - d is not its own inverse.

   (c) Suppose also that $c \diamond c = d$. Fill in the rest of the table.

   (d) Is this group commutative? Why or why not?

3. There are 19,683 different operation tables for the set {1, 2, 3}.

   (a) Justify this statement.

   (b) Prove that at most three of these tables represent groups.

4. In Section 6.6 you learned about modular addition. In particular, you learned that the operation ⊕ (mod 12) on the set {0, 1, ..., 11} forms a group. This is a question about the same operation, ⊕ (mod 12), but this time think of it on the entire set of whole numbers, {0, 1, 2, 3, ...}.

   (a) Does closure hold? Why or why not?

   (b) The operation ⊕ (mod 12) is associative on this set. Write out an example to illustrate this fact.

   (c) Is there an identity element? If so, what is it? If not, how do you know?

   (d) Does every whole number have an inverse? If so, specify inverses for 5, 15, and 25. If not, explain why not.

   (e) Do the Cancellation Laws hold in this system? Justify your answer.

   (f) Is this system a group? Why or why not?

5. One of the following two statements is true; the other is false. Which is which?

   (i) If a and b are any elements of any group, $(G, \diamond)$, then

   $$(a \diamond b)' = a' \diamond b'$$

   (ii) If a and b are any elements of any group, $(G, \diamond)$, then

   $$(a \diamond b)' = b' \diamond a'$$

   Prove the true statement and find a counterexample for the false one.

6. (a) There are only four symmetries of a rectangle that is not a square. Describe them as movements and as permutations.
   (b) Make an operation table for this system of symmetries.
   (c) Justify the claim that this system is a group.
   (d) Is this group commutative? Justify your answer.
   (e) Point out one way in which the table pattern for this group differs from the pattern of the table for addition mod 4 in Display 6.14.

7. (a) List all the symmetries of a regular pentagon, both as movements and as permutations.
   (b) This set of symmetries forms a group under composition. Identify the inverse of each symmetry.

8. **Prove** If a group contains an even number of elements, then at least one element besides the identity is its own inverse.

6.8 Number Systems

In this section, groups return to what suggested them—addition and multiplication of numbers.

In Section 6.5, the group axioms were suggested by looking at ways in which addition and multiplication are similar.

6.71

1. Solve the equations $147 + x = 882$ and $147 \cdot x = 882$ in a way that illustrates the similar use of the group axioms for addition and multiplication.

2. The following questions ask for a particular number. In each case, say what the number is, and then explain how it was used in your solution for part 1.

   (a) What is the identity for addition?

   (b) What is the identity for multiplication?

   (c) What is the additive inverse of 147? What's a more common name for the additive inverse of a number?

   (d) What is the multiplicative inverse of 147? What's a more common name for the multiplicative inverse of a number?

A group is a set with a single operation on it. Various parts of the number system can be viewed as groups by focusing on one operation or another. However, people usually think of the number system as having at least four basic operations—addition, subtraction, multiplication, and division—all at once. Even so, the group axioms provide a useful way to organize and simplify the rules for using these four operations.

We begin by thinking of just the two operations that suggested the group axioms. In the number system, addition and multiplication exist side by side, so to speak. As the previous questions illustrate, they have parallel group properties. They also have another useful property that we have seen in some groups: They are commutative. That is, switching

Learning Outcomes

After studying this section you will be able to:

Describe the structure of the real number system in terms of the axioms for a field

Define subtraction and division of numbers as addition and multiplication using inverses

Explain how the group axioms and the field axioms are related

Use modular arithmetic to construct finite fields of numbers.

the order in which two numbers are added or multiplied does not change the answer. Display 6.25 lists all these properties side by side to highlight the parallel structure.

Addition (+)	Multiplication (·)
closed	closed
associative	associative
has an identity (0)	has an identity (1)
each x has an inverse $(-x)$	each $x \neq 0$ has an inverse $\left(\dfrac{1}{x}\right)$
commutative	commutative

Display 6.25

What does "closed" mean in Display 6.25?

6.72

　　All but one of the essential properties of addition and multiplication of numbers appear in Display 6.25. Something very important is missing. None of those properties connects the two operations. That is, nothing in Display 6.25 tells us how addition and multiplication interact with each other. We need one more rule to complete the picture, a law that you have used many times before—Distributivity. Display 6.26 completes the picture. It shows all the laws that govern the standard arithmetic of numbers.

Addition (+)	Multiplication (·)
closed	closed
associative	associative
has an identity (0)	has an identity (1)
each x has an inverse $(-x)$	each $x \neq 0$ has an inverse $\left(\dfrac{1}{x}\right)$
commutative	commutative
· is distributive over +	

The number system operations

Display 6.26

1. Give a numerical example of the fact that multiplication is distributive over addition. Then state the Distributive Law algebraically (using letters to represent any numbers).

6.73

2. Which property in Display 6.26 justifies the fact that

$$a \cdot (b + c) = (b + c) \cdot a$$

for any numbers *a, b,* and *c*?

3. What would it mean to say that addition is distributive over multiplication? Give a numerical counterexample to show that this is *not* true.

Even though Display 6.26 just lists properties of addition and multiplication, it actually contains all the essential information about subtraction and division, as well. That's because we can define subtraction and division in terms of addition, multiplication, and inverses.

For any numbers *a* and *b*, $a - b = a + (-b)$.

For any numbers *a* and *b*, $a \div b = a \cdot \left(\frac{1}{b}\right)$, where $b \neq 0$.

The divisor, *b*, cannot equal 0 in the definition of division because 0 does not have an inverse under multiplication. Why not? Can't we just define a multiplicative inverse for 0? Can't we just make up a new number and call it $\frac{1}{0}$? Not if we want the properties in Display 6.26 to hold! Here's why.

Suppose there were a number $\frac{1}{0}$, an inverse for 0 under multiplication. Then, by the definition of inverse

$$0 \cdot \frac{1}{0} = 1$$

because 1 is the identity for multiplication. But 0 times anything is 0, isn't it? Must it be? How do you know?

Let's prove a theorem.

Theorem In any system with the properties in Display 6.26, the additive identity, 0, multiplied by anything *must* be 0.
In symbols,

$$a \cdot 0 = 0$$

for any a.

Proof Let a be any element in the system. By the definition of additive identity,

$$0 = 0 + 0$$

so

$$a \cdot 0 = a \cdot (0 + 0) = (a \cdot 0) + (a \cdot 0)$$

by distributivity. But, since 0 is the additive identity, adding it to the term on the right doesn't change the value of that term, so we have

$$(a \cdot 0) + 0 = (a \cdot 0) + (a \cdot 0)$$

Now, the properties of + contain the axioms for a group, so we can use cancellation to remove $(a \cdot 0)$ from both sides of the equation, getting

$$0 = a \cdot 0$$

and we're done.

6.74

1. **Is the proof of this theorem direct or indirect? Explain.**

2. **Using this theorem, finish the proof that $\frac{1}{0}$ cannot exist. Is your proof direct or indirect? Explain.**

You may have noticed that references to the number system have not specified the kind of numbers we're talking about. That has been deliberate. All the numbers you have used in **MATH** *Connections* are part of a large system called the *real numbers*. Chapter 7 explains the different types of numbers that make up the reals. Some of those different types can be considered as number systems themselves. All the properties in Display 6.26 hold for the real numbers. However, that is not true of some of the systems contained within the real numbers.

6.75

Answer these questions for each of the following sets of numbers with usual addition and multiplication.

(a) **Which properties in Display 6.26 hold for the system? Give a counterexample for each property that does not hold.**

(b) **Are subtraction and division operations within this system? Why or why not?**

1. The natural numbers, {1, 2, 3, 4, 5, ...}

2. The integers, { ..., -3, -2, -1, 0, 1, 2, 3, ...}

3. The rational numbers, which are are all the common fractions (that is, all quotients $\frac{a}{b}$, where a and b are integers and $b \neq 0$)

The properties in Display 6.26 completely determine the behavior of addition, subtraction, multiplication, and division of real numbers. *All* the arithmetic rules for those operations follow from these eleven statements. That is, if we think of the statements of Display 6.26 as axioms, all the other rules for those operations can be proved as theorems. You already saw one example of such a theorem, the fact that 0 times any number equals 0. Some others will appear shortly.

6.76

Thinking of the properties in Display 6.26 as axioms pays off in another way, too. It turns out that there are other useful systems besides the real numbers that have all these properties. Any theorem proved from these properties will be true for all those other systems, as well. Thus, we can use the usual arithmetic of the real numbers to find and verify efficiently many properties that hold in all these other systems, just as they do in the real number system. The axiomatic system described by the properties in Display 6.26 is called a *field*. It is defined as follows:

A Word to Know: A **field** is a set with two operations that have the following properties:
- both operations are associative and commutative

- there are identity elements for both operations

- every element has a first-operation inverse

- every element except the first-operation identity has a second-operation inverse

- the second-operation is distributive over the first.

To avoid the clumsy wording of this definition, it is customary to borrow notation from the number system. The first operation is denoted by + and the second operation is denoted by · (even though they may not be the usual addition or multiplication). The symbols 0 and 1 are used for the first and second operation identities, respectively (whether or not they are numbers at all). The first and second operation inverses are denoted by $-x$ and x^{-1}, respectively. Using these customs, the axioms for a field can be summarized as in Display 6.27.

First Operation (+)	Second Operation (·)
closed	closed
associative	associative
has an identity (0)	has an identity (1)
each x has an inverse ($-x$)	each $x \neq 0$ has an inverse $\left(x^{-1}\right)$
commutative	commutative
· is distributive over +	

The axioms for a field

Display 6.27

As we have seen, the real number system is an instance of a field. So is the system of rational numbers. A larger number system called the **complex numbers** is a field containing the reals. There are also much smaller instances, fields that contain only a finite number of elements. These finite fields turn out to be very useful for a wide variety of things, including code breaking and the design of scientific experiments. Typical examples of finite fields use the remainder arithmetic you studied in Section 6.6. Here are a few questions to remind you of how that arithmetic works.

6.77

1. Recall from Section 6.6 that $\oplus$ (mod 5) is defined as
   $a \oplus b =$ the remainder of $a + b$ divided by 5
   Calculate $3 \oplus 4$ $3 \oplus 2$ $0 \oplus 4$ $2 \oplus 1$ $4 \oplus 4$

2. Similarly, $\otimes$ (mod 5) is defined as
   $a \otimes b =$ the remainder of $a \cdot b$ divided by 5
   Calculate $3 \otimes 4$ $3 \otimes 3$ $0 \otimes 4$ $2 \otimes 1$ $4 \otimes 2$

3. Define $\oplus$ (mod 6) and $\otimes$ (mod 6). Then calculate mod 6: $4 \oplus 2$, $4 \oplus 3$, $4 \otimes 3$, $3 \otimes 5$.

4. Define $\oplus$ (mod 7) and $\otimes$ (mod 7). Then calculate mod 7: $4 \oplus 2$, $4 \oplus 3$, $4 \otimes 3$, $3 \otimes 5$.

A typical instance of a small field is the set of whole numbers {0, 1, 2, 3, 4} with addition and multiplication mod 5. Its two operation tables appear in Display 6.28.

⊕	0	1	2	3	4
0	0	1	2	3	4
1	1	2	3	4	0
2	2	3	4	0	1
3	3	4	0	1	2
4	4	0	1	2	3

⊗	0	1	2	3	4
0	0	0	0	0	0
1	0	1	2	3	4
2	0	2	4	1	3
3	0	3	1	4	2
4	0	4	3	2	1

A field of five numbers

Display 6.28

These questions refer to the field in Display 6.28.

6.78

1. What is the identity for ⊕? For ⊗? How can you tell from the tables?

2. Which number is –2? List the first operation inverses of the other elements. Use the ⊕ table to justify your answers.

3. Which number is 3^{-1}? List the second operation inverses of the other elements. Use the ⊗ table to justify your answers.

We can define ⊕ and ⊗ mod n for any natural number n from 2 on, just as you did for 5, 6, and 7 earlier. These operations work on the set of all whole numbers strictly less than the modulus. How can we tell which modulus numbers give us a field and which do not? Checking each case one at a time is a hopeless task! Fortunately, there's an easier way. As this chapter's final example of the power of axiomatic systems, we shall settle infinitely many cases all at once by proving a single theorem.

You know that the usual product of two nonzero real numbers can never be zero. What you may not know is that this is a property of all fields. That is

Theorem If a and b are two elements of a field and $a \cdot b = 0$, then either $a = 0$ or $b = 0$. "0" is the first operation identity, and "product" refers to the second operation of the field.

Proof Suppose that a and b are two elements of a field such that $a \cdot b = 0$ and $a \neq 0$. We shall prove the theorem by showing that b *must be* 0. We have already proved that, in any field, 0 multiplied by anything must be 0. Thus,

$$a \cdot b = a \cdot 0$$

Since $a \neq 0$, it has a second operation inverse, $a - 1$. Multiply both sides of this equation by $a - 1$, regroup by associativity, and apply the definitions of inverse and identity.

$$a \cdot b = a \cdot 0$$

$$a - 1 \cdot (a \cdot b) = a - 1 \cdot (a \cdot 0)$$

$$(a - 1 \cdot a) \cdot b = (a - 1 \cdot a) \cdot 0$$

$$1 \cdot b = 1 \cdot 0$$

$$b = 0$$

The power of a theorem within an axiomatic system comes from the fact that it must be true in *all* instances of the axioms. Thus, no field can ever have two nonzero elements whose product is 0. Now look back at your calculations for $\otimes$ (mod 6). One of the examples was $4 \otimes 3 = 0$. Neither 4 nor 3 is 0, so *this can't be happening in a field*. In other words, {0, 1, 2, 3, 4, 5} with $\oplus$ and $\otimes$ (mod 6) cannot be a field!

This idea generalizes to any composite modulus number—that is, to any modulus number that is the product of two smaller numbers. For example, $10 = 5 \cdot 2$, so {0, 1, 2, ..., 9} with $\oplus$ and $\otimes$ (mod 10) cannot be a field. Why not? Because $5 \otimes 2 = 0$ (mod 10).

6.79

1. In each of the following equation forms, find nonzero numbers less than the modulus that make the equation true.

    (a) __ $\otimes$ 2 = 0 (mod 8)

    (b) 7 $\otimes$ __ = 0 (mod 21)

    (c) __ $\otimes$ __ = 0 (mod 12)

    (d) __ $\otimes$ __ = 0 (mod 365)

2. For what kind of modulus number is it impossible to find examples like those in part 1?

Thus, the only modulus numbers that can possibly be used for these fields are the primes. We haven't proved that all the primes actually work, of course. However, that can be done, too. Knowing that these modular fields only come in prime number sizes is a big help to the people who apply them to coding or decoding, to the design of reliable experiments, and to various other real-world situations.

REFLECT

This chapter was about the power of logic and abstraction working together. You saw how the properties of arithmetic and other familiar systems are abstracted to form axioms. The axioms are used to prove theorems, other properties that must be true whenever the axioms hold. The power of this process comes from the fact that every theorem is automatically true in the many instances of a single axiomatic system. Thus, when these axiomatic systems are applied to describe different real-world situations, all their theorems are automatically reliable facts about those situations.

As examples of this process at work, you studied groups and fields, two fundamental axiomatic systems that are used throughout mathematics and science. You have worked with typical instances of each system in different settings that included numbers of various kinds, the movements of geometric figures, and functions. In particular, you have seen how the arithmetic of numbers is related to groups and fields. This idea will be revisited in Chapter 7 as you learn more about the infinite sets of numbers at the heart of mathematics.

Problem Set: 6.8

1. Write out complete operation tables for the field formed by $\oplus$ and $\otimes$ (mod 3). It only contains three numbers. Then answer the following questions:

   (a) What is the identity for $\oplus$? For $\otimes$?
   (b) Which number is -1? Which number is -2? Justify your answers.
   (c) Which number is 1^{-1}? Which number is 2^{-1}? Justify your answers.

2. This problem refers to the field of numbers $\{0, 1, 2, 3, 4\}$ with $\oplus$ and $\otimes$ (mod 5). Use the tables in Display 6.28 to help you answer these questions:

   (a) Which number is -1? Which number is -2? How do you know?
   (b) Which number is 2^{-1}? Which number is 4^{-1}? How do you know?
   (c) Which number is 3^2? Which number is 3^3? Which number is 3^4? Explain.
   (d) Calculate $\quad 1 - 4 \quad 4 - 1 \quad 1 \div 2 \quad 4 \div 3 \quad 3 \div 4$

(e) Solve the following equations in this field. In each case, explain your solution. To check your answers, substitute for x and see if you get true statements.

(i) $2 \oplus x = 1$
(ii) $3 \otimes x = 4$
(iii) $(3 \otimes x) \oplus 2 = 1$
(iv) $2 \otimes (x \oplus 4) = 3$

3. (a) Do the nonzero numbers in the field of integers mod 5 form a group under $\otimes$? If so, list the identity and the inverse of each number. If not, explain why not. Display 6.28 might help you.

(b) Prove or disprove. All the elements of a field except for the first operation identity form a group under the second operation.

4. **Prove** In any field containing at least two elements, the first operation identity and the second operation identity must be different elements. (*Hint*: Try an indirect approach.)

5. You probably know that the equation $x^2 - y^2 = (x + y)(x - y)$ is true for all real numbers x and y.

(a) Prove that this equation holds for any two elements of any field. You may use the fact that $a \cdot (-b) = -(a \cdot b)$ for any elements in any field.

(b) Use the numbers 3 and 4 to check an example of this equation in the mod 5 field of Display 6.28.

6. Which numbers are in the field formed by $\oplus$ and $\otimes$ (mod 7)? Write out the complete operation tables for this field. Then answer the following questions:

(a) Which number is -5? Which number is -3? How do you know?

(b) Which number is 2^{-1}? Which number is 3^{-1}? How do you know?

(c) Solve the following equations in this field. In each case, explain your solution. To check your answers, substitute for x and see if you get true statements.
(i) $5 \oplus x = 4$
(ii) $3 \otimes x = 5$
(iii) $(3 \otimes x) \oplus 5 = 2$

(d) What is the square root of a number? Which nonzero numbers have square roots in this field? What are the square roots in each case?

ELK The herd
fluctuate. Is it t

K.C. Cole
Discovering the Beauty in Math

K.C. Cole is by her own account a "professional amateur scientist." As the science writer for *The Los Angeles Times* and a senior editor at *Discover* magazine, her job is to translate the ideas and advances of the world's leading scientists into terms we can all understand. She has published articles on subjects ranging from virtual reality to invisible planets and the animals that live on our eyelashes. Incredibly she has even written a book about math, *The Universe and the Teacup*, with no math in it.

"Math allows us to live outside of ourselves and think about big ideas," says K.C. "What is truth? Why are we here? Through mathematics we can obtain a comfort level with the world and find our place in the Universe." K.C. has been writing professionally since 1972, and while it is accurate to say that she has little formal math or science background, she is quick to point out that she "had the best education possible, because I've had the best scientists as mentors."

In addition to writing, Cole works with museums and schools developing materials and exhibitions which expose the value and excitement of math and science.

"The trouble with a great deal of typical math and science education is that we never show people the beauty of mathematics and science. Compare it to the way we teach music. What if we only allowed students to learn to play scales? It would be boring. There must be an emphasis on the sense of beauty and fun."

Infinity–The Final Frontier?

CHAPTER 7

7.1 A Brief History of Infinity

Every occurrence of the Olympic games sees new records set. But what does it really mean to say that the record for the 100-meter dash is 9.2 seconds? Does it mean that it took exactly 9.2 seconds to run 100 meters? In fact, all we know is that before the digital timer's display moved from the 9.2 reading to the 9.3 reading, the race was over. It could have taken 9.21 seconds or 9.217 seconds or 9.2179 seconds to run the 100 meters and our clock would still show 9.2 seconds. But what if we developed more sophisticated clocks that could time races to more accurate times? Would this mean we could be certain that we had the exact time? Can time be divided into shorter and shorter units indefinitely or do we finally reach a point where the unit of time is indivisible? These questions are profound ones and often disturbing because they involve concepts related to *infinity*.

For thousands of years, humans have looked up at the stars and wondered about the infinity of space and time. The idea that things such as space and time might not have an end is somehow disturbing.

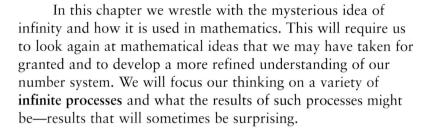

About Words

The word *infinity* comes from the Latin *infinitas* which means boundary free.

About Words

Although some might think that a *paradox* is a couple of physicians, the dictionary defines it as a statement that seems to contradict either itself or common sense.

In this chapter we wrestle with the mysterious idea of infinity and how it is used in mathematics. This will require us to look again at mathematical ideas that we may have taken for granted and to develop a more refined understanding of our number system. We will focus our thinking on a variety of **infinite processes** and what the results of such processes might be—results that will sometimes be surprising.

Our intuition about infinite things is often useful, but at times it may lead us astray. In this chapter, you will learn several concepts that involve infinity. Ancient Greek mathematicians grappled with some of them when they tried to solve *paradoxes* posed by the philosopher Zeno of Elea (496–435 B.C.).

7.1   In modern form, one of these paradoxes goes something like this.

A spider and a snail decide to have a race. The spider can move at 1 foot per second which is 10 times as fast as the snail who can only crawl at $\frac{1}{10}$ foot per second. Being a good sport, the spider decides to give the snail a 100 foot start. Will the spider ever overtake the snail?

Assume that the spider and the snail are on a number line as illustrated in Display 7.1.

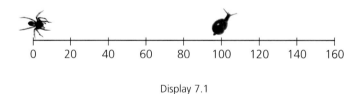

Display 7.1

Although our intuition tells us that the spider will soon overtake the snail, plausible arguments can be made to justify two different answers.

Argument 1 Yes, the spider will overtake the snail. Recall that the speeds of the spider and the snail are 1 foot per second and $\frac{1}{10}$ foot per second respectively. After 200 seconds the spider has traveled $(200)(1) = 200$ feet and the snail has traveled $(200)\left(\frac{1}{10}\right) = 20$ feet. The spider is now 200 feet from the starting point and the snail is only $100 + 20 = 120$ feet from the starting point. Clearly the spider has overtaken the snail.

Argument 2 No, the spider will never be able to overtake the snail. By the time the spider has moved 100 feet the snail has moved 10 feet. Their relative positions are shown on the diagram in Display 7.2.

| 100 | 110 | 120 | 130 |

Display 7.2

They are now 10 feet apart. When the spider has gone 10 more feet to catch up to the snail, the snail will have gone 1 more foot, and so they are now 1 foot apart. When the spider has gone 1 more foot to catch up to the snail, the snail will have gone $\frac{1}{10}$ foot and so they are now 0.1 foo81t apart. We can examine what happens each time the spider moves forward to try to close the gap between them.

Copy and complete Display 7.3 and use it to establish the relative positions of these two after various distances.

7.2

Distance Traveled by Spider	Spider Position	Distance Traveled by Snail	Snail Position
0	0	0	100
100	100	10	110
10	110	1	111
1			
0.1			
0.01			
0.001			
0.0001			
0.00001			

Display 7.3

It appears from the chart that there will always be a small distance between the two, so the spider will never overtake the snail!

1. Could this process be continued indefinitely? Explain.

2. Will the number representing the position of the spider ever be greater than that of the snail? Explain.

7.3

3. What assumptions are being made about space and time in this argument? Are they valid?

4. Which of the two arguments—the spider will overtake the snail or the spider will never overtake the snail—do you think is correct? Why?

The brilliant ancient Greek mathematicians did not see any fallacy in Argument 2. In fact, this particular paradox was not fully understood until sometime in the 19th century. What makes this apparently simple problem so difficult to pin down? It is the occurrence of an *infinite process* for which the result is uncertain. The two mathematical ideas nested in this problem—limits and infinity—are both somewhat difficult to understand with our finite minds.

Furthermore, Argument 2 makes certain assumptions, namely that time can be subdivided into shorter and shorter periods and that lengths (the distances traveled by the spider and the snail) can also be made smaller and smaller without limit.

7.4 As noted, Argument 2 depends on an infinite process. We need to be able to establish the result of the infinite process. We will revisit the Paradox of Zeno later in this chapter after we have developed a few more tools with which we can shape our ideas about infinity. Before we do that, let's take a closer look at why anyone would want to understand the concept of infinity, given that every human's experience of space and time is always finite.

7.5 As strange as it may seem, much of the mathematics that you have already learned has to do with situations that involve infinity. We have made infinite models for finite things. Consider the graph of the linear function $f(x) = 3x$ as shown in Display 7.4.

Although we draw a graph by using a table of ordered pairs that satisfy the relationship $y = 3x$, we don't feel the need to calculate infinitely many ordered pairs to draw the graph. Once the pattern is clearly established we *assume* that it continues *for all values of x* including those that are either larger or smaller than the ones we used to draw the graph. The arrows on the line are used to indicate this fact.

We also assume that there are infinitely many points on the line, so we draw a solid line through the plotted points. Perhaps surprisingly, it is also true that there are infinitely many points between any two distinct points on the line!

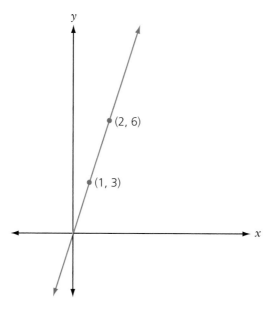

Display 7.4

Recall that to find the midpoint of a segment we average the coordinates of the endpoints. To find the midpoint of the segment from $(1, 3)$ to $(2, 6)$ we calculate $\frac{1+2}{2}, \frac{3+6}{2} = (1.5, 4.5)$.

7.6

1. Find two distinct points on the line $y = 3x$, as close as you like. Exchange these points with a partner and challenge your partner to find another point on the line that is somewhere between them.

2. Verify that the point your partner gave you as the answer to your challenge is between the points you specified and also on the line $y = 3x$.

3. If you wanted to give your partner two more points even closer than before, which points could you use? Could you repeat this process over and over again? Explain.

This *infinite process* illustrates that there are infinitely many points between any two points on this line, no matter how close the original points are! This statement is true not because we can find a point between *some* points on the line, but because we can find a point between *any* two points on the line. It is useful for us to have mathematical skills that allow us to say things about *all* points on a graph, even if there are infinitely many of them. In fact, much of mathematics has been developed to deal with *continuous functions*, that is, those without gaps in their graphs. So, we may *choose* to use an infinite model for a finite phenomenon because we have many mathematical tools to use when solving problems involving such functions.

For example, in an earlier chapter of **MATH** *Connections* we developed a trigonometric function to model the number of hours of daylight for each day of the year (Display 7.5). This function, $y = 3.035 \sin\left(\frac{360}{365}x\right) + 12.1$, assumes that any value of x will produce a valid value for y.

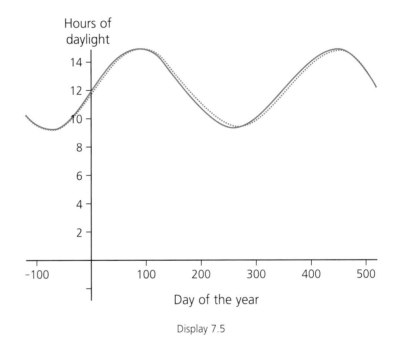

Display 7.5

Although the mathematical model allows us to compute a y-value for any given x-value, these values are not meaningful in terms of the physical reality. For practical purposes, x cannot have a value that is anything other than a whole number. This variable represents the number of any particular day of the year, therefore it does not make sense for this value to be a fraction. We have used an infinite model to represent a finite situation because we happen to know quite a bit about the sine function, which is a continuous curve. The concept of infinity is often embedded in the common mathematics that we use *even though we may not realize it.*

Problem Set: 7.1

1. Consider the line segment from A:(1, 4) to B:(3, 8).
   (a) Find the midpoint of AB and call this M_1.
   (b) Find the midpoint of AM_1 and call this M_2.
   (c) Find the midpoint of AM_2 and call this M_3.
   (d) Repeat this procedure to find the coordinates of M_4, M_5, M_6, and M_7.
   (e) In theory, could this process be continued indefinitely? Explain.
   (f) What point(s) do you think would be the result of this process?

2. Consider the line segment from A:(1, 4) to B:(3, 8).
   (a) Find the midpoint of AB and call this X.
   (b) Find the midpoints of AX and XB and label them.
   (c) Find the midpoints of each line segment in your diagram.
   (d) How many line segments did you have in parts (a), (b), (c)?
   (e) In theory, could this process be continued indefinitely? How many line segments would be the result? Explain.

3. Earlier in **MATH** *Connections* we introduced the formula $P = 0.0085e^{0.0065x}$ to model the population of the world, where P is the population and x is the year. According to this formula,
   (a) What was the population in 1950?
   (b) What population is projected for the year 2020?
   (c) Is this an infinite model for a finite phenomenon? Explain why or why not?
   (d) What assumptions are made by this formula? Are they reasonable?

7.2 The Natural Numbers and Proof by Induction

Perhaps the first encounter that you had with the idea of an infinite or **unbounded quantity** was when thinking about the counting numbers. Although now they appear to be very simple, this set of numbers is the foundation for much of the more sophisticated mathematics. We will examine the counting numbers in more detail to see how they fit into our discussion of infinity.

The set of counting numbers were the first numbers used by humans in their daily lives. Recall that this set is also called the set of natural numbers. The set of natural numbers is denoted by the letter $\mathbb{N}$. This set may be written as

$$\mathbb{N} = \{1, 2, 3, 4, 5, \ldots\}$$

It is not difficult to show that the set of natural numbers is infinite because it has no largest number in it. No matter what number anyone might claim to be largest, we can always find another number that is larger simply by adding 1 to the number that is given. For example, 1,000,000 is not the largest natural number because 1,000,001 is a larger natural number.

In this sense then, the set of natural numbers is infinite because we have a way to construct a number larger than any *arbitrarily* large finite value. This notion of arbitrariness is crucial here—the set isn't infinite because we can construct a number larger than *some* value, it is infinite because we can construct a number larger than *any* given value, no matter what initial value we choose.

7.7   This argument that the set of natural numbers is infinite is intuitively reasonable. However, infinity is not a number and it does not have a value; consequently, we should not be surprised if it does not behave like numbers with which we are familiar. In part, the common tendency to think that infinity has a value is due to the fact that the word has its own symbol, ∞.

Unlike the symbols π and e that each represents a number, the symbol ∞ does not have a value. That is, the symbol ∞ is used to convey an idea. This symbol was first used by the British mathematician John Wallis (1616–1703). The set of natural numbers is said to be infinite. The idea is that each natural number greater than one can be determined from the previous one by the addition of 1.

7.8

The natural numbers are used in proving many **conjectures** by mathematical induction. Recall that proving a conjecture in mathematics means that you must show it to be true for all possible situations. So, you may be required to prove something to be true for infinitely many values, using only finite methods.

About Words

A *conjecture* is a statement of something that you suspect to be true but have not proven.

This is exemplified by German mathematician Karl Friedrich Gauss (1777-1855) who at the early age of 10 made conjectures that allowed him to do things more quickly than anyone else. One day in school the teacher asked the students to find the sum of all of the numbers from 1 to 100. The teacher expected that this task would keep the pupils busy for some time. Gauss, who was 10 at the time, immediately wrote down the answer! Apparently he had visualized the numbers written out in a line like this

Karl Friedrich Gauss

$$1 + 2 + 3 + \ldots + 98 + 99 + 100$$

and realized that if you added $(1 + 100)$, $(2 + 99)$, $(3 + 98)$ and so on you would get 101 each time. Since there were 100 numbers in total, there would be 50 pairs of numbers, each of which added up to 101, to give a grand total of $(50)(101) = 5050$.

From this result we can form the conjecture that

$$1 + 2 + 3 + 4 + 5 + \ldots + n = \frac{n(n + 1)}{2} = \frac{n^2 + n}{2}$$

It is easy to show that it works for any particular value of n that we might want to check. For example if $n = 5$ then the left side of the conjecture becomes $1 + 2 + 3 + 4 + 5 = 15$ while the right side is given by $\frac{5^2 + 5}{2} = \frac{25 + 5}{2} = 15$.

7.9 **Verify that this conjecture is correct for $n = 7$, $n = 10$, $n = 14$, and $n = 1,000,000$.**

Wait a minute! Trying to verify this conjecture for a large number such as 1,000,000 will be very time consuming; and, it still doesn't prove that it is true for *all values of n*. Fortunately, the principle of *mathematical induction* comes to the rescue. It says that *if* we can show that *the truth of the conjecture for some arbitrary value implies its truth for the next one in the chain, then* all we have to do is prove the conjecture is true for $n = 1$. This chaining property proves its truth for all the natural numbers. The proof that a given conjecture is true for all natural numbers consists of two steps.

1. Prove the conjecture true for $n = 1$.

2. Show that the truth of the conjecture for an arbitrary value of n, say k, guarantees the truth of the conjecture for $k + 1$, which is the next value of n.

If we could show these two things, we would know that the conjecture would be true for $n = 1$ (Step 1) and true for $n = 1 + 1 = 2$ (Step 2). Now because of Step 2 it is true for $n = 2 + 1 = 3$ (because it was true for $n = 2$). Now of course, it is true for $n = 4$. So we know it is true for $n = 2$, $n = 3$, $n = 4$.

Let's look at the full proof for this particular conjecture.

$$1 + 2 + 3 + 4 + 5 \ldots + n = \frac{n(n + 1)}{2} = \frac{n^2 + n}{2}$$

Step 1 Prove true for $n = 1$. When $n = 1$, we test to see if

$$1 = \frac{n^2 + n}{2} = \frac{1^2 + 1}{2} = \frac{2}{2} = 1$$, so the conjecture is true when $n = 1$.

Step 2 Show that *if* it is true for $n = k$, *then* it is also true for $n = k + 1$. Note that we are not claiming it to be true for $n = k$, we are saying that *if it is*, then it must also be true for $n = k + 1$.

If the conjecture is true for $n = k$ then we know that $1 + 2 + 3 + \ldots + k = \frac{k^2 + k}{2}$. Now let's examine the conjecture if $n = k + 1$. We are trying to establish a value for $1 + 2 + 3 + 4 + \ldots + k + (k + 1)$. Since we are assuming the

conjecture is true for $n = k$, we can replace
$$1 + 2 + 3 + 4 + \ldots + k \text{ with } \frac{k^2 + k}{2}$$

That is, we add the next term, $(k + 1)$, to both sides.
$$1 + 2 + 3 + 4 + \ldots + k + (k + 1) = \frac{k^2 + k}{2} + (k + 1)$$

We can add the terms on the right if we get a common denominator first.
$$\frac{k^2 + k}{2} + (k + 1) = \frac{k^2 + k}{2} + \frac{2k + 2}{2} = \frac{k^2 + 3k + 2}{2}$$

But what would we expect to get if the conjecture is true for $n = k + 1$? Well, if we substitute $k + 1$ for n on the right hand side of the original $\frac{n^2 + n}{2}$ conjecture, we would get

$$\frac{(k + 1)^2 + (k + 1)}{2} = \frac{(k^2 + 2k + 1) + (k + 1)}{2} = \frac{k^2 + 3k + 2}{2}$$

which we have shown is equal to the left side of the conjecture when $n = k + 1$.

This proves that if the conjecture is true for any natural number, it is also true for the next natural number, which means the conjecture is true for all natural numbers—even though there are infinitely many!

Proof by mathematical induction is a very important and powerful method of proof; it bridges the gap from the finite to the infinite. Induction illustrates quite nicely that *infinity can sometimes be managed—if we have the right tools.*

7.10

1. (a) Copy and complete Display 7.6 to help you in establishing a formula (conjecture) for the sum of
$1 + 3 + 5 + 7 + \ldots + (2n - 1)$
for any natural number, n.

Number of Terms	Terms to Sum	Sum
1	1	1
2	1 + 3	4
3		
4		
5		

Display 7.6

(b) Copy and complete Display 7.7 and use your conjecture to complete the chart.

n	Left Side of Conjecture	Right Side of Conjecture	Value of Left Side	Value of Right Side
2	1 + 3		4	4
3	1 + 3 + 5		9	9
6				
10				
5				
9				
k				
$k + 1$				

Display 7.7

(c) Prove this conjecture by the principle of mathematical induction.

2. Conjecture: $2 + 4 + 6 + 8 + \ldots + 2n = n^2 + n$ for all natural numbers.

(a) Use this conjecture to complete the chart in Display 7.8.

(b) Prove this conjecture by the principle of mathematical induction.

(c) Prove this conjecture and the results of question 1 above using Gauss' conjecture about the sum of the natural numbers.

n	Left Side of Conjecture	Right Side of Conjecture	Value of Left Side	Value of Right Side
2	$2 + 4$	$(2)^2 + 2$	6	6
3	$2 + 4 + 6$	$(3)^2 + 3$	12	12
6				
10				
5				
9				
k				
$k + 1$				

Display 7.8

Problem Set: 7.2

1. Use mathematical induction to prove the conjecture that for all natural numbers,
$$5 + 1 + (-3) + (-7) + \ldots + (9 - 4n) = -2n^2 + 7n$$

2. Use mathematical induction to prove the conjecture that for all natural numbers,
$$1 + 5 + 9 + \ldots + (4n - 3) = 2n^2 - n$$

3. Use mathematical induction to prove the conjecture that for all natural numbers,
$$2 + 8 + 14 + \ldots + (6n - 4) = 3n^2 - n$$

4. Given the conjecture $1 + 2 + 3 + 4 + \ldots + n = \frac{1}{2}\left(n + \frac{1}{2}\right)^2$

   (a) Show that if the conjecture is true for $n = k$ it is also true for $n = k + 1$.

   (b) Is this conjecture correct? Explain.

5. Use mathematical induction to prove that the number of different arrangements of n things is given by $n!$

6. Use mathematical induction to prove that the number of different subsets of a set with n elements is 2^n.

7.3 Rational Number Properties

Learning Outcomes

After studying this section, you will be able to:

Demonstrate understanding the historical development of the sets of natural numbers, the integers, and the rational numbers

Recognize to which number set(s) various numbers belong

Describe the relationship that the three sets have to each other

Identify the group properties of the sets of natural numbers, the integers, and the rational numbers.

About Symbols

The symbol 0 that we use for zero is the one used by Hindu mathematicians who formalized the place value systems. The Mayans used a half-open eye as a placeholder for zero.

7.11   The natural numbers provided the basis for much of the mathematics needed by early societies. Although simple to think of in terms of counting, they do have some shortcomings. For example, in the set of natural numbers there is no way to indicate *nothing* or the absence of something. With the development of the concept zero, an identity element for addition and inverses was produced. Using zero and additive inverses, the set of natural numbers was extended to form the set of **integers** (denoted by the letter I).

$$I = \{0, 1, -1, 2, -2, 3, -3, 4, -4, \ldots\}$$

where each element other than zero is written paired with its inverse element. The set of natural numbers is infinite because it has no largest member. The set of integers has no largest or smallest member, and it is customary to write it in a way that emphasizes this fact. So, we typically see the set of integers written as

$$I = \{\ldots, -3, -2, -1, 0, 1, 2, 3, \ldots\}$$

You have already studied a number of mathematical systems that are closed under various operations (for example, the set of rotations of an equilateral triangle). The set of integers is closed under addition, subtraction and multiplication, because every time you add, subtract or multiply two integers, the result is an integer. But it is not closed under the operation of division. Dividing $100 equally among three people has no answer in the set of integers. However, there is a number system that is closed under the four arithmetic operations and it is based on the *ratio* of two integers. This is the set of **rational numbers,** and it consists of all possible ratios of integers with the restriction that we cannot place zero in the denominator. In symbolic form, we define the rational numbers as the set $\mathbb{Q}$ consisting of all numbers $\frac{a}{b}$ where a and b are integers and $b \neq 0$.

Recall that division by zero is not defined because it would contradict other important properties of the rational numbers. To investigate the possibility of division by zero, examine the question $\frac{3}{0} = x$. This statement would mean that $0x = 3$. There is no value for x that makes this statement true, so we conclude that division of a nonzero number by zero is undefined.

> **If we use $\mathbb{N}$ for the natural numbers and I for the integers, why would we use $\mathbb{Q}$ for the rational numbers?**

7.12

The set of rational numbers is very useful. It is closed under addition, subtraction and multiplication. Since we cannot divide by zero, we have inverses for every element of the set except zero.

> 1. **What is the identity element for addition?**
>
> 2. **What is the additive inverse of $\frac{2}{3}$? Of $-\frac{1}{2}$?**
>
> 3. **What is the identity element for multiplication?**
>
> 4. **What is the multiplicative inverse of $\frac{2}{3}$? Of $-\frac{1}{2}$?**
>
> 5. **Is 4 a rational number? How about -3?**
>   **Justify your answers in each case.**

7.13

One common misconception is to think of these three sets of numbers ($\mathbb{N}$, I and $\mathbb{Q}$) as somehow separate from each other. If we think of their historical development, however, we need to keep in mind that each one grew out of a need to extend the previous one. It is easy to see the relationship of these sets of numbers to one another in a Venn diagram in Display 7.9.

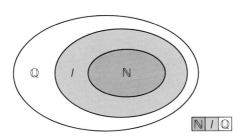

Display 7.9

7.14   This means that some numbers can belong to several different sets. People are like this too—you can live in Arizona, the United States and North America all at the same time. But being from the United States doesn't guarantee you are from Arizona and neither does a number being an integer guarantee that it is also a natural number. However, being from Arizona does guarantee that you are from the United States, just as a natural number is guaranteed to be an integer.

7.15

1. Given the following list of numbers, copy the chart below and place each number into every set to which it belongs.

$$-3, \frac{3}{7}, 0, 5, -\frac{2}{3}, -5, -\frac{4}{2}, \frac{10}{5}, \frac{-6}{-3}$$

Natural Numbers	
Integers	
Rational Numbers	

Display 7.10

2. Draw a Venn diagram and place each number in question 1 in the appropriate place to indicate to which set(s) it belongs.

7.16   The diagram in Display 7.9 also suggests another question. Although all three sets of numbers are infinite, it appears that the set of rational numbers is somehow larger than the set of integers and the set of integers is larger than the set of natural numbers. Is this reasonable? Is this idea just because of the way the diagram is drawn or does it have some merit? Write one or two paragraphs on your thoughts about the relative size of these three sets of numbers. We will come back to this idea in the last section of the chapter.

The historical development of the rational numbers was based on the need for solving problems that did not have integral solutions. It turns out that the rational numbers have properties that allow us to describe the properties of the system of rational numbers in a simple way. Display 7.11 summarizes these properties.

The Rational Number System Q	
Addition (+)	Multiplication (·)
Closure	Closure
Associativity	Associativity
Identity (0)	Identity (1)
Inverses for all	Inverses for all but 0
Commutativity	Commutativity
· is distributive over +	

Display 7.11

1. Illustrate each of the properties in Display 7.11 with a numerical example.

7.17

2. Why do we not list the operations of subtraction and division?

Problem Set: 7.3

1. Given the set of numbers
   $A = \{5, 7, \frac{-2}{3}, \frac{3}{-2}, \frac{1}{3}, \frac{-10}{-5}, \sqrt{4}, -2, -\sqrt{36}, \frac{0.1}{0.3}\}$
   list all the members of the set A that belong to

   (a) the natural numbers

   (b) the integers

   (c) the rational numbers

   (d) none of these

2. Draw a diagram similar to the one in Display 7.9 and place each of the numbers of set A of problem 1 in the appropriate place to indicate which set(s) it belongs to.

3. Explain why the system of rational numbers, along with the operations of addition and multiplication, is a more useful number system than the integer or the natural number systems.

4. $+$ and $\cdot$ are operations on $\mathbb{N}$ and I. Copy Display 7.12, then put $\mathbb{N}$ next to each property that holds in the system of natural numbers, put I next to each property that holds in the system of integers and put $\mathbb{Q}$ next to each property that holds in the system of rational numbers.

Addition (+)	Multiplication (·)
Closure	Closure
Associativity	Associativity
Identity (0)	Identity (1)
Inverses for all	Inverses for all but 0
Commutativity	Commutativity
· is distributive over +	

Display 7.12

7.4 Rational Numbers

We began this chapter with a discussion of the
Paradox of Zeno. One of the arguments that was presented
involved decimal numbers. Although you are familiar with
decimal numbers, perhaps we need to take a closer look at
what they really mean in order to understand them well enough
to sort out the apparent contradictions in Zeno's Paradox. As
the number systems that we have to deal with become more
complicated, it is helpful to be able to get a visual sense of the
relative sizes of sets of numbers. One familiar tool for this
purpose is a number line (Display 7.13).

7.18

Learning Outcomes

After studying this
section, you will be
able to:

Locate rational numbers
on the number line in
both fractional form and
decimal form

Change rational fractions
to decimal form

Locate infinite repeating
decimals on the number
line

Explain how a repeating
decimal is the result of
an infinite process.

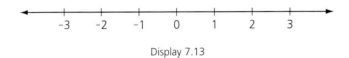

Display 7.13

Remember that this is just a tool to help us visualize
numbers. Any line is made up of points and points have no
size, only position. Consequently, the points on the number line
are *represented* by dots that we can see. Keep in mind,
however, that although a dot may have size, the point that it
represents does not.

**You are already familiar with the placement of many
numbers on the number line.**

7.19

(a) Does the decimal 0.111... represent a number?

(b) Does it have a position on the number line?

(c) Exactly where would that be?

Finding the position for 0.111... would be difficult
because it is infinite. Despite our familiarity with the number
line, we need to deepen our understanding of it before we will
be able to find the position of infinite decimals.

It is easier to start by finding the position of a fraction
such as $\frac{3}{4}$. The number $\frac{3}{4}$ signifies 3 parts out of 4 parts.

One method for dividing the segment in question into 4 equal portions and establishing the position for the number $\frac{3}{4}$ is illustrated in Display 7.14.

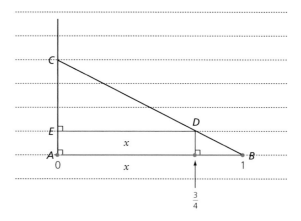

Display 7.14

1. Using lined paper, draw a perpendicular at 0.

2. Join the point C (four lines up) to B at the end of the segment AB that is one unit long.

3. Draw the line ED.

4. Draw a line from D perpendicular to the original segment AB.

The arrow indicates the point that represents the number $\frac{3}{4}$.

7.20

1. $\triangle\ CED$ and $\triangle\ CAB$ in Display 7.14 are the same shape but different sizes. What do you call triangles such as these?

2. If the distance between the lines on your page is a, then how long is AC? CE?

3. What other ratio is the ratio $\frac{DE}{AB}$ equal to?

4. What is the value of DE? What is the value of x?

5. Does this method depend on how far apart the lines are on your page? Explain.

6. Draw a sketch to illustrate how you could find the position for the number $-\frac{1}{3}$.

7. Could any fraction be located by this method? Explain.

7.4 Rational Numbers

Obviously we don't need to go through an accurate construction such as this one every time we want to establish the position of a number on a number line. However, now we know there is a way to find the exact positions of rational numbers. Let's see if this helps us to find the position for numbers expressed in decimal form. Sometimes when we are very familiar with a concept, we forget the underlying meaning behind it. What *do* decimal numbers really mean in our number system?

7.21

The place value system that we use to write numbers makes use of a very important and subtle idea. The value of a digit depends on its position in the number relative to the decimal point. For example, in the number 1222.2 the four twos all have different values; one represents 200, one represents 20, one represents 2 and the other represents $\frac{2}{10}$ or 0.2. The ideas behind a positional system of numeration developed over a long period of time, but the linking of the fundamental ideas behind it is generally considered to have been done by Hindu mathematicians around A.D. 600.

7.22

The diagram in Display 7.15 illustrates that 0.75 and $\frac{3}{4}$ have the same position on the number line.

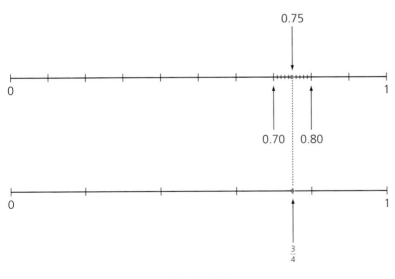

Display 7.15

Note that the position for 0.75 and the position for $\frac{3}{4}$, although arrived at in somewhat different ways, is exactly the same because *the fractional and decimal representations are just different ways to write the same number.*

7.23   The procedure for finding the position for a decimal such as 0.17564 would be similar. Subdivide the interval between 0 and 1, then the interval between 0.1 and 0.2, then the interval between 0.17 and 0.18 and so on. This process makes the size of the interval in which we find the number's position smaller and smaller and it is quite similar to using the ZOOM button on a calculator. As you ZOOM in, the scale changes to a smaller one which allows you to read values with more accuracy. It is starting to sound a little bit like the situation in Zeno's Paradox, except in that case, we were dealing with an infinite process rather than a finite one. In the finite case, we can always find the position of a fraction; but, it turns out that when rational numbers are expressed in decimal form there are two possibilities.

1. The resulting decimal is finite (contains a finite number of nonzero digits) such as 0.7500...

2. The resulting decimal is infinite, but repeats a string of digits, such as

$$\frac{1}{7} = 0.142857142857142857... = 0.\overline{142857}$$

We place a bar over the top of the digits that repeat to shorten the writing of these repeating decimals. Remember that it is not the numbers that are changing here, but the way they are represented. The number that we normally represent by the symbol $\frac{1}{7}$ can also be represented by the symbol $0.\overline{142857}$.

7.24   **Use your calculator to express each of the following fractions as decimals. State whether the decimal is finite or infinite. If the decimal repeats, write the sequence of repeating digits and the number of digits in that sequence.**

(a) $\frac{4}{5}$ (b) $\frac{2}{3}$ (c) $\frac{1}{9}$ (d) $\frac{1}{8}$

(e) $\frac{1}{3}$ (f) $\frac{3}{7}$ (g) $\frac{5}{19}$

7.25   **As you noticed in part (g) above, the number of digits of accuracy given by the calculator makes it impossible to tell if $\frac{5}{19}$ is a finite or an infinite repeating decimal. As it turns out $\frac{5}{19} = 0.\overline{263157894736842105}$. If you were to multiply 19 and 0.263157894736842105 by hand, do you think the result would be 5? Explain.**

1. For each of the following, establish the number of repeating digits.

   (a) $\frac{6}{7}$ (b) $\frac{2}{13}$ (c) $\frac{7}{17}$ (d) $\frac{5}{23}$

   Use these results to make a conjecture about the *maximum* number of digits that can occur in the decimal representation of $\frac{a}{b}$, $b \neq 0$ before a pattern starts to repeat. Explain the reason behind your conjecture.

2. Is it possible that a rational number will ever turn out to be an infinite decimal that *does not* repeat? Explain.

This discussion about fractions and repeating decimals is not just a mathematical curiosity. If the number represented by the symbols $\frac{1}{9}$ and 0.111... is the same, then the number they represent should occupy only one position on the number line. Finding a place for infinite repeating decimals on the number line is a bit troublesome, however. It is not difficult to establish the position of the number $\frac{1}{9}$, but when it is written as 0.1 or 0.111111... it is a bit more complicated. Why? Because it involves an infinite process; and as we have seen previously, the results of infinite processes are rarely obvious.

Although we may not know how to graph an infinite repeating decimal, we do know how to graph a finite decimal. We can find an upper and lower bound for the decimal even if we can't establish an exact position right away. Clearly 0.111... is larger than 0.1 and smaller than 0.2 so it will have a position somewhere in this interval.

Thinking Tip

Try to get off to a good start. Sometimes when faced with a new situation we suffer from the paralysis of analysis and are unable to get started. When you don't know what to do a good rule of thumb is do the only thing you can—it will get your thinking started and it will often lead you to a correct conclusion.

7.27

1. Copy Display 7.16 into your notebook and then fill in the upper and lower bounds for various approximations of the decimal 0.111.... The first two have been done for you.

Approximation	Lower Bound	Upper Bound	Length of Interval
0.1	0.0	1.0	1.0
0.11	0.10	0.20	0.10
0.111			
0.1111			
0.11111			
0.111111			
0.1111111			

Display 7.16

2. As the approximation becomes more accurate, what happens to the upper and lower bounds?

3. As the approximation becomes more accurate, what happens to the length of the interval?

This chart gives only a few steps in the infinite process of establishing a position for the infinite repeating decimal 0.1111.... As humans with a finite life span, we can't ever carry out an infinite process, but we can imagine what the result would be *if it were carried out*. It seems reasonable to conclude that the process is zooming in on a particular position. And, the result of this infinite process would be a single point because if the process were carried out infinitely many times, the *length of the interval* in which the position of the number is found will be zero. Furthermore, because $0.\overline{1}$ and $\frac{1}{9}$ are different symbols for the same number, they have the same unique position on the number line.

7.28   There is an important point in this discussion that needs to be emphasized. *When you establish the interval in which your decimal number is to be found, the next digit in the number can never take you outside of this interval.* The interval is then subdivided into 10 pieces (because we use a base ten number system) and the largest possible next digit of 9 represents $\frac{9}{10}$ of that interval which still leaves you inside the interval. Now you establish a new interval and the next digit can never take us outside of that interval. So, the position of the number in question is limited to a smaller and smaller

interval, the more digits of accuracy you use. We call the result of this kind of infinite process a *limit*.

We now return to the Paradox of Zeno and see what would happen if we try to decide where the spider and the snail would end up as a result of the infinite process. Go back and read the Paradox of Zeno and the two arguments.

7.29

The second argument implies the positions of the spider and snail will be given by the following expressions:

Spider: $0 + 100 + 110 + 111 + 111.1 + 111.11 + \ldots$

Snail: $100 + 110 + 111 + 111.1 + 111.11 + 111.111 + \ldots$

Consequently, both the spider and the snail will have a position represented by the same rational number, 111.111.... We could find the position on the number line for this number after infinitely many steps just as we did for the number 0.1111... And, we know that the result of that infinite process was a single point. As a matter of fact it would take exactly $\frac{1000}{9}$ seconds for the two to be at exactly the same spot. After that number of seconds, their positions are

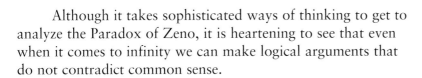

Spider: $0 + 1 \cdot \dfrac{1000}{9} = \dfrac{1000}{9}$

Snail: $100 + \dfrac{1}{10} \cdot \dfrac{1000}{9} = \dfrac{900}{9} + \dfrac{100}{9} = \dfrac{1000}{9}$

Although it takes sophisticated ways of thinking to get to analyze the Paradox of Zeno, it is heartening to see that even when it comes to infinity we can make logical arguments that do not contradict common sense.

To finish off this tour of the rational numbers and their position in the number line, let's return to the idea discussed at the beginning of the chapter, that between any two distinct points on a line there are infinitely many points, so between any two rational numbers there are infinitely many rational numbers.

Imagine the segment of the number line from 0 to 1. Clearly, 0.5 is in this interval. Now, pick either end and find another point halfway between this end and 0.5. If we picked 0, then the number halfway between 0 and 0.5 would be 0.25. This process can be continued as many times as we like and we will always be able to find a point between two distinct points just by finding the average. A set of points with the property that there are infinitely many points between any two distinct points is said to be a **dense set**.

A Fact to Know: The set of rational numbers is a **dense set**.

The rational numbers form a dense set of points on the number line. It is natural to ask if there are any gaps in the number line between the rational numbers. That is, are there any positions on the number line that do not correspond to a point that we would find by averaging two rational numbers? The surprising answer is yes, there are infinitely many gaps in the number line if only the rational numbers are located on it! This claim is surprising to say the least; but, it can be illustrated by an interesting activity.

EXPLORATION

7.30 In this **Exploration** you are going to play the Chaos Game. We'll see why it is called that later. Your teacher will provide you with a diagram of an isosceles triangle with the three vertices labeled as *A, B* and *C*. You will also need a ruler with centimeters and millimeters on it and a die. The rules of the Chaos Game are simple.

(a) Put a dot at point *B*. This is the starting point for everyone.

(b) Pick either point *A* or *C* and find the point (call it *P*) that is exactly halfway between *B* and the vertex you picked. This can be done by using a ruler to line up the points and then measuring to find the midpoint.

(c) Now roll the die.

   (i) If a 1 or 2 turns up, put a dot midway between *P* and *A* and label it as 1.
   (ii) If a 3 or 4 turns up, put a dot midway between *P* and *B* and label it as 1.
   (iii) If a 5 or 6 turns up, put a dot midway between *P* and *C* and label it as 1.

   Be as accurate as you can and draw the dots so that they can be seen clearly. Repeat this process using the new point as your point *P* and label each new point in turn as 2, 3, and so on. Do this for at least 15 points.

(d) The beginning of a sample game is shown in Display 7.17. In this game, the person picked *C* and then drew in the point labeled *P* midway between *B* and *C*. The first roll of the die was 2 (which means to use vertex *A*) and this yielded the point labeled as 2. The second roll of the die was 3 which resulted in the point labeled 2. The third roll of the die was 1 which resulted in the point labeled 3.

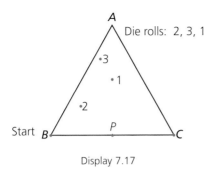

Display 7.17

Everyone will get a different result because the process is a random one. However, your teacher will show the results when there are many points in the triangle on a transparency so that you can see if any patterns emerge.

(e) Find the midpoint of AB and call it X, the midpoint of AC and call it Y and the midpoint of BC and label it Z. Join XYZ to form a triangle. Are any of your points inside this triangle? Check with the students around you. Are any of their points inside triangle XYZ? Explain.

Explorations such as this one are tedious to do by hand but can be done quickly by a computer. The diagram in Display 7.18 shows a computer generated version of the Chaos Game (about 150 points) with the points enlarged to make them easier to see. The Chaos Game is another example of an infinite process as the process can be repeated infinitely.

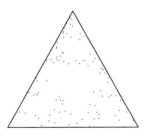

Display 7.18.

It seems that the points generated will always fall inside the original triangle and so the points produced by this process are *bounded*. Furthermore, if we think of each point as having an ordered pair associated with it, when we find the midpoint of the line we are just finding the average of the two coordinates of the end points. This procedure is quite similar to what we did to illustrate that there were infinitely many rational numbers between any two points on the number line. We would expect, therefore, that if we carried out this process enough times, the entire triangle would eventually get filled. Display 7.19 is a computer generated version of the Chaos Game with 500,000 points, each one as small as the computer can display.

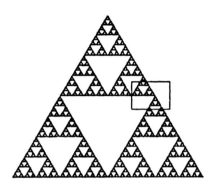

Display 7.19

The Chaos Game is based on the random roll of a die and the location of the points appear to be chaotic (not be in a pattern). A deeper look however, reveals a very well defined pattern. **Chaos Theory** has become very important in recent years because it gives mathematicians a new way to look at real world events that were perceived to be chaotic but were found to have patterns. For example, the populations of various animal species vary from year to year in an apparently random way. Applying the techniques of *Chaos Theory* has allowed scientists to examine the records of animal populations and find clear patterns.

Surprised? This strange mathematical creation was first conceived in a very different way by the Polish mathematician Waclaw Sierpinski long before computers were invented. However, the Sierpinski Triangle is one example of a mathematical entity that has become very important in the last 20 years—it is called a **fractal**. The designs of *Fractal Geometry* are used in many diverse applications—from special effects for movies to modeling blood flow in the arteries of the human body. They can be generated by computers and there are an infinite variety of patterns that can be produced.

About Words

The word *fractal* was invented in 1975 by Benoit Mandelbrot. He used the Latin root *fractus,* meaning broken, to make the word *fractal* which is both a noun and an adjective that describes these curious shapes.

One defining feature of fractals is that they are self-similar. In other words, if you pick a piece of the figure and enlarge it, the same pattern appears over again, and again, and again. This repetitive pattern continues no matter how deeply you look.

For example, look at the rectangular region in Display 7.19: when it is enlarged, the diagram in Display 7.20 is the result. We can see immediately that the same pattern of empty triangles is appearing on a smaller and smaller scale—but the pattern is still there.

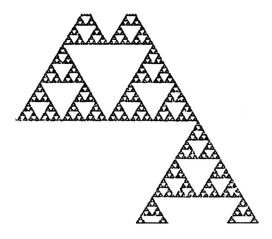

Display 7.20

An identical pattern would be produced if this region were enlarged again.

What is important for mathematics is that it is possible to have infinitely many points (generated by an averaging process) inside a boundary and still have infinitely many places where there are no points! This idea is very similar to the claim that was made previously about the rational numbers. Although there are infinitely many points on the number line and between any two distinct points we can always find another, there will still be infinitely many gaps between rational numbers that do not represent rational numbers. Unlike a number line which has gaps that we cannot see, the Sierpinski Triangle has gaps (or holes in this case) that can be seen clearly.

Are these gaps between rational numbers in a number line empty or are they positions for a different kind of number? This question leads us to the study of irrational numbers.

Problem Set: 7.4

1. Find the decimal representation for the numbers $\frac{2}{11}$ and $\frac{9}{11}$. Add the fractional forms together and the decimal forms together. Explain your result.

2. Find the decimal representation of $\frac{1}{3}$ and $\frac{2}{3}$. If you add the two fractions what do you get? If you add the decimal representations what do you get? Explain.

3. Explain why the decimal representation of a rational number will be either finite, or infinite and repeating.

4. We have shown that every rational number will produce a decimal that either repeats or terminates. Is this the same as showing that every decimal that repeats or terminates will produce a rational number? Explain. What word is used to describe the relationship between these two claims?

5. The Sierpinski Triangle is an example of a self-similar object because the same pattern occurs on smaller and smaller scales. Give an example of a self-similar object in the real world.

7.5 The Irrational Numbers and the Reals

In the previous section we suggested that there are positions in a number line that will never be filled by rational numbers. We also claimed that there were numbers in these positions. These numbers cannot be rational fractions, terminating decimals or repeating decimals because these are all just different ways of writing rational numbers.

> **We know that the decimal number e and the number π do not terminate nor repeat. Create a number different from e and π that does not terminate nor repeat a pattern. Write it down.**

7.31

The numbers e and π are not rational numbers—they do not terminate or repeat a pattern. They are called **irrational numbers**. The set of irrational numbers is denoted by $\mathbb{Q}'$. In our previous work we have seen examples of irrational numbers whose decimal positions do not repeat or end.

For example, the number e is

2.71828182845904523536028747135266249775724709369999574966967627724076630353547594571382178525 14...

and the number π, is

3.14159265358979323846264338327950288419716939937510582097494459230781640628620899862803482534 2116...

and the number $\sqrt{2}$ is

1.41421356237309504880168872420969807856967187537694807317667973799073247846210703885038753432 7641...

Mathematicians have proven that π does not repeat or end, a result that is illustrated whenever π has been evaluated to many millions of digits on large computers. If you wish, you can try your hand at searching for patterns; just a few digits are given in Display 7.21.

Learning Outcomes

After studying this section you will be able to:

Describe irrational numbers

Find the position of irrational numbers on the number line in decimal and radical form

Explain the relationship of the sets of the rational and irrational numbers to the set of real numbers.

A Piece of Pi
3.14159265358979323846264338327950288419716939937510582097494459230781640628620899862803482534211706798214808651328230664709384460955058223172535940812848111745028410270193852110555964462294895493038196442881097566593344612847564823378678316527120190914564856692346034861045432664821339360726024914127372458700660631558817488152092096282925409171536436789259036001133053054882046652138414695194151160943305727036575959195309218611738193261179310511854807446237996274956735188575272489122793818301194912983367336244065664308602139494639522473719070217986094370277053921717629317675238467481846766940513200056812714526356082778577134275778960917363717872146844090122495343014654958537105079227968925892354201995611212902196086403441815981362977477130996051870721134999999837297804995105973173281609631859502445945534690830264252230825334468503526193118817101000313783875288658753320838142061717766914730359825349042875546873115956286388235378759375195778185778053217122680661300192782766111959092164201989380952572010654858632788659361533818279682303019520353018529689957736225994138912497217752834791315155748572424541506959508295331168617278558890750983817546374649393192550604009277016711390098488240128583616035637076601047101819429555961989467678374494482553797747268471040475346462080466842590694912933136770289891521047521620569660240580381501935112533824300355876402474964732639141992726042699227967823547816360093417216412199245863150302861829745557067498385054945885869269956909272107975093029553211653449872027559602364806654991198818347977535663698074265425278625518184175746728909777727938000816470600161452491921732172147723501414419735685481613611573525521334757418494684385233239073941433345477624168625189835694855620992192221842725502542568876717904946016534668049886272327917860857843838279679766814541009538837863609506800642251252051173929848960841284886269456042419652850222106611863067442786220391949450471237137869609563643719172874677646575739624138908658326459958133904780275901...

Display 7.21

Interestingly, this characteristic of π played a major role in one of the original *Star Trek* episodes. The Enterprise's computer was being taken over by an evil force, so Mr. Spock (who studied **MATH** *Connections* on Vulcan) asked the computer to calculate the *exact* value of π. The computer (that had not studied **MATH** *Connections* at IBM) busily went away to do so. As it computed more and more digits without getting an exact value, it used up more and more memory and eventually crowded out the alien, evil force. Now who says that irrational numbers aren't useful!

It might be thought that numbers like this are hard to find. However, we don't have to search for such numbers because we can easily make up our own.

Consider the number represented by the decimal

7.32

$$0.10110111011110111110111110...$$

1. Use the pattern to list the next 10 digits.

2. Will the decimal ever repeat? Explain.

3. Make up an irrational number of your own.

Although they might seem to be a bit unwieldy, irrational numbers can be assigned a unique position on a number line just as numbers such as 1 have unique positions. Placing the number 0.10110111011110... on a number line is done by using the same method that we used to find the position of the infinite repeating decimal 0.111... . Each digit in the decimal number tells us where to go inside a new smaller subinterval, and the result of this infinite process is the position of the number under consideration.

We can also examine the placing of irrational numbers such as $\sqrt{2}$. It is true that $\sqrt{2}$ cannot be expressed exactly as a decimal, but it is not necessary to find its exact position on a number line. It can be placed by a simple geometrical construction illustrated in Display 7.22.

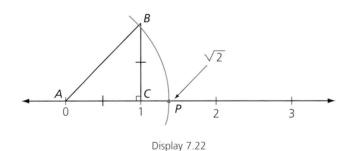

Display 7.22

Because each side of the right triangle ABC is 1 unit then $(AB)^2 = 1^2 + 1^2 = 2$.

Consequently, $(AB)^2 = 2$ and $AB = \sqrt{2}$. This length can then be measured along a number line to establish the point associated with the number represented by $\sqrt{2}$ without ever making a decimal approximation. Hence, the point P is its *exact* position.

7.33 Now that we know the exact position of $\sqrt{2}$, we can use it to find the position of $\sqrt{3}$ (Display 7.23). We know from the Pythagorean Theorem that $(AC)^2 + (BC)^2 = (AB)^2$. $(AB)^2 = 1^2 + (\sqrt{2})^2 = 1 + 2 = 3$. So, $(AB)^2 = 3$ and $AB = \sqrt{3}$. We now use a compass to measure a length on the number line exactly equal to AB and this will fix the position of the irrational number $\sqrt{3}$. We can use this method to establish the position for square roots of positive whole numbers.

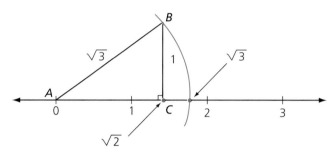

Display 7.23

7.34

1. Use the Blackline Master your teacher gives you to find the position of $\sqrt{2}$, $\sqrt{3}$, $\sqrt{4}$, $\sqrt{5}$.

2. Use this number line to find approximate values for each of these numbers.

3. Compare these values with those produced by your calculator. How close are they?

4. Is $\sqrt{4}$ an irrational number? Explain.

The set of irrational numbers is somewhat different from the other sets of numbers $\mathbb{N}$, I, and $\mathbb{Q}$ that we have studied so far. They form a distinct and separate set not contained in any of the other three sets. Recall that sets that have no members in common are said to be *disjoint*. This relationship is illustrated in Display 7.24.

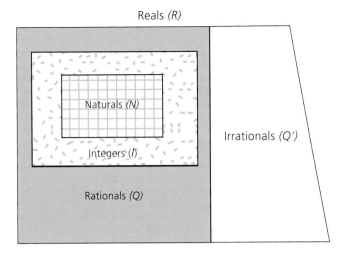

Display 7.24

Although the set of rational numbers is dense, there are still gaps in the number line when only the rationals are included. These gaps are filled by the irrational numbers, so the number line is now complete. The set of rational numbers combined with the set of irrational numbers form the set of real numbers, denoted by the letter $\mathbb{R}$.

Most of the mathematics that we have done so far have been with the real numbers, and unless stated otherwise it is normally assumed to be the case. The reals are chosen because they are a set of numbers with a wide range of useful properties. Because a real number line is a continuous line without gaps, we can graph functions using real numbers by plotting enough points to see the pattern and then joining them in an appropriate way.

Are there any numbers that do not belong to the set of real numbers? The answer is yes, the **complex numbers**, and they have an important role in mathematics. However, all complex numbers cannot be placed on a real number line. We will leave the discussion of complex numbers until another time.

7.35

Problem Set: 7.5

1. Copy Display 7.25 and then write in each of the numbers below in the correct set.

$$0.2, 0.\overline{2}, 0.12112111211112..., 3, -5, +\frac{-10}{3}, \frac{-15}{3}, 0, \sqrt{4},$$
$$-\sqrt{9}, \sqrt{5}, \pi, 0.333..., e$$

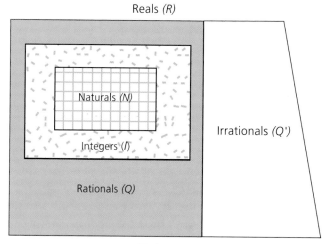

Display 7.25

2. Explain the difference between an irrational number and a rational number.

3. Will a fraction written as a decimal ever produce an irrational number? Explain.

4. Determine an irrational number between 1 and 2.

5. Prepare a frequency table for 200 digits of π starting at some randomly chosen place in Display 7.21. If there is no pattern to these digits, what should be the frequency of each digit's occurrence? Based on your results, how confident are you that there is no hidden pattern to the digits?

7.6 Infinite Series

The previous sections have dealt with some subtle ideas about infinite processes and their results. Although most of the discussion has been in terms of these ideas in mathematics, some of these ideas can arise in everyday life. For example, many companies offer discount coupons in an effort to increase their profit. Consider the following situation.

The Champion Chip Company has decided to offer a free coupon on the outside of each bag of chips to try to improve sales. If you save 10 coupons and redeem them, you can get a free bag of chips. What fraction of a bag of chips is one coupon worth?

Write down your answer to this question. You may want to do some calculations or the answer may seem obvious to you. Either way, you must come up with a possible answer even if you are not certain about it.

7.36

Learning Outcomes

After studying this section, you will be able to:

Use the Method of Exhaustion to evaluate infinite series

Demonstrate understanding the mathematical concept of a limit

Convert repeating decimals to rational fractions

Find the sum (limit) of an infinite geometric series.

An obvious answer is that because 10 coupons can be exchanged for a bag of chips, 1 coupon would be worth $\frac{1}{10}$ of a bag. Unfortunately, this "obvious answer" is not correct because with each bag of chips comes a coupon that also has some value. Let's examine this problem in a bit more detail.

$$10 \text{ coupons} = 1 \text{ bag} + 1 \text{ coupon}$$
$$1 \text{ coupon} = \frac{1}{10} \text{ bag} + \frac{1}{10} \text{ coupon}$$

But we wanted the value of one coupon in terms of a bag of chips only, so the $\frac{1}{10}$ coupon on the right side of the equation needs to be replaced. The value of 1 coupon is given by

$$1 \text{ coupon} = \frac{1}{10} \text{ bag} + \frac{1}{10}(\frac{1}{10} \text{ bag} + \frac{1}{10} \text{ coupon})$$
$$1 \text{ coupon} = \frac{1}{10} \text{ bag} + \frac{1}{100} \text{ bag} + \frac{1}{100} \text{ coupon}$$

Similarly the value of $\frac{1}{100}$ coupon can be calculated to be $\frac{1}{1000}$ bag $+ \frac{1}{1000}$ coupon. The value of 1 coupon now becomes

$$1 \text{ coupon} = \frac{1}{10} \text{ bag} + \frac{1}{100} \text{ bag} + \frac{1}{1000} \text{ bag} + \frac{1}{1000} \text{ coupon}.$$

This substitution can be continued indefinitely and so we have another example of our old friend the infinite process! The value of 1 coupon in terms of a bag of chips is given by the expression,

$$\frac{1}{10} + \frac{1}{100} + \frac{1}{1000} + \frac{1}{10,000} + \frac{1}{100,000} + \ldots$$

7.37

1. What would this expression become in decimal form? Write it as a repeating decimal.

2. What fraction do you think is equivalent to this repeating decimal? Experiment with your calculator for a few minutes and see if you can come up with a conjecture.

Maybe we can do this question in another way entirely. We know that 10 coupons = 1 bag + 1 coupon, so 9 coupons = 1 bag. This means that 1 coupon is exactly the same as $\frac{1}{9}$ bag of chips!

7.38

1. Verify that the decimal you found in question 1 above is the same as $\frac{1}{9}$ by using your calculator.

2. The kind of imprecise thinking that might lead one to think that a coupon is worth $\frac{1}{10}$ of a bag of chips can have serious consequence. In this case what originally appeared to be a 10% discount is actually a discount of approximately 11%. If the sales volume for the Champion Chip Company is $23,000,000 per year, how much would an error in thinking like this cost the company?

Although this problem might seem straightforward now, it contains many mathematical ideas, including the problem of how to find the sum of infinitely many terms in an expression such as 0.1 + 0.01 + 0.001 + ... Expressions such as this involving infinite sums are called *infinite series*. The study of infinite series is a very important mathematical topic with many applications. The famous Greek mathematician Archimedes wrestled with infinite series in some aspects of his work. His approach is a good one to use for our purposes because we can look at the problem of infinite series concretely by using what is called the **Method of Exhaustion.**

Gold foil is made by pounding a piece of gold into thin sheets. One ounce of gold will yield 25 square meters of foil! Three artisans have a square of gold foil to divide among them. Because gold foil is so valuable they want to divide it equally. How might they do this?

Let's say that the square of gold foil is 1 unit in area. One way to proceed would be to take the square and cut it into four equal pieces and give each person one of the four pieces. Repeat the process with the leftover piece and once again give each person one of the four pieces and keep one piece to subdivide.

Display 7.26 shows three steps in the process with the pieces going to three people A, B, and C.

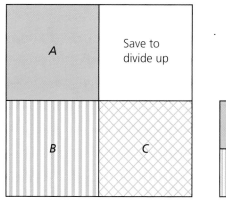

Display 7.26

If it were possible to continue this process indefinitely, would each person get the required one-third of a unit?

7.39   Display 7.27 illustrates how the pieces belonging to person *A* would fit back into the original square. This diagram makes it clear that the shaded portion is exactly one third of the whole thing since there are three of every different sized piece that make up the whole.

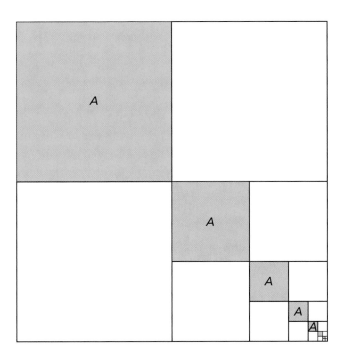

Display 7.27

Now each person has a pile of pieces that is supposed to be worth $\frac{1}{3}$ of the whole. But is it?

Well, the first piece is $\frac{1}{4}$ and the second is one quarter of this or $\frac{1}{4} \times \frac{1}{4} = \frac{1}{16}$, the next is one quarter of this again or $\frac{1}{4} \times \frac{1}{16} = \frac{1}{64}$ and so on.

Mathematically we can write that the total area of all of the shaded squares, no matter how many there are, is given by

$$\frac{1}{4} + \frac{1}{16} + \frac{1}{64} + \frac{1}{256} + \ldots$$

but we also know that the area of the shaded portion is exactly $\frac{1}{3}$ of the whole thing. So we can see that

$$\frac{1}{4} + \frac{1}{16} + \frac{1}{64} + \frac{1}{256} + \ldots = \frac{1}{3}$$

Once again we have an infinite series of terms having a finite value (in this case $\frac{1}{3}$), which we call the **limit** of the series.

7.40

1. Rewrite the series using powers of 4 in the denominators. What is the 10th term? The 25th term? The nth term?

7.41

2. Copy and complete Display 7.28.

Number of Terms	Series	Sum
1	$\frac{1}{4}$	
2	$\frac{1}{4} + \frac{1}{16}$	
3		
4		
5		

Display 7.28

A computer program gave the following sum of the first 90 terms of this series.

0.333333333333333333333333333333333333333333 3333333333333115

accurate to 57 decimal places. This does not prove that the value of the series is 0.333... , but it certainly looks plausible.

One common misconception about the limits of infinite series is that they are not exact. That is, people are happy to agree that this series might be very close to $\frac{1}{3}$, but because we can't ever really add up infinitely many terms, the value of the infinite series will never be exactly $\frac{1}{3}$. This logic is limited (pun intended) by our inability to add up infinitely many terms of anything. No one said that we have to be able to *do* it—rather we are saying that this number would be the result of the infinite process implied by the series. For example, as we saw when the repeating decimal 0.333... was put on a number line, it occupied the same position as $\frac{1}{3}$, so the two are equal.

7.42

7.43   This argument that $\frac{1}{4} + \frac{1}{16} + \frac{1}{64} + \frac{1}{256} + ... = \frac{1}{3}$ is plausible and convincing, but it does not prove anything about the limit of this series—that will have to wait until a later time. For now let's examine another similar situation.

7.44   In each of the following questions use the ideas of the Method of Exhaustion. If you find it useful to draw a sketch, please do.

1. Write each of the following as an infinite series.

   (a) $\frac{1}{4}$ (b) $\frac{1}{9}$ (c) 1

2. Verify that your results are reasonable in each part of question 1.

3. What fraction would be the limiting value of each of the following infinite series?

   (a) $\frac{1}{5} + \frac{1}{25} + \frac{1}{125} + ...$

   (b) $\frac{1}{7} + \frac{1}{49} + \frac{1}{343} + ...$

   (c) $1 + \frac{1}{2} + \frac{1}{4} + \frac{1}{8} + \frac{1}{16} + \frac{1}{32} + ...$

4. In what way(s) is the expression in question 3(c) different from 3(a) and 3(b)?

7.45   Several important patterns need to be noted here. Each term, after the first, in these series can be produced from the previous one by multiplying by a constant value. For example, in the series $\frac{1}{4} + \frac{1}{16} + \frac{1}{64} ...$, each term, after the first, is found by multiplying the previous term by $\frac{1}{4}$.

Phrases to Know: A series where each term, after the first, is formed by multiplying the previous term by a constant value is called a **geometric series**. The constant value is called the *common multiplier*.

Note that in each of the cases we have considered, the constant multiplier is a fraction. Although a geometric series can have a common multiplier that is not a fraction, it is not always true that the resulting infinite series has a sum.

7.46   1. A series has a first term of 10. Write out the first four terms of the resulting series for a common multiplier of

(a) 2   (b) 1   (c) -1
(d) 0   (e) $\frac{1}{4}$ (f) $-\frac{1}{2}$

2. **Which (if any) of these infinite series has a sum? Explain.**

A Fact to Know: To have a geometric series that has a finite sum, the common multiplier must be a number with absolute value less than 1.

We can now develop a method for finding the sum of infinite geometric series.

If a geometric series has a first term of 3 and a common multiplier of $\frac{1}{2}$ then the series would be

$$3 + \frac{3}{2} + \frac{3}{4} + \frac{3}{8} + \frac{3}{16} + \ldots$$

Another way to look at this same series is to rewrite it in the form

$$3 + 3 \cdot \frac{1}{2} + 3 \cdot \frac{1}{2^2} + 3 \cdot \frac{1}{2^3} + 3 \cdot \frac{1}{2^4} + \ldots$$

If we denote the sum of this infinite series as S_∞, then we can write

$$S_\infty = 3 + 3 \cdot \frac{1}{2} + 3 \cdot \frac{1}{2^2} + 3 \cdot \frac{1}{2^3} + 3 \cdot \frac{1}{2^4} + \ldots$$

Now multiply both sides by $\frac{1}{2}$ to produce

$$\frac{1}{2} \cdot S_\infty = 3 \cdot \frac{1}{2} + 3 \cdot \frac{1}{2^2} + 3 \cdot \frac{1}{2^3} + 3 \cdot \frac{1}{2^4} + \ldots$$

Note that every term in the original series has a corresponding term in the new series after we multiplied by $\frac{1}{2}$. This means we can pair up almost all of the terms of the original series with corresponding terms in the other, so we can subtract them with confidence.

$$S_\infty = 3 + 3 \cdot \frac{1}{2} + 3 \cdot \frac{1}{2^2} + 3 \cdot \frac{1}{2^3} + 3 \cdot \frac{1}{2^4} + \ldots$$

$$\frac{1}{2}S_\infty = 3 \cdot \frac{1}{2} + 3 \cdot \frac{1}{2^2} + 3 \cdot \frac{1}{2^3} + 3 \cdot \frac{1}{2^4} + \ldots$$

This subtraction produces the expression $S_\infty - \frac{1}{2}S_\infty = 3$

Using the Distributive Property yields $S_\infty (1 - \frac{1}{2}) = 3$

$$S_\infty = \frac{3}{1 - \frac{1}{2}} = \frac{3}{\frac{1}{2}} = 6$$

7.47 Check that this limit is reasonable by adding the first seven terms.

About Symbols

The letter *r* comes from the word ratio because in a geometric series, the ratio of any two consecutive terms is the same.

In general, if the first term of a geometric series is denoted by the letter *a*, the common multiplier (often called the *common ratio*) is denoted by the letter *r*, and the sum of the infinite series (if there is one) is denoted by S_∞, then the series would be given by

$$S_\infty = a + ar + ar^2 + ar^3 + ar^4 + \ldots$$

Now, if we multiply both sides of this equation by *r* the result is,

7.48 $$rS_\infty = ar + ar^2 + ar^3 + ar^4 + \ldots$$

The important thing to recall is that every term except the first one in the original series has a corresponding term in the new series. That is, *a* in the original series does not have a corresponding term in the new series. However, the *ar* in the first series corresponds to the *ar* in the new series, the ar^2 in the first one corresponds to the ar^2 in the second and so on. Consequently, we can subtract the two equations with confidence because for each term in the original series, except the first term, there will be a corresponding term in the second series to cancel it out. This subtraction produces the expression

$$S_\infty - rS_\infty = (a + ar + ar^2 + ar^3 + \ldots) - (ar + ar^2 + ar^3 + \ldots) = a$$

We use the Distributive Property to produce $S_\infty(1 - r) = a$.

Finally divide both sides by the quantity $(1 - r)$ to produce $S_\infty = \dfrac{a}{1 - r}$, provided that $|r| < 1$.

In order to confirm that this formula does work as it should, let's use it on a series for which we already know the infinite sum. By using the Method of Exhaustion we found that

$$\frac{1}{3} = \frac{1}{4} + \frac{1}{16} + \frac{1}{64} + \ldots$$

In this case the first term *a* is $\dfrac{1}{4}$ and the common multiplier *r* also happens to be $\dfrac{1}{4}$ so we get

$$S_\infty = \frac{\frac{1}{4}}{1 - \frac{1}{4}} = \frac{\frac{1}{4}}{\frac{3}{4}} = \frac{1}{4} \cdot \frac{4}{3} = \frac{1}{3}$$

The advantage of using the formula $S_\infty = \dfrac{a}{1-r}$ is that for $-1 < r < 1$, it also works on series that have not been derived from the Method of Exhaustion.

Consider the series $1 + \dfrac{1}{2} + \dfrac{1}{4} + \dfrac{1}{8} + \dfrac{1}{16} + \dfrac{1}{32} + \ldots$ (that we looked at earlier), which was not derived from using the Method of Exhaustion. The first term is 1 and the common multiplier is $\dfrac{1}{2}$, so the sum of this series is given by

$$S_\infty = \frac{1}{1 - \dfrac{1}{2}} = \frac{1}{\dfrac{1}{2}} = 1 \cdot \frac{2}{1} = 2$$

Sum the first 10 terms of this series. Is the sum close to 2?

7.49

This result seems plausible and can be visualized from the diagram in Display 7.29.

$$1 + \frac{1}{2} + \frac{1}{4} = \frac{1}{8} + \frac{1}{16} + \frac{1}{32} + \ldots = 2$$

Display 7.29

Although it isn't possible to indicate the area of each of the tiny rectangles, it is clear that none will ever fall outside of the large rectangle. The area of this rectangle is 2 square units and so the infinite sum of the series is bounded with a limit of 2.

A Fact to Know: The infinite sum, S_∞, of a geometric series with common multiplier r such that $|r| < 1$ and the first term is a, is given by

$$S_\infty = a + ar + ar^2 + ar^3 + \ldots = \frac{a}{1-r}$$

Another way to confirm that this formula does produce correct results is to use it to change a repeating decimal into a fraction and then check the result using a calculator. So, let's try to change 0.153153153... to a fraction and then check the results.

7.50

1. Change the number 0.153153153 into a series.

2. Find S_∞ using 0.001 as the common multiplier.

3. Verify that this result is correct by changing $\frac{17}{11}$ to a decimal.

You can now convert repeating decimals to their fractional forms. This is a nontrivial result! We now know for certain that *all* repeating decimals are rational numbers because we can convert any repeating decimal to a rational number. Before this discussion, all we knew for sure was that rational numbers in decimal form would either be finite or infinite and repeating. Recall that irrational numbers (nonrepeating infinite decimals) cannot be converted to rational form.

7.51

1. • Write each of the following repeating decimals as infinite geometric series.

• State the first term *a* and the common multiplier *r*.

• Use the formula to change each repeating decimal into a fraction.

• Check your results using a calculator.

(a) $0.\overline{123}$ (b) $0.\overline{428571}$

(c) $0.\overline{63}$ (d) $0.\overline{9}$

(e) $0.\overline{103}$

2. Do you think the fraction that results in (e) is correct? Explain.

Often in mathematics we find there are alternate ways to do things once we understand the theory behind them. Converting a repeating decimal to a fraction is no exception. Let's say we wanted to convert $0.\overline{123}$ to a fraction.

We could let the value of this decimal be x, then set $x = 0.123123123...$. This is an equation we can multiply both sides of by 1000 to get $1000x = 123.12312123...$. Now subtract the two equations

$$1000x = 123.123123123...$$
$$x = 0.123123123...$$

$$999x = 123$$

$$x = \frac{123}{999} = \frac{41}{333}$$

1. Why did we choose to multiply by 1000?

7.52

2. If you wanted to convert $0.\overline{51}$ to a fraction by this method, what number would you multiply $0.\overline{51}$ by?

3. If you wanted to convert $0.\overline{3}$ to a fraction by this method, what number would you multiply $0.\overline{3}$ by?

4. Use this new method to convert each of the following decimals to fractions in lowest terms.

   (a) $0.\overline{12}$ (b) $0.\overline{63}$

   (c) $0.\overline{103}$ (d) $0.\overline{9}$

5. Verify your answers using a calculator.

It is important to note that we are multiplying both sides of an equation by the same number even though one side is infinite. This step produces a valid result because any repeating decimal does have a finite and precise value. It is this fact that allows us to use infinite repeating decimals in equations and to solve them using our standard methods.

In this section you have seen how infinite series are linked to repeating decimals and that infinite geometric series can sometimes have limits that allow us to find their sum. But can we prove it? There is a big difference between checking a few values and making an educated guess at what numbers those values approach and *proving* the limit to be a particular value. To prove that a number we believe to be the limit of a series is the limit, we would need to show that *no matter how close to the claimed limit someone asks us to get, we can always say how many terms would need to be added to get that close or closer.*

For example, look back to the series $\frac{1}{4} + \frac{1}{16} + \frac{1}{64} + \frac{1}{256} + ... = \frac{1}{3}$, (Display 7.28) and the various decimal approximations that you filled in the table. If someone asked you to get closer than say 0.001 to 0.333333... , five terms would be more than enough. Still this does not guarantee that we can *always* say how many terms we need to be closer than *any* desired value. To show something to be true for all possible cases we need to show it is true for the general case only once, then the job is done. This process is something that is learned in the study of calculus.

Problem Set: 7.6

1. Find the sum of the series $\frac{1}{2} + \frac{1}{4} + \frac{1}{8} + \frac{1}{16} + \dots$. Illustrate this result with a diagram.

2. In the tool and die industry, CAMs (Computer Assisted Machines) are used to mill parts to accurate tolerances. A particular lathe is set up to take a round bar of steel that is 1.5 inches in diameter and reduce it to 1 inch in diameter, plus or minus one thousandth of an inch. The CAM programmer decides to do this by removing 0.25 inches from the diameter on the first pass, 0.125 inches on the second, 0.0625 on the third and so on until the bar is as close to 1 inch as is desired. Then all that has to be done is to establish how many cuts need to be taken to produce the required final product.

   (a) Show that no matter how many cuts the lathe makes, it cannot produce a finished piece of work with diameter less than 1 inch.

   (b) How many cuts by the lathe would be needed to produce a part that is within one thousandth of an inch of a 1 inch diameter?

3. Draw an equilateral triangle and think of its area as 1 square unit. Join the midpoints of all three sides to make a new equilateral triangle. Then join the midpoints of the sides of this new equilateral triangle to form another smaller triangle inside it. If this process were continued indefinitely, what would be the sum of all the combined areas of all of the smaller triangles in the diagram? Treat each area as a separate one, ignore that it is contained in other triangles.

4. Draw any square and join the midpoints of all four sides to make a new square. Then join the midpoints of the sides of

this new square to form another square. Assume the original square has an area of 4 square units.

(a) If this process were continued indefinitely, what would be the sum of the areas of all of the squares in the diagram?
(b) What would be the total length of all of the sides of all of the squares in the diagram? Treat each area separately; ignore that it is contained in other squares.

5. Consider the series $4 + 2 + 1 + \frac{1}{2} + \frac{1}{4} + \ldots$.

(a) Is it a geometric series? Explain.
(b) What is the value of the first term and the common multiplier or ratio?
(c) Find the sum of this infinite series.
(d) The partial sum of an infinite series is the sum of some fixed number of terms starting with the first. Copy and complete Display 7.30, then draw a graph with Number of Terms on the x-axis and Partial Sum on the y-axis.

Number of Terms	Partial Sum
1	4
2	6
3	7
4	
5	
6	
7	
8	
9	

Display 7.30

(e) Does the set of ordered pairs form a function? Why or why not? Explain.
(f) Should you draw a smooth curve through the points? Why or why not? Explain.
(g) Does the resulting graph have an asymptote? If so, what is its equation? Explain.

6. Use the Method of Exhaustion to express the number $\frac{3}{4}$ as an infinite series.

7. Use the calculator to find the fractional equivalent of the decimal $0.7\overline{9}$. Is $\frac{4}{5}$ the same as $0.7\overline{9}$? If so, why? If not, what number would be between them on the number line?

8. In three different ways, show that $0.\overline{9}$ is equal to 1.

7.7 Finding Area Under a Curve

One of the most famous aircraft of WW II was the British Spitfire. The Spitfire had wings which were *elliptical* (oval shaped) in cross section. The fuel tanks were designed in elliptical shape because they were placed inside the wings.

Designers needed to know exactly how much fuel the tanks contained to be able to calculate the weight of the fuel. But how can you find the volume of a tank that is elliptical rather than circular? Recall your study of three dimensional figures in an earlier chapter of **MATH** *Connections*. You learned that if a solid had a constant cross section, the volume could be found by multiplying the area of the cross section by the height of the object. So, for example, a cylinder has a volume of $\pi r^2 h$ because πr^2 is the area of its cross section, which is a circle. The real problem in finding the volume of the Spitfire's fuel tanks is to find the area of the elliptical cross section because the volume is the product of the cross sectional area and the length of the tank.

Although Archimedes had nothing to do with designing the Spitfire, he did investigate the problem of finding areas of irregular shapes. In this section we examine this problem as another example of an infinite process. Unlike Archimedes, we have the advantage of knowing how to graph curves with a graphing calculator. Thus, our job is much easier.

We will return to the Spitfire later. First let's investigate how to find the area between the curve $y = \dfrac{1}{4 - x}$ and between $x = 1$ and $x = 3$ on the x-axis. The function and the area are shown in Display 7.31. Although you may not be able to find the exact area right away, you can get a rough estimate by approximating the area as a series of rectangles.

Learning Outcomes

After studying this section, you will be able to:

Find the area under a curve by approximation

Demonstrate understanding the mathematical concept of integration

Explain how the area under a curve is the limit of an infinite process

Use the TI-84 Plus (TI-83 Plus) to find the area under a curve.

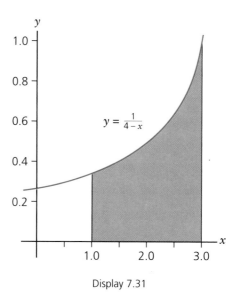

Display 7.31

We start by dividing the interval into 4 segments of equal length and drawing in the rectangles, using the left side of the rectangle as the height (Display 7.32). The cross-hatched region is the area to be found. The darker shading represents the error in approximating this area by rectangles. If you want to know the height of a rectangle you need to find the value of y for the appropriate value of x. In this diagram, when $x = 1$, the corresponding y-value is given by $y = \dfrac{1}{4 - x} = \dfrac{1}{4 - 1} = \dfrac{1}{3} \approx 0.33$.

You can see in the diagram that this looks about right for the height of the first rectangle. Because we have subdivided the region from 1 to 3 into four segments of equal width, each rectangle has a width of 0.5.

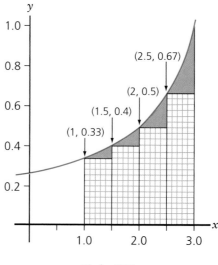

Display 7.32

1. Copy and complete Display 7.33.

7.53

Rectangle	x-value	y-value	Rectangle Width	Rectangle Height	Rectangle Area
1	1.0	0.33	0.5	0.33	0.165
2					
3					
4					

Display 7.33

2. **What is the approximate area between this curve and the *x*-axis?**

3. **Is this estimate too big or too small? Explain.**

In the previous estimate, we used the left side of the rectangle as the height, but we could have used the right side just as easily (Display 7.34).

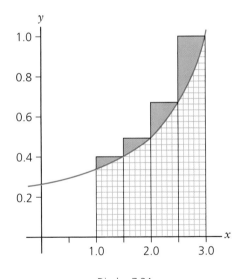

Display 7.34

This time the *x*-values of 1.5, 2.0, 2.5 and 3.0 are used to get the heights of the four rectangles. For example, if $x = 1.5$ then the *y*-value is given by $y = \dfrac{1}{4 - 1.5} = \dfrac{1}{2.5} = 0.4$; and, again this looks reasonable according to the diagram.

7.54

1. Copy and complete Display 7.35.

Rectangle	x-value	y-value	Rectangle Width	Rectangle Height	Rectangle Area
1	1.5	0.4	0.5	0.4	0.2
2					
3					
4					

Display 7.35

2. What is the approximate area between this curve and the x-axis?

3. Is this estimate too large or too small? Explain.

What we have done is find an *upper bound* and a *lower bound* for the required area. We don't know what the area is exactly, but we do know that it is between 0.9500 and 1.2833. We can calculate a better approximation by using more rectangles.

7.55

This kind of repetitive process is exactly the kind of thing that calculators and computers do well. Your calculator has a short program stored in it called RECTANG that draws rectangles and finds the area, just as you have done.

1. Enter the function $y = \dfrac{1}{4 - x}$ as Y_1 and set the WINDOW so that and $0 \le x \le 3.5$ and $0 \le y \le 2$.

2. Press PRGM and select the program called RECTANG. Pressing ENTER will run the program. You are now asked for information.

START X1
?   Enter the first x-value, in this case 1

END X2
?   Enter the second x-value, in this case 3

NUMBER   Enter the number of rectangles to use,
                   in this case 4
?

RIGHT(1)
LEFT(0)
?   Enter 0 to use the left side of the
                   rectangle for the height and 1 to use the
                   right side of the rectangle for the height.

If you used 0, the screen should look like Display 7.36.

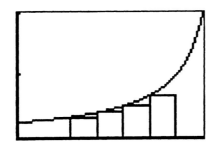

Display 7.36

3. After the graph and rectangles are drawn, the calculator pauses until you press ENTER again and this gives the value for the area. Calculate the upper bound and lower bound for the area using 4 rectangles. Verify that the values given by the program for the area using 4 rectangles are the same as you found.

4. Copy and complete the table below and use the program RECTANG to fill it in. Round your results to 6 decimal places.

N	Upper Bound for Area	Lower Bound for Area	Difference	Average
2				
4	1.28333	0.950000	0.333333	1.116666
8				
16				
32				
64				
128				
256				

Display 7.37

The table illustrates that as the number of rectangles is increased, the difference between the upper and the lower bounds approaches zero. You can see why the error decreases when the number of rectangles is increased by looking at the change in one rectangle when it is split into two. (See Display 7.38.) The table also illustrates that the average approaches some limiting value—another example of an infinite process that has a result that converges to a limit. This suggests that there is a finite result for this infinite process and that there is an exact value for the area.

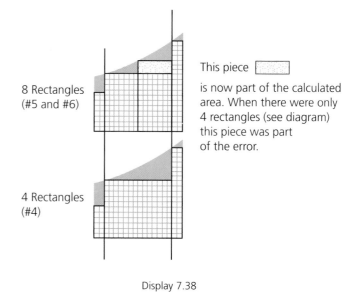

8 Rectangles
(#5 and #6)

This piece is now part of the calculated area. When there were only 4 rectangles (see diagram) this piece was part of the error.

4 Rectangles
(#4)

Display 7.38

7.56 Use the program RECTANG to evaluate the area accurate to 2 decimal places.

(a) **Explain the method you used.**
(b) **How many rectangles were required?**
(c) **Which method is most efficient?**

The idea of finding the area under a curve by approximating it with rectangles is the fundamental idea of **integral calculus.** Calculus is one of the most commonly used mathematical tools in science and engineering. When you study more mathematics, or study social sciences such as sociology, psychology, business or economics, you will certainly come across it again. As you can see from your investigation, the *idea* of finding the area this way isn't difficult, even if the detail of doing it is sometimes a little tricky. Perhaps this is why Archimedes and a number of other mathematicians came very close to developing integral calculus but were not able to take the final step.

Calculus was developed by an English mathematician, Sir Isaac Newton (1642–1727), and by a German mathematician, Gottfried Wilhelm Leibnitz (1646–1716), independently of each other. However, it now seems clear that Leibnitz did publish his findings before Newton. The controversy about who had really developed calculus was bitter and raged on in England and Europe for many years. It is believed by some historians that this is the reason that Newton retired from mathematics and took a position managing the Royal Mint. Some have suggested that stress induced by the controversy contributed to Leibnitz's death.

The method that we have used of numerically finding an approximate value for the area under a curve is useful in many situations; however, *the real power of calculus is that it provides a method of algebraically calculating the exact area!*

Isaac Newton

In our previous illustration the area under the curve $y = \dfrac{1}{4 - x}$ between two values of x, say $x = a$ (the smaller value) and $x = b$ (the larger value) is given by the formula $A = ln\,(4 - a) - ln\,(4 - b)$, provided $a < 4$ and $b < 4$. You studied natural logs earlier in **MATH** *Connections* and your calculator has a natural log key. Let's use it to verify that the values we have already established for the area under $y = \dfrac{1}{4 - x}$ from $x = 1$ to $x = 3$ agrees with the one predicted by the formula

$$A = ln(4-1) - ln(4-3) = ln(3) - ln(1)$$
$$A = 1.098612289 - 0 = 1.098612289$$

which is very close to our other answers. The reason that the algebraic method is such a powerful technique is that we can now find the area between $x = 2$ and $x = 3.5$ or $x = 0$ and $x = 2.4$, for example, without having to do any more work, other than use the formula—even if we wanted 8 decimal places of accuracy! Showing how this formula is developed is something that you'll learn when you study calculus.

1. Use your calculator and the program RECTANG to find the area under the curve $y = \dfrac{1}{4-x}$ (two decimal places) between each of the following x-values:

   7.57

   (a) $x = 1$ and $x = 3.5$

   (b) $x = 0$ and $x = 3$

   (c) $x = 1.5$ and $x = 3.7$

2. Use the formula given in this section to calculate each of these same areas. Do the answers agree?

3. In the beginning of this section we mentioned that the Spitfire had wings that were *elliptical* in cross section. The fuel tanks were placed inside the wings so they were *elliptical* shaped tanks. Designers needed to know exactly how much fuel such tanks contain to be able to calculate the weight of the fuel. But how can you find the volume of a tank that is elliptical rather than cylindrical?

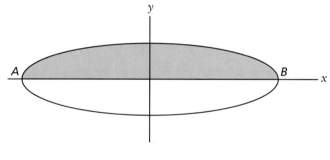

Display 7.39

The cross section of the fuel tank is shown in Display 7.39. The top half of this ellipse is defined by the function $f(x) = \sqrt{\dfrac{4 - x^2}{36}}$.

(a) Find the coordinates of the points A and B.

(b) Use your calculator to find the shaded area.

(c) Find the total area of the ellipse.

(d) If the tank is 6 feet in length, then how many cubic feet of fuel can it hold?

(e) If there are 7.48 gallons in 1 cubic foot, how many gallons of fuel will the tank hold?

The volumes of other shapes can also be calculated using this method—what we need to know is the equation of the curve of the cross section.

Problem Set: 7.7

1. Find the area between the curve $y = 3x^2$ and the x-axis and $x = 2$ and $x = 6$. Find this area by using

   (a) your calculator

   (b) the formula $A = b^3 - a^3$ where $b = 6$ and $a = 2$. What are a and b in general?

2. The top half of a circle with a radius of 1 unit is defined by the function $y = \sqrt{1 - x^2}$.

   (a) Use your calculator to find the area between this curve and the x-axis.

   (b) Find the area of the full circle. Explain.

3. Find the area between the curve $y = e^x + 1$ and the x-axis between $x = 0$ and $x = 1$.

   (a) Using your calculator, find this area.

   (b) Do you recognize this number? What is it?

4. One thing that gasoline station attendants have to do during every shift is what is called "the dips." Basically, they take a long wooden stick and insert it into a small pipe that leads down to the underground tanks. They retrieve the stick and based on the length of wood that is wet with gasoline they can calculate how much gasoline is in the tank. This is important as a check on how much gasoline has been pumped and as a reminder of when gasoline tanks need to be replenished.

   The gasoline is stored in large circular cylindrical tanks that are laying on their side. A typical tank would be 6 feet in diameter and as much as 20 feet in length. The cross section of such a tank is a circle and the top half of this circle is defined by the function $f(x) = \sqrt{9 - x^2}$.

   (a) If the tanks must never be filled to more than 95% capacity, what is the maximum capacity of a tank in gallons?

   (b) Suppose an attendant does the dips at the end of her shift and finds that 4 feet of the stick is wet. How many gallons of gasoline are in the tank?

7.8 Countable Sets

Learning Outcomes

After studying this section, you will be able to:

Distinguish among different sizes of infinity

Show sets to be equivalent by establishing a one-to-one correspondence between them

Describe the differences between the infinite characteristics of the sets of rational numbers, irrational numbers, and the real numbers.

Georg Cantor

In this chapter we have looked at infinity from a number of perspectives. We found that an infinite process can have finite results and that these results can often be calculated exactly. The last thing that we will look at in our voyage into the great unknown is how to go about counting infinite things. This idea seems silly at first because if we can't count something, that is our first clue that it must be infinite! This is true, so we have to rethink what it means to count things that are infinite rather than finite collections of objects.

7.58

1. **Does it make sense to discuss equality between sets that are infinite?**

2. **How can we talk about equality between infinite quantities if we don't know the values of the things that are supposed to be equal?**

We know that finite collections of objects can be counted and we can use this value to determine if one set is larger than another or the same size.

A similar idea that makes use of the natural numbers can be used with infinite sets. Although some of the basic ideas about infinite sets had been around since the early time of the Greek mathematicians, it was not until the 19th century that a more formal and mathematically defensible method was developed for discussing infinite sets. The mathematician Georg Cantor (1845–1918) established the principle that the set of natural numbers was a countably infinite set while the set of real numbers was not. What then does it mean to be countably infinite?

Although the set of natural numbers is infinite, it is not infinite in the same way as the set of real numbers. The real number system represents all the points on a line. The natural numbers represent relatively few of those points, each a fixed distance from the nearest one on each side of it. This idea suggests (but does not prove) that there might be different kinds of infinite sets; those that can be paired with the natural numbers, and those that cannot. Pairing allows us to compare infinite sets by size, even though we cannot actually count them. Sometimes this comparison leads to puzzling results.

For example, let's say we form a set of numbers by doubling each element of the natural numbers and call this the set A. Because each element of A comes from doubling an element of the set $\mathbb{N}$ it is easy to pair the elements of $\mathbb{N}$ with the elements of A. That is, it is easy to put the elements of set A into a one-to-one correspondence with the natural numbers, for example,

$$\mathbb{N} = \{1, 2, 3, 4, 5, ...\}$$

$$A = \{2, 4, 6, 8, 10, ...\}$$

The problem is that the set A, which is essentially the set of all even natural numbers, appears to be the same *size* as all of the natural numbers that contain both the even and odd numbers!

7.59

Similarly the set of all odd numbers can be put into a one-to-one correspondence with the natural numbers by using the function $f(n) = 2n - 1$. In this case $1 \to 1$, $2 \to 3$, $3 \to 5$, so each natural number can be paired with an odd number. We have a peculiar situation where it appears that half of something is just as big as the whole thing! This idea is confusing until we recall that an infinitely large quantity is **not a number** in the same sense as 5, 16, or 123,459, and it does not make sense to think about finding half of it or twice it.

Words to Know: Sets that can be put into a one-to-one correspondence with the natural numbers are said to be **countable** (even though they are infinite sets) or *countably infinite*.

Are there other sets that can be put into a one-to-one correspondence with the natural numbers? For example, can we put the set of integers,

$$I = \{..., -3, -2, -1, 0, 1, 2, 3, ...\}$$

into a one-to-one correspondence with the set of natural numbers? It is important when doing the matching that the pattern be clear. There must be no possibility that following the pattern will inadvertently leave out some values. Also, any matching must be clearly illustrated by a pattern that will hold for any finite number of the set that we list. In this case it can be accomplished by rewriting the integers slightly.

$$\mathbb{N} = \{1, 2, 3, 4, 5, \ldots\}$$

$$I = \{0, -1, 1, -2, 2, \ldots\}$$

Now the one-to-one correspondence is easier to see.

$$1 \rightarrow 0$$
$$2 \rightarrow -1$$
$$3 \rightarrow 1$$
$$4 \rightarrow -2$$
$$5 \rightarrow 2$$
$$6 \rightarrow -3$$
$$7 \rightarrow 3$$

and so on for as many terms as you list.

7.60

1. **List the next 10 members of the set of natural numbers and the integers with which they would match.**

2. **Are there any integers that would not have a natural number paired with them? If so, which ones? If not, explain why not.**

3. **What natural number would be paired with the following integers?**

   (a) −123   (b) 64   (c) −90   (d) 55

4. **What natural number would be paired with the integer x?**

5. **Earlier in MATH *Connections* you learned about functions as ways of associating pairs of numbers. Express the pairing in this case as a function where the domain is the set of natural numbers. Such a function is called a *sequence*. Recall that a sequence is a function that has the set of naturals as its domain.**

Let's try to find other sets of numbers that can be put into a one-to-one correspondence with the natural numbers. Consider the set of all fractions of the form $\frac{a}{b}$ where a and b are both natural numbers and $b \neq 0$. If we list all of the fractions by grouping those where the numerator and denominator add up to

1, 2, 3, 4, 5, ... , we will make sure that we don't leave out any. For example, if we wanted to list all of the fractions for which the numerator and denominator add up to 6 we would list,

$$\frac{1}{5}, \frac{2}{4}, \frac{3}{3}, \frac{4}{2}, \frac{5}{1}$$

Furthermore, if we omit those that are not in lowest terms we will ensure that we don't count the same one twice. Written this way, the set of all positive fractions then looks like this:

$$\mathbb{N} = \{1, 2, 3, 4, 5, 6, 7, 8, 9, 10, ...\}$$
$$F = \{\frac{1}{1}, \frac{1}{2}, \frac{2}{1}, \frac{1}{3}, \frac{3}{1}, \frac{1}{4}, \frac{2}{3}, \frac{3}{2}, \frac{4}{1}, ...\}$$

and it can be put into a one-to-one correspondence with the counting numbers. This means that the set of positive fractions, the set of integers and the set of natural numbers are all equivalent. That is, any two of the sets can be put into a one-to-one correspondence.

7.61

1. **List the next 10 elements in the set F of positive fractions.**

2. **Which fractions did you leave out because they are not in lowest terms?**

3. **Would a fraction with the value $\frac{28.3}{1184.6}$ ever occur in this listing? Explain.**

4. **Are you confident that this method will ensure that all possible positive fractions are listed? Explain the reason(s) for your answer.**

In a similar fashion, we can put the set of all rational numbers that comprises all numbers of the form $\frac{a}{b}$ where a and b are both integers and $b \neq 0$ into a one-to-one correspondence with integers that have already been matched with the natural numbers. This means that the set of rational numbers is also considered to be countable. Remember, any rational number can be converted into a decimal that is either finite or repeating. It follows, then, that the set of all decimals that are finite or repeating is countable. Because of this equivalence between finite or repeating decimals and fractions, we could think of the pairing between the natural numbers and the positive fractions in this way.

$$\mathbb{N} = \{1, 2, 3, 4, 5, 6, 7, 8, 9, 10, ...\}$$
$$D = \{0, 1.0, 0.5, 2.0, 0.\overline{3}, 3.0, 0.25, 0.\overline{6}, 1.5, 4.0, ...\}$$

In fact this is exactly what we had before because the numbers in the pairing haven't changed, *just the symbols we use to represent them.*

This discussion of the decimal and fractional representation of numbers shows that all of the repeating decimals and finite decimals form a set that is countable because this set is another way of denoting the fractions that can be paired in a one-to-one correspondence with the natural numbers.

7.62 **Back in Section 7.2 you wrote your thoughts about the relative *sizes* of the sets of natural numbers, the integers, and the rational numbers. Have your ideas changed? If so, how? If not, why not?**

What, then, is not a countable set? Well, note that nonrepeating, nonterminating decimals (the set of irrational numbers) are not included in the rational numbers. We know that the *irrational numbers* can be put on a number line just like the rational numbers, but does this mean that *all* decimals can also be put into a one-to-one correspondence with the natural numbers?

To begin, let us consider all possible decimals between 0 and 1, including 0, since all real numbers can be formed from this set by adding or subtracting a whole number. If we want to find a one-to-one correspondence between this set of decimal numbers and the natural numbers, we must find some clear pattern or scheme to follow that shows how each nonnegative decimal less than 1 could be paired with a natural number. And, this pattern must ensure that no numbers are omitted.

We use an indirect proof here—assume there is such a list and then show that this assumption produces a contradiction. Suppose someone comes to you with a scheme that they claim will achieve these two objectives stated above. First let's assume that there is such a pattern in the following list:

0.16625273564...

0.36482362344...

0.20500000091...

0.45231823123...

0.60000000001...

0.83487348539...

and so on. Then, to prove that this list is incomplete, all that is needed is to show that the list fails to take into account some decimal. We can always make up such a number by making up a decimal using the following rule.

Look at the first digit of the first number. If the digit is not 5 then write down a 5. If it is 5, write down a 6. Now look at the second digit of the second number. Repeat the process. Repeat with the third digit of the third number and so on. This process is illustrated in Display 7.40.

$$
\begin{array}{l}
\overline{\hspace{3cm}} \text{ not } 5 \rightarrow 5 \\
0.16625273564\ldots \\
\quad\overline{\hspace{2.6cm}} \text{ not } 5 \rightarrow 5 \\
0.36482362344\ldots \\
\quad\quad\overline{\hspace{2.2cm}} \text{ is } 5 \rightarrow 6 \\
0.20500000091\ldots \\
\quad\quad\quad\overline{\hspace{1.8cm}} \text{ not } 5 \rightarrow 5 \\
0.45231823123\ldots \\
\quad\quad\quad\quad\overline{\hspace{1.4cm}} \text{ not } 5 \rightarrow 5 \\
00.60000000001\ldots
\end{array}
$$

Display 7.40

So the number 0.55655... will never be in this listing because of the way that the listing is constructed. Now, if the person who made up the original list said, "All right, I forgot that one, add it to the list" we could go back and make up another number (using a similar procedure) that would not be there and repeat this procedure indefinitely. Therefore, the set of nonnegative decimal numbers less than 1 cannot be put into a one-to-one correspondence with the natural numbers.

It turns out that the set of all decimals representing both rational and irrational numbers, what we call the set of real numbers, represents another kind of infinity, different from the one defined by the set of natural numbers. It appears that not all infinities are created equal, after all!

REFLECT

This ends our tour of the world of the infinite. It has introduced you to many important but sometimes puzzling ideas. Many of these concepts can only be fully developed over time as you see more and more pieces of the picture that mathematics paints. In the words of the famous British mathematician G. H. Hardy (1877–1947):

> "The mathematician, like a painter or a poet, is a maker of patterns. If the mathematician's patterns last longer it is because they are made with ideas."

Problem Set: 7.8

1. For each of the following sets, determine if the set is countable or not. Explain.

   (a) The set of all multiples of 3.
   (b) The set of points between 0 and 1 on a real number line.
   (c) The set of all numbers of the form $2n + 1$ where n is a natural number.
   (d) The set of all positive fractions with denominator 5.
   (e) The set of points between 0 and 2 on a real number line.

2. Use a geometrical approach to illustrate that there is the same number of points on a line of 1 unit in length and one of any arbitrary length.

3. Recall that a set of numbers is said to be *dense* if between any two distinct numbers it is possible to find infinitely many numbers. Is the set of integers *dense*? How about the set of rational numbers? Explain your reasons for each case.

4. Prepare a frequency table for 200 digits of π starting at some randomly chosen place in Display 7.21. If there is no pattern to these digits, what should be the frequency of each digit's occurrence? Based on your results how confident are you that there is no hidden pattern to the digits? Explain.

Michio Kaku
The Explanation of Everything

Michio Kaku, professor of theoretical physics at City College in New York, believes a unified explanation of everything is attainable in his lifetime and he is only 51 years old. "Euclidean geometry deals with two dimensions. We now go to 10 dimensions with room to unify the fundamental forces in one framework. The explanation of everything begins with the four forces: electromagnetic, gravitational, and weak and strong nuclear energy," explains Dr. Kaku, "and it will be an equation one inch long ($E=MC^2$ is 1/2 inch). We think we're close to having the answer."

"The dominant theory of our time is the super-string theory supported by several Nobel Laureates," continues Dr. Kaku, who is well known for his abilities to explain and translate highly technical complicated mathematical principles to ordinary people.

"It uses analytic geometry to chart the location and movement of particles. We believe these particles are actually strings which vibrate in ten dimensions." In this theory each vibration is viewed as a point-like elementary particle just as the vibration of a musical string is perceived as a distinct note.

Dr. Kaku grew up in Palo Alto, California and has always had a passion for math and science. "When Albert Einstein died it was big news around the world. I always knew that I wanted to work on completing his dream of finding the theory that explains everything." Michio successfully built an atom smasher in high school despite limited scientific resources and after graduating from Harvard University he made a vow to talk to children about the joys of science. "I was blessed with real physicists as teachers and I understand that science is not about memorizing things you will forget tomorrow. Scientists do not spend time naming things. Math and science are about finding the handful of basic principles."

"In the future when we unify the four forces it will reveal the secrets of space and time. It may allow for time travel and it will explain everything from black holes to the creation of the Universe."

Axioms, Geometry, and Choice

CHAPTER 8

8.1 Can Any Statement Be an Axiom? Consistency

8.1

Learning Outcomes

After studying this section you will be able to:

Describe what it means to say that an axiomatic system is consistent

Test an axiomatic system to see if it is consistent

Identify some real-life situations that can be described in terms of axiomatic systems.

Answer these questions in your own words.

1. What is an axiom?

2. What is an axiomatic system? What are the essential parts of an axiomatic system?

3. What is an instance of an axiomatic system?

4. Is Quick Six an axiomatic system? Why or why not?

5. What is the essential difference between an axiom and a theorem?

6. Can any statement be an axiom?

Can any statement be an axiom? What does this question mean? Maybe we ought to ask first:

> Where do axioms come from?

The simplest answer is:

> Somebody makes them up.

But why? There are various reasons. Axioms often arise as part of the process of making a mathematical model of some real-world situation as you saw in Chapter 6. But sometimes an axiomatic system is designed to test a mathematical theory or to answer a question of logic. In such cases, the makers of the axioms may not know or care about any instance of the system.

Put aside the model↔instance connection for now and look at axiomatic systems by themselves. From this point of view,

- The axioms of a system are made-up statements about some basic, undefined terms.

- The axioms are true within the system because we say so. That is, they are declared to be the logical starting points for the system.

- A statement within the system is valid if it can be proved from the axioms.

The question is:

Can *any* statement about the basic terms of a system be an axiom?

For example, suppose we start to make up an axiomatic system using the undefined terms *drib*, *drab*, and *drop*. Yes, the words are silly, but they make more grammatical sense than *x*, *y*, and *z*. Dr. Seuss, the author of *The Cat in the Hat* and many other children's books, made a fortune using words like this!

- Could we choose

    "Every drib drops a drab."

    as an axiom? Of course! In this system, would it be true? Of course! Why? Because we said so by making it an axiom.

- Could we choose

    "Some drib does not drop a drab."

    as an axiom? Of course! In this system, would it be true? Of course! Why? Because we said so by making it an axiom.

- Could we choose both of these statements as axioms at the same time?

Well, *could* we choose both of these statements as axioms at the same time? Why or why not?

8.2

Those two statements, taken together, form a contradiction. Any system containing them would violate the Law of Contradiction.

8.3

"So what?" you might say. "Can't we set up our own laws when we make up an axiomatic system?"

Yes and no. You certainly can set up your own axioms, but you can't violate the laws of reason. The point of having axioms is to have a starting place for logical arguments about whatever the system describes. If you begin with something illogical, then your system will be useless. In the real world, any useful axiomatic system has to have an instance, a situation in which the axioms are true statements about something real. A system containing a contradiction cannot have an instance; self-contradictory objects simply do not exist in the real world. This is a fundamental principle of reasoning, so we'll put a star next to it and say it again.

(★) If an axiomatic system contains a contradiction, it cannot have an instance.

Actually, the contrapositive form of statement (★) is more useful to us.

8.4

1. What is the contrapositive of statement (★)?

2. How are the truth values of a statement and its contrapositive related?

Of course, nobody puts a contradiction into an axiomatic system *on purpose*, but sometimes one might be built in by accident. And when one is, it's not always easy to find.

Both of the following sets of axioms are about the same undefined terms.

8.5

Undefined terms: point, line, on
System I
Axioms
(a) There are exactly three points.
(b) There are exactly three lines.
(c) Each line is on exactly two points.
(d) Every pair of points is on exactly one line.

System II
Axioms
(a) There are exactly four points.
(b) There are exactly four lines.
(c) Each line is on exactly two points.
(d) Every pair of points is on exactly one line.

These two systems are very much alike, but one contains a contradiction and the other doesn't. Which is which? Justify your answer.

About Words

The literal meaning of *con-sist*, from Latin, is to stand with. Thus, statements are *consistent* if they can stand together logically.

Statements that do not contradict each other are said to be **consistent.** If the axioms of a system do not contain or lead to any contradictions, then they are consistent with respect to each other. This idea of consistency within the system is usually expressed as follows:

Words to Know: An axiomatic system that does not contain any contradictions is said to be **consistent.** An axiomatic system that contains a contradiction is said to be **inconsistent.**

Did you discover which of the two axiomatic systems, I or II, is inconsistent? If so, how did you do it? Did you use the contrapositive of Statement (★)? That's the key. Now that we have the proper vocabulary, we can restate this important statement more concisely. This time, we'll give it two stars.

(★★)   An axiomatic system that has an instance must be consistent.

By now you probably found an instance of System I. If not, stop here and try again. Think about a triangular diagram of some sort. What are the "points"? What are the "lines"? What does "on" mean in this situation? This means that System I is consistent, so the contradiction must be in System II.

"That works if you've already told us that one of the systems contains a contradiction," we heard somebody say. "But what if you're wrong? Or what if we run into an axiomatic system we don't know anything about?"

Didn't anybody ever tell you that authors are *never* wrong? Do you really believe that?! O. K., it's a good question. Maybe we've tricked you and there is no contradiction in System II. Or maybe we made a mistake.

Axioms, Geometry, and Choice

8.1 Can Any Statement Be an Axiom? Consistency

How can you be sure? And if this axiomatic system does contain a contradiction, what is it?

A good way to find a contradiction in a system is to try to make an instance of the axioms. When you run into trouble, look carefully at what's getting in your way. That's usually a clue to the contradiction. For example, we think that System II contains a contradiction, but we don't know what it is. So we try to build an instance and see where we run into trouble.

In System II

- Axiom (a) says: "There are exactly four points," so any instance must contain exactly four things called *points*. Let's name these *points A, B, C* and *D*. Remember: The basic terms of a system are undefined, so *points* may not mean points in space and lines may not mean lines.

- Axiom (b) says: "There are exactly four *lines*." Before naming these *lines*, let us see how they are supposed to be related to the *points*.

- Axiom (c) says: "Each line is on exactly two points." This tells us that we could name each *line* by the pair of *points* on it. But which *points* are on *lines*?

- Axiom (d) tells us. It says: "Every pair of points is on exactly one line."

8.6

> **Because of axioms (c) and (d), we can name each *line* by the pair of *points* on it.**
>
> 1. *AB* represents a *line*. Does *BA* represent the same *line* or a different one? How do you know?
>
> 2. By axioms (c) and (d), how many *lines* are in this system? Name them.
>
> 3. What's the contradiction?

Now that you see where the contradiction lies, it becomes easy to write a much clearer, shorter proof that System II is inconsistent.

Proof By axiom (a), there must be four points. By axiom (d), each pair of points is on exactly one line, and, by axiom (c), two different pairs of points cannot be on the same line. Thus, there are as many lines as there are pairs of points. Now, there are six pairs of points (because $_4C_2 = 6$), so there must be six lines. But this contradicts axiom (b), which says that there are exactly four lines. Therefore, System II is inconsistent.

Find a contradiction in this axiomatic system.

8.7   Undefined terms: mole, widget, hold
Axioms
(a) There are exactly 20 moles.
(b) Each widget is held by exactly three moles.
(c) Every mole holds exactly one widget.

Write a clear, careful proof of the fact that the mole-
widget axiomatic system of the preceding question is
inconsistent.

8.8

Summary

To determine whether or not an axiomatic system is consistent,
find (or make) an instance of it.

1. Finding an instance proves that the system is consistent.

2. If you cannot find an instance, look carefully at how the
   axioms are getting in your way.

3. Use your observations about what's getting in your way to
   find two statements that contradict each other.

4. Prove that the system is inconsistent by showing how both
   of the contradictory statements follow from the axioms.

Does this consistency stuff relate to the real world, to
your real world? You bet!

- Every contract describes an axiomatic system. When you
  take out a credit card, or buy a car, or rent an apartment,
  you sign an agreement about what you get and how you pay
  for it. The dealings between you and your bank, car dealer,
  or landlord are required by law to be consistent with that
  agreement.

- A collective bargaining agreement between a labor union
  and the management of a company (or a sports league) is an
  axiomatic system. It declares that the actions of all
  employees and their bosses will be consistent with the rules
  (axioms) of the contract. In this setting, a union grievance is
  a claim that the managers did something that contradicted
  some part of that contract.

- On July 4, 1776, representatives of the 13 American colonies
  broke away from Great Britain by agreeing to an axiomatic
  system, the Declaration of Independence. After a brief

opening paragraph, the axioms are stated clearly and explicitly, as shown in Display 8.1. The document goes on to prove a fundamental theorem: The 13 American colonies are justified in breaking away from Great Britain and forming an independent country—the United States of America!

We hold these truths to be self-evident:
~ That all men are created equal;
~ That they are endowed by their creator with certain unalienable rights;
~ That among these are Life, Liberty, and the pursuit of Happiness;
~ That to secure these rights, Governments are instituted among Men, deriving their just powers from the consent of the governed;
~ That whenever any Form of Government becomes destructive to these ends, it is the Right of the people to alter or abolish it, and to institute new Government, laying its foundation on such principles and organizing its powers in such form, as to them shall seem most likely to effect their Safety and Happiness.

An important list of axioms

Display 8.1

- The laws of the United States form a long, complex axiomatic system based on the Constitution. Each time a law is passed, it becomes a new axiom of this system. Every year, many new laws are passed by Congress and the state legislatures. These laws must be consistent with the Constitution. The Supreme Court has the job of ensuring that consistency. In doing this job, the Court does not decide whether a particular law is a good idea or a bad idea from some point of view. It simply considers whether or not that law contradicts some part of the Constitution. If it does, the Court declares it unconstitutional, thereby throwing out the law and the contradiction with it.

8.9

Here are three cases in which the Supreme Court declared a law unconstitutional.

- 1954: Brown v. Board of Education of Topeka, Kansas, 347 U.S. 483 (1954)

- 1971: Reed v. Reed, 404 U.S. 71 Idaho (1971)

- 1974: United States v. Nixon, 418 U.S. 683 (1974)

Look up one of these rulings in the library or on the Internet. Write a brief description of the issue. How does the outcome of the case affect you and other people today?

Problem Set: 8.1

1. Consider this axiomatic system

   Undefined terms: point, line, on
   Axioms
   (a) There is at least one line.
   (b) Every line is on at least three points.
   (c) No point is on every line.

(i) Prove that this axiomatic system is consistent.

(ii) Add an Axiom (iv) that makes the system inconsistent. Justify your answer.

(iii) Suppose we were to choose as Axiom (d) this statement,

(d) There are exactly four points.

Is this expanded system consistent or inconsistent? Justify your answer.

2. In Chapter 6 you saw how family relationships among students named Janovic or Masryk could be described as a list of three axioms. The following axiomatic system repeats those same three axioms in a slightly more abstract form and adds a place for a fourth axiom.

Undefined terms: *J, M,* related to

Axioms

(a) There are exactly three *J*s.

(b) Every *J* is related to at least two *M*s.

(c) No *M* is related to more than two *J*s.

(d) _____

• Justify the claim that the system consisting of Axioms (a), (b), and (c) is consistent.

• Consider each of the following statements in turn as Axiom (d). For which ones is the system consistent, and for which ones is it inconsistent? Justify each answer.

(i) Some *M* is related to all the *J*s.

(ii) Some *J* is related to all the *M*s.

(iii) Not every *M* is related to a *J*.

(iv) There are only two *M*s.

(v) There are twelve *M*s.

(vi) Some *M* is related to only one *J*.

(vii) Every *M* is related to only one *J*.

(viii) Some *J* is related to only one *M*.

(ix) There are more *J*s than *M*s.

(x) There are more *M*s than *J*s.

3. Here is a set of axioms that we shall call System **A**.

   Undefined terms: point, line, on

   Axioms
   A1 There is at least one point.
   A2 Every point is on at least two lines.
   A3 Every line is on at least two points.
   A4 Given any two points, there is exactly one line on both of them.

   (a) Is System **A** consistent? Why or why not?
   (b) Write out ~ **A2**, the negation of Axiom **A2**. Is the system composed of the Axioms **A1**, ~ **A2**, **A3**, and **A4** consistent? Justify your answer.

4. Consider the following axioms.

   Undefined terms: point, line, on

   Axioms
   (a) There are at least one point and one line.
   (b) Given any two (distinct) points, there is exactly one line on both of them.
   (c) Given any two (distinct) lines, there is exactly one point on both of them.
   (d) Every line is on at least three points.
   (e) Not all points are on the same line.

   Is this a consistent system? Prove your answer.

5. Explain how Statement (★★)—An axiomatic system that has an instance must be consistent—is the contrapositive of Statement (★)—If an axiomatic system contains a contradiction, it cannot have an instance. (*Hint:* Think about Statement (★★) in *if ... then ...* form.)

8.2 The Geometry of Euclid

This is the story of the world's most famous axiomatic system. It was constructed 2300 years ago in Alexandria by a teacher named Euclid. It was studied by Greek and Roman scholars for a thousand years. Around A.D. 800 it was translated into Arabic and studied by Arab scholars, too. It became the standard for logical thinking throughout medieval Europe. It has been printed in more than 2000 different editions since it first appeared as a typeset book in the 15th century. Its influence has become a part of almost every field of thought.

- In the 13th century, Saint Thomas Aquinas used its form to organize his writings on religion.

- In the 17th century, the British scientist Isaac Newton and the Dutch philosopher Benedict de Spinoza used the form of this system to present their ideas.

- In the 18th century, Thomas Jefferson used its form in writing the Declaration of Independence.

- In the 19th century, Abraham Lincoln carried a copy of it with him and studied it at night by candlelight in order to become a better lawyer.

This famous axiomatic system is Euclid's plane geometry, the first part of his most famous work, *The Elements*. Only the Bible has been printed more often.

1. Where is the city of Alexandria in which Euclid lived? What major river is it near? Of what country is it a part now? Of what country was it a part in 300 B.C.? After whom was it named?

8.10

2. When and where was movable type printing first used in Europe? Who was the European printer credited with first using movable type to print a book? What was the first book he printed?

Euclid

The Greeks had developed a lot of mathematics by 300 B.C. The work of Pythagoras and his followers had been around for two centuries, and many other people had written about their own mathematical discoveries, too. Plato's philosophy and Aristotle's logic were firmly established by then, so scholars knew that mathematical facts should be justified logically. Apparently many of these mathematical results had been proved from more basic ideas. But even these proofs were disorganized, each one starting from its own assumptions, without much regard for consistency. Of all the people who tried to put this jumble of mathematical ideas in order, Euclid was by far the most successful. He was so successful, in fact, that his system has lasted for 2300 years!

Euclid wanted to put all of mathematics on a unified logical foundation. The *elements* of mathematics were to be the principles making up that foundation. In 300 B.C., all of Greek mathematics was related either to geometry or to number theory. Euclid set out to rebuild those fields "from the ground up." He organized *The Elements* into 13 parts, called "Books." They probably were long papyrus scrolls.

About Words

In chemistry, the *elements* are the basic substances from which all matter is made.

— Books I, III, IV, and VI are about two-dimensional (plane) geometry.

— Books XI, XII and XIII are about three-dimensional (solid) geometry.

— The other six books are about numbers and measurement.

These books contained a total of 465 **propositions** (we would call them theorems), each one proved from statements that came before it. With a touch of genius, Euclid connected his entire work to Plato's philosophy with the last proposition of the last book: He proved that the only possible types of regular polyhedra are the five Platonic Solids, which symbolized for Plato the basic elements of the entire universe! The Platonic Solids were described earlier in **MATH** *Connections*.

8.11

What are the names of the five Platonic Solids? Describe each one geometrically. According to Plato, which basic element of the universe did each one represent?

Book I begins with ten basic assumptions[1]. Your teacher will give you a list of these Common Notions and Postulates so that you may refer to them easily.

Common Notions

1. Things equal to the same thing are also equal to each other.

2. If equals are added to equals, the results are equal.

---

[1]These and other statements of Euclid are adapted from Sir Thomas L. Heath's translation, *The Thirteen Books of Euclid's Elements*, 2nd Edition, 1925.

3. If equals are subtracted from equals, the remainders are equal.

4. Things that coincide with one another are equal to one another.

5. The whole is greater than the part.

Postulates

1. Exactly one straight line can be drawn from any point to any point.

2. A finite straight line can be extended continuously in a straight line.

3. A circle can be formed with any center and distance (radius).

4. All right angles are equal to one another.

5. If a straight line falling on two straight lines makes the sum of the interior angles on the same side less than two right angles, then the two straight lines, if extended indefinitely, meet on that side on which the angle sum is less than the two right angles.

In the language of Chapter 6, all ten of these statements are the axioms, the starting point statements for Euclid's plane geometry. The Greeks used the word *axiom* only for the "Common Notions," statements that applied to any objects in any context. Specific assumptions about a particular subject were called **Postulates.** Nowadays people usually use *axiom* and *postulate* interchangeably; we shall, too. In this chapter, the axioms of Euclid's system mean his Common Notions *and* his Postulates.

About Words

In everyday English, to *postulate* something is to assume that it is true.

Do you understand what Postulate 5 says? Draw a diagram for it and explain it in your own words.

8.12

In Euclid's view, all ten of these statements are obviously true, once you know what the words mean. Do you agree? To clarify the meanings of the words, he provided 23 definitions. The first few of those definitions are pretty strange, probably because Euclid was trying to leave no geometric terms undefined. For instance,

A *point* is that which has no part.

A *line* is length without breadth.

A *straight* line is a line which lies evenly with the points on itself.

Euclid was not trying to define words such as *point* and *line* from scratch, as if no one had ever heard of them before. Surely everyone, including Euclid, thought of points as locations and of straight lines as paths that could go through any point and stretch out in any direction. They understood that whenever two lines intersected there was a point at the intersection, and so on. Euclid was just trying to sharpen the everyday use of these well known words by pointing out properties needed for their use in geometry. He wanted people to understand that:

> A point in geometry is a location so precise that it cannot be divided into smaller parts; it has no size.

> A line in geometry has only one dimension of size; it has no breadth or thickness.

Scholars have wondered about his definition of straightness for centuries. However, to study his system, we should not rely on what we guess Euclid might have meant. We are better off thinking of *point, (straight) line, plane (surface)*, etc., as undefined terms, taking their meanings from the ways they are used in the axioms and theorems.

Most of Euclid's other definitions describe familiar figures in more or less familiar ways. For example,

- A *plane angle* is the inclination to one another of two lines in a plane if the lines meet and do not lie in a straight line.

- When a straight line crossing a straight line makes the adjacent angles equal to one another, each of the equal angles is called a *right angle,* and the straight line crossing the other is called a *perpendicular* to that other line.

- A *circle* is a plane figure contained by one line such that all the straight lines falling upon it from one particular point within the figure are equal. That particular point is called the *center* of the circle.

- Of the trilateral figures, an *equilateral triangle* is one which has its three sides equal, an *isosceles triangle* has two of its sides equal, and a *scalene triangle* has its three sides unequal.

- *Parallel* straight lines are straight lines in the same plane that, if extended indefinitely in both directions, do not meet one another in either direction.

Recall from Section 6.2 the requirements for a good definition. Use those requirements to evaluate Euclid's definitions of:

8.13

1. point
2. straight line
3. plane angle
4. right angle
5. perpendicular
6. equilateral triangle
7. isosceles triangle
8. scalene triangle
9. parallel

Which of these definitions are good ones? Which are not so good? Justify your opinions.

From this simple beginning—23 definitions, five Common Notions, and five Postulates—Euclid reconstructed the entire theory of plane geometry. In the rest of this section and the next, we look more closely at parts of Book I of *The Elements*. We do this for three reasons,

- to show you the power of this small list of axioms
- to give you more experience with careful reasoning
- to explain (in Section 8.5) one of the great surprises of modern mathematics.

But before going any further, we must be clear about one thing

> *The Elements* is not about how to build things; it's about how to think!

Not just about mathematics. Euclid shows us how to think logically about anything—how to build a complex theory one step at a time, with each new piece firmly attached to what has already been built. In fact, each theorem of the *The Elements* is introduced as a *proposition* because it is only *proposed* or suggested as true until its proof is complete.

In Book I, Euclid proved 48 propositions. Your teacher will give you a list of the ones we use in this chapter, so that you can refer to them as we go along.

The first one is:

> On any finite straight line, an equilateral triangle can be constructed.

To understand how this is proved, we must first know what Euclid meant by constructed. Earlier in **MATH** *Connections* we told you that the only tools allowed for a geometric construction were a straightedge (an unmarked ruler) and a compass. You probably thought that was pretty strange. Here's the reason: A construction is actually a proof that something can be made within the rules of Euclid's system. Look back at Postulates 1, 2, and 3.

- Postulate 1 says that a straight line (we'd call it a line segment) can be drawn between any two points, and Postulate 2 says that any line segment can be extended as far as we please. Both of these things can be done with a straightedge.
- Postulate 3 says that a circle can be drawn with any center point and any radius. This can be done with a compass.
- No other postulates or axioms say anything about what can be drawn, so *no other tools are allowed.*

Anything you can draw with just these two tools is guaranteed to be a legitimate part of the system. Now here is Euclid's proof of the first proposition.

Proposition 1 On any finite straight line, an equilateral triangle can be constructed.

Proof (See Display 8.2.) Let *AB* be the given segment (finite straight line).

(a) Draw a circle with center *A* and radius *AB*.

(b) Draw a circle with center *B* and radius *AB*.

(c) From an intersection point C of the two circles, draw segments *AC* and *BC*.

(d) Since *A* is the center of the circle through *B* and *C*, *AC* equals *AB*.

(e) Since *B* is the center of the circle through *A* and *C*, *BC* equals *AB*.

(f) By steps (d) and (e), *BC* also equals *AC*.

(g) Since the three segments *AB*, *AC*, and *BC* all are equal, the triangle *ABC* is equilateral, as required.

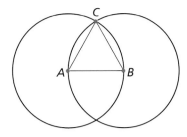

Proposition 1

Display 8.2

Each step of the proof of Proposition 1 can be justified by an axiom (a Common Notion or a Postulate) or by a definition. State as many of these reasons as you can.

8.14

In step (c) of the proof of Proposition 1, how do we know that the two circles have an intersection point?

8.15

Euclid's Propositions 2 and 3 prove that a fixed length can be transferred from one place to another. This is a technical detail, in some sense, but it is interesting to see how he uses Proposition 1 to justify it. Problems 1 and 2 at the end of this section show you these proofs and ask you to justify their steps.

Proposition 2 A line segment equal to a given line segment can be placed with one end at a given point.

Proposition 3 Given two unequal line segments, a length equal to the shorter one can be cut off from the longer one. This extends Proposition 2 by allowing you to specify the direction of the moved segment, as well as its length.

In the first part of Book I, Euclid goes on to prove many of the facts about straight lines and triangles that you studied in previous work in **MATH** *Connections*. Display 8.3 lists ones that we shall need in this section and the next. Don't try to memorize them, but remember where to find them. They are also on your handout list. The proofs of some of these propositions appear in the **Problem Set**. You may regard the others as proved, by Euclid and by many, many other people.

PROPOSITION 4: (SAS) IF TWO SIDES OF ONE TRIANGLE ARE EQUAL RESPECTIVELY TO TWO SIDES OF ANOTHER AND IF THE ANGLES FORMED BY THESE TWO PAIRS OF SIDES ARE EQUAL, THEN THE TWO TRIANGLES ARE CONGRUENT. (THAT IS, THE THIRD SIDE OF ONE TRIANGLE EQUALS THE THIRD SIDE OF THE OTHER AND THE REMAINING ANGLES OF ONE ARE EQUAL RESPECTIVELY TO THE REMAINING ANGLES OF THE OTHER.)

PROPOSITION 5: THE ANGLES OPPOSITE THE EQUAL SIDES OF AN ISOSCELES TRIANGLE ARE EQUAL TO ONE ANOTHER; AND, IF THE EQUAL SIDES ARE EXTENDED FURTHER, THE ANGLES MADE WITH THE THIRD SIDE WILL BE EQUAL.

PROPOSITION 8: (SSS) IF THREE SIDES OF ONE TRIANGLE ARE EQUAL RESPECTIVELY TO THREE SIDES OF ANOTHER, THEN THE RESPECTIVE ANGLES OF THE TWO TRIANGLES ARE ALSO EQUAL. (THE TRIANGLES ARE CONGRUENT.)

PROPOSITION 9: (CONSTRUCTION) HOW TO BISECT A GIVEN ANGLE.

PROPOSITION 10: (CONSTRUCTION) HOW TO BISECT A GIVEN LINE SEGMENT.

PROPOSITION 11: (CONSTRUCTION) HOW TO DRAW A STRAIGHT LINE AT RIGHT ANGLES TO A GIVEN STRAIGHT LINE FROM A GIVEN POINT ON IT.

PROPOSITION 13: WHEN A STRAIGHT LINE SET UP ON ANOTHER STRAIGHT LINE MAKES ADJACENT ANGLES, IT WILL MAKE EITHER TWO RIGHT ANGLES OR ANGLES WHOSE SUM EQUALS TWO RIGHT ANGLES.

PROPOSITION 15: IF TWO STRAIGHT LINES INTERSECT, THE VERTICAL ANGLES ARE EQUAL TO ONE ANOTHER.

PROPOSITION 16: IN ANY TRIANGLE, IF ONE SIDE IS EXTENDED, THE EXTERIOR ANGLE IS GREATER THAN EITHER OF THE OPPOSITE INTERIOR ANGLES.

PROPOSITION 23: (CONSTRUCTION) HOW TO CONSTRUCT AN ANGLE EQUAL TO A GIVEN ANGLE AT A GIVEN POINT ON A GIVEN STRAIGHT LINE.

PROPOSITION 26: (ASA AND AAS) IF TWO TRIANGLES HAVE TWO ANGLES AND ONE SIDE OF ONE TRIANGLE EQUAL RESPECTIVELY TO TWO ANGLES AND THE CORRESPONDING SIDE OF THE OTHER, THEY WILL ALSO HAVE THE REMAINING SIDES AND ANGLE OF THE ONE TRIANGLE EQUAL RESPECTIVELY TO THE CORRESPONDING REMAINING SIDES AND ANGLE OF THE OTHER. (THE TRIANGLES ARE CONGRUENT.)

Some propositions from Book I of Euclid's *The Elements*

Display 8.3

1. Draw two diagrams to illustrate the two parts of Proposition 13.

8.16

2. Why do you suppose Euclid used a phrase like "set up on," instead of "intersecting"? What distinction do you think he had in mind?

Why do you think we have included the original proposition numbers here? What is the *mathematical* purpose for this?

8.17

Does it seem a little strange to you that Euclid's Postulate 5 was longer and more complicated than the other four postulates? It must have bothered Euclid, too, because he avoided using his fifth postulate as long as he could. The fifth postulate is about a very important idea: parallel lines.

What important ideas are related to parallel lines? Identify as many as you can. Think back to your previous work in MATH *Connections.*

8.18

Euclid put off talking about parallel lines until Proposition 27. Maybe he was looking for a way to prove Postulate 5 as a theorem. Maybe he just thought that the propositions were best organized in this way. No one really knows. However, once he started using the fifth postulate, Euclid used it with power. The remaining 22 propositions of Book I establish all the essential properties of parallel lines, parallelograms, and squares, ending with a proof of the Pythagorean Theorem *and its converse.*

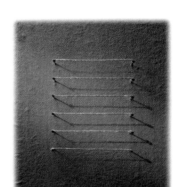

1. What does the Pythagorean Theorem say? What is its hypothesis? What is its conclusion?

8.19

2. How is the Pythagorean Theorem related to parallel lines?

3. What does the converse of the Pythagorean Theorem say?

In the next section you will see how Euclid used his fifth postulate to justify all the basic properties of parallel lines. The proof of the Pythagorean Theorem rests on some of those properties, so we shall not do it yet. However, the proof of its converse is a clever, elegant ending for Euclid's Book I. In the spirit of Euclid, we end this section with it.

Here's the situation: Proposition 47 is the Pythagorean Theorem. *Assume that it has already been proved.* Now we want to prove its converse.

8.20 **Proposition 48** If the square on one side of a triangle equals the sum of the squares on the other two sides, then the angle opposite the largest square is a right angle.

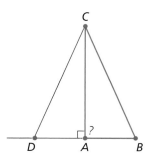

Proposition 48

Display 8.4

Proof (See Display 8.4.) Let *ABC* be a triangle for which the square on side *BC* equals the sum of the squares on sides *AB* and *AC*. We must show that ∠*BAC* is a right angle.

(a) Draw a line from *A* at right angles to line *AC*. [Proposition 11]

(b) Mark off a point *D* on it so that *AD* equals *AB*. [Proposition 3]

(c) Draw *DC*. [Postulate 1]

(d) Since *AD* equals *AB*, the square on *AD* equals the square on *AB*. [Definition of a square]

(e) Add the square on *AC* to each; then the sum of the squares on *AD* and *AC* is equal to the sum of the squares on *AB* and *AC*. [Common Notion 2]

(f) But the sum of the squares on *AD* and *AC* equals the square on *CD* because ∠*DAC* is right; [Proposition 47, the Pythagorean Theorem itself]

(g) ... and the square on *BC* equals the sum of the squares on *AB* and *AC*. [our hypothesis]

(h) Therefore, the square on *CD* equals the square on BC [by Common Notion 1], so side *CD* equals side BC.

(i) Now, since *AD* is equal to *AB* [by step (b)] and *AC* is common to both, △ *ABC* and △ *ADC* are congruent, so ∠*BAC* equals ∠*DAC*. [Proposition 8 (SSS)]

(j) But ∠*DAC* is a right angle. [step 1]

Therefore, ∠*BAC* is a right angle, as required.

Problem Set: 8.2

These problems are proofs of propositions in Book I of Euclid's *The Elements*. Your list of propositions will help you answer many questions. In each case, any reason you give to justify a step must be one of the following things:

- an earlier step in the proof

- a Common Notion

- a Postulate

- one of Euclid's definitions from this section

- a proposition *with a lower number than the one you're working on.*

1. Here is Euclid's proof of Proposition 2. It begins with a given point, *A*, and a given line segment, *BC*, as shown in Display 8.5.
   - Copy Display 8.5. Then add to it, step by step, as you work through this proof.

   - Give a reason to justify each step of this proof, according to the general instructions above. In this case, only one proposition has a lower number.

   Proposition 2 A line segment equal to a given line segment can be placed with one end at a given point.

The Beginning of Proposition 2.

Display 8.5

Proof Point *A* and segment *BC* are given. We must construct a line segment with A as an endpoint and with the same length as *BC*.

(a) Draw segment *AB*.

(b) On *AB*, construct an equilateral triangle *DAB*.

(c) Draw a circle with center *B* and radius *BC*.

(d) Extend *DB* to intersect this circle at a point *E*.

(e) Draw a circle with center *D* and radius *DE*.

(f) Extend segment *DA* to intersect this circle at a point *F*.

(g) Since both *C* and *E* are on the circle with center *B*, *BC* and *BE* are equal.

(h) Since both *E* and *F* are on the circle with center *D*, *DE* and *DF* are equal.

(i) But *DA* is equal to *DB*.

(j) Therefore, the remainders *AF* and *BE* are equal.

(k) Since *BE* was proved equal to *BC* (in step (g)), *AF* and BC must also be equal.

Therefore, *AF* is a line segment with *A* as an endpoint and with the same length as *BC*, as required.

2. Justify each step in this proof of Proposition 3. (See Display 8.6.)

Proposition 3 Given two unequal line segments, a length equal to the shorter one can be cut off from the longer one.

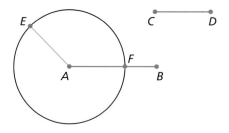

Proposition 3

Display 8.6

Proof Let AB and CD be the two given unequal line segments, with AB the longer one. We must cut off from AB a line segment of length equal to CD.

(a) At A place a line segment AE of length equal to CD.

(b) Draw a circle with center A and radius AE, intersecting CD at point F.

(c) Since A is the center of this circle, AE equals AF.

(d) But, since AE also equals CD, it follows that CD equals AF, as required.

3. Here is Euclid's proof of Proposition 5. Justify each numbered step in it. Display 8.7 is a partially completed figure for this proof. Copy it and complete it according to Euclid's description in the proof.

Proposition 5 The angles opposite the equal sides of an isosceles triangle are equal to one another; and, if the equal sides are extended further, the angles made with the third side will be equal.

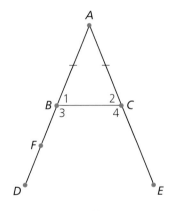

Proposition 5

Display 8.7

Proof Let ABC be an isosceles triangle with sides AB and AC equal.

(a) Extend AB and AC in straight lines beyond B and C, to points D and E, respectively.

Euclid does not say how far away D and E should be chosen, but it is clear from the rest of the proof that they should be far enough away to be out of the way of the rest of the argument.

We must show that ∠2 equals ∠1 and that ∠4 equals ∠3. Choose a random point *F* on *BD*.

(b) From *AE* (the longer segment) mark off *AG* equal to *AF* (the shorter segment).

(c) Draw segments *FC* and *GB*.

(d) Now, *AF* equals *AG* (by step (b)), and *AB* equals *AC* (by hypothesis), and these respective pairs of sides contain a common angle, ∠*GAF*, so △ *ACF* and △ *ABG* are congruent, implying that

side *FC* equals side *GB*

∠*ACF* equals ∠*ABG*

∠*AFC* equals ∠*AGB*.

(e) Since *AF* equals *AG* and *AB* equals *AC*, the remainders *BF* and *CG* are equal.

(f) But we also know [from step (d)] that *FC* equals *GB* and that ∠*BFC* equals ∠*CGB*, so △ *BFC* and △ *CGB* are congruent, implying that

∠*FBC* equals ∠*GCB*

∠*BCF* equals ∠*CBG*.

(g) Now, ∠*ABG* was proved equal to ∠*ACF*. In which step? In these angles, ∠*CBG* equals ∠*BCF*, so the remaining angles, ∠1 and ∠2, are equal, as required.

Finally, note that ∠*FBC* is identical with ∠3, and ∠*GCB* is identical with ∠4, so [by step (f)] ∠4 equals ∠3, as required.

4. Proposition 11 justifies the construction of a straight line at right angles to a given straight line from a given point on it. Euclid's proof is outlined here.
   - Draw the figure that he describes.
   - Give a reason for each step.
   - Complete the argument according to this outline by supplying the additional steps and reasons needed.

Proposition 11 How to draw a straight line at right angles to a given straight line from a given point on it.

Proof Let *AB* be a straight line and let *C* be a point on it. We must draw from *C* a straight line at right angles to *AB*. Choose a point *D* at random on *AC*.

(a) Find a point *E* on *CB* such that *CE* equals *CD*.
(b) On *DE* construct an equilateral triangle, △ *FDE*.
(c) Draw *FC*.

Euclid claims that the straight line *FC* has been drawn at right angles to *AB*. To complete Euclid's argument, use SSS to prove that △ *DCF* and △ *ECF* are congruent, implying that the adjacent angles, ∠*DCF* and ∠*ECF*, are equal. Then apply the definition of *right angle*. You should need four or five steps to fill in these details.

5. Draw the figure described at the beginning of the following proof. Then complete the proof by answering the questions below.

   Proposition 15 If two straight lines intersect, the vertical angles are equal to one another.

   Proof Suppose that straight lines *AB* and *CD* intersect at point *E*.

   (a) Which angles of this figure must we show to be equal?
   (b) What does Proposition 13 tell you about the angles made by the line AB and the segment *CE*?
   (c) What does Proposition 13 tell you about the angles made by the line *CD* and the segment *BE*?
   (d) What conclusion can you draw from parts (b) and (c) by using Postulate 4 and Common Notion 1?
   (e) Finish the argument showing that ∠*AEC* and ∠*BED* are equal.
   (f) By mimicking parts (b)—(e), write out the proof that the other two vertical angles are equal.

About Words

To *bi-sect* something means to cut it into *two* equal *sections;* that is, to divide it in half.

6. Give a reason to justify each numbered step of the following construction. Then finish the proof. Remember, you can use only the propositions numbered lower than 9.

Proposition 9 (Construction) How to bisect a given angle.

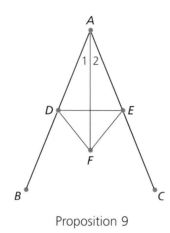

Proposition 9

Display 8.8

Proof (See Display 8.8.) Let ∠*BAC* be the given angle, and choose a point *D* at random on *AB.*

(a) On *AC*, mark off a segment *AE* equal to *AD.*
(b) Draw *DE.*
(c) Construct the equilateral triangle *DEF.*
(d) Draw *AF.*

　　Claim: *AF* bisects ∠*BAC.* That is, ∠1 equals ∠2. Prove it. (*Hint:* Use SSS somehow.)

7. Draw the figure described in the following construction, and give a reason to justify each numbered step. Then finish the proof. Remember: You can use only the propositions numbered lower than 10.

Proposition 10 (Construction) How to bisect a given line segment.

Proof Let *AB* be the given line segment.

(a) Construct the equilateral triangle *ABC.*
(b) Construct the angle bisector of ∠*ACB*, and let *D* be the point at which this line intersects *AB.*

　　Claim: The point *D* bisects *AB.* Prove it.

8. Earlier in **MATH** *Connections* you learned a different method for bisecting a line segment. Describe it. Then prove that it works.

9. Justify each step in the following proof. See Display 8.9.

   Proposition 16 In any triangle, if one side is extended, the exterior angle is greater than either of the opposite interior angles.

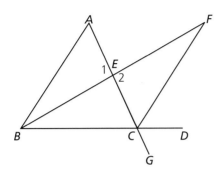

Proposition 16

Display 8.9

   Proof Let *ABC* be a triangle with side *BC* extended to a point *D*. We must show that ∠*ACD* is greater than each of the opposite interior angles, ∠*CBA* and ∠*BAC*.

   (a) Let *E* bisect *AC*.
   (b) Draw *BE*.
   (c) Extend *BE* past *E* to a point *F* …
   (d) … such that *EF* equals *EB*.
   (e) Draw *FC*.
   (f) Extend *AC* past *C* to some point *G*.
   (g) Now, ∠1 equals ∠2,
   (h) and *AE* equals *EC*,
   (i) and *EB* equals *EF*;
   (j) so △ *ABE* is congruent to △ *CFE*, implying that ∠*BAE* equals ∠*ECF*.
   (k) But ∠*ACD* is greater than ∠*ECF*.
      Therefore, ∠*ACD* is greater than ∠*BAE* (which is the same as ∠*BAC*), as required.

10. Prove that ∠*ACD* is greater than ∠*CBA* by bisecting *BC* and mimicking steps (a)–(k). Draw a new diagram for this case. (*Hint:* Begin by applying Proposition 15.)

8.3 Euclid and Parallel Lines

Learning Outcomes

After studying this section you will be able to:

Explain how Euclid's Fifth Postulate is related to the idea of parallel lines

Prove a few of Euclid's propositions on your own (with a little help)

Identify logical connections between parallel lines, the angle sum of triangles, and squares.

Remember,

The Elements is about how to think.

In the entire history of the world, Euclid was one of the best at organizing a complicated set of ideas. For the past 2300 years his axiomatic system for geometry has been studied as a model of logical structure by kings and presidents, judges and politicians, doctors and lawyers, artists and writers, teachers and business executives, and just about every other educated person in our civilization. Now it's your turn.

Euclid's work wasn't perfect (whose is?), but it was very, very good. So good, in fact, that it took more than 2000 years for scholars to unravel a mystery right at its heart. The rest of this chapter tells the story of that mystery and the search for its solution. The story has a surprise ending that leads to another mystery. But we're getting ahead of ourselves. Before you can understand an answer, you have to know what the question is. In this section you will study the part of *The Elements* that contains the question. Sections 8.4 and 8.5 explain its surprising answer, leading to the deeper mystery described in Section 8.6.

The story begins with Euclid's Fifth Postulate.

8.21

1. What, exactly, does Euclid's Fifth Postulate say?

2. Do you think that the Fifth Postulate is a reasonable assumption to make about straight lines?

3. What can be said about straight lines that don't satisfy the hypothesis of the Fifth Postulate? Do such lines exist? How do you know?

In Section 8.2 we said that the Fifth Postulate is about parallel lines. Notice that *this postulate does not say that parallel lines exist.* It just points out a property of pairs of lines that are not parallel. However, it can be used to prove the existence of parallel lines (as we shall see in Propositions 27—31). For that reason, the Fifth Postulate is usually called the *Parallel Postulate.*

1. What is the converse of the Parallel Postulate?

2. What is the contrapositive of the Parallel Postulate?

8.22

3. Which of these two statements must be true in Euclid's geometry? Why?

Euclid may have been bothered by his Fifth Postulate, but not because he doubted that parallel lines exist. Surely he thought of parallel lines (such as the opposite sides of squares and rectangles) as natural ideas for any system of shapes in a plane. Most likely, he avoided using the Fifth Postulate in his first 26 propositions because he hoped to prove it as a theorem. We'll never really know.

We do know that once Euclid started to use his Fifth Postulate, he used it well. This section follows Euclid's footsteps as he guides us from knowing nothing about parallel lines to the most important properties of parallelograms, rectangles, and squares. It ends with his proof of how to construct a square, the shape at the core of everything about area that you learned earlier in **MATH** *Connections*. The journey begins with the definition of *parallel lines*, which Euclid defined as follows:

> **A Phrase to Know:** Parallel lines are straight lines (or segments) in the same plane that, if extended indefinitely in both directions, do not meet one another in either direction.

What characteristic property of parallel lines is not part of Euclid's definition?

8.23

Remember—just defining parallel lines doesn't make them exist. You could *define* a three headed, purple unicorn, but that won't make one appear! Proving their existence was the first part of this job for Euclid.

Proposition 27 If a straight line falling on two straight lines makes the alternate angles equal to each other, the two straight lines will be parallel to each other.

Proof Suppose that straight lines *AB* and *CD* are crossed by a straight line at *E* and *F*, as in Display 8.10, and suppose that alternate angles 1 and 2 are equal. We must prove that *AB* and *CD* are parallel.

1. If not, then *AB* and *CD*, when extended, will meet either in the direction of *B* and *D* or in the direction of *A* and *C*. Why?

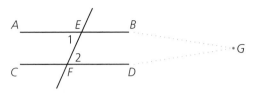

Proposition 27

Display 8.10

Suppose first that they meet in the direction of *B* and *D*, and call their intersection point *G*. Then, by hypothesis and the definitions of interior and exterior angles, ∠1 is an exterior angle of △ *GEF* that is equal to an opposite interior angle, ∠2.

2. But this is impossible. Why?

Therefore, *AB* and *CD*, when extended, will not meet in the direction of *B* and *D*. Similarly, it can be proved that they will not meet in the direction of *A* and *C*. (See problem 1.) But, by definition, straight lines that do not meet in either direction are parallel. Therefore, *AB* is parallel to *CD*, as required.

8.24

1. Justify each of the two numbered steps in the proof of Proposition 27 by an axiom, a definition, or an lower-numbered proposition that appears in Section 8.2.

2. Does Proposition 27 guarantee that parallel lines exist? Why or why not?

3. Proposition 27 is an example of an indirect proof. Explain. What's an indirect proof? How can you tell that this is one?

A more modern way of stating Proposition 27 is:

If two lines cut by a **transversal** have alternate interior angles equal, then the lines are parallel.

8.25

1. What does the prefix *trans-* mean in English? Write down three English words that use this prefix, and also write down their meanings.

2. What is a *transversal?* Write a definition for this term.

3. What are *alternate interior angles*? Write a definition for this term. Find two pairs of alternate interior angles in Display 8.10.

4. What do you think *alternate exterior angles* might be? Can you name them in Display 8.10? Write a definition for this term.

Proposition 28 If a transversal across two straight lines makes the exterior angle equal to the opposite interior angle on the same side, or makes the sum of the interior angles on the same side equal to two right angles, the two straight lines will be parallel to each other.

Euclid's language is a little confusing here. Display 8.11 and the beginning of the proof clarify what's going on.

Proof Suppose that *EF* crosses lines *AB* and *CD* in such a way that (a) the exterior angle 1 equals the opposite interior angle 3, or (b) the sum of the interior angles on the same side (of the transversal), $\angle 2$ and $\angle 3$, equals two right angles. In each case, it must be shown that *AB* is parallel to *CD*.

Part (a): Since $\angle 1$ equals $\angle 3$, and $\angle 1$ also equals $\angle 6$ by Proposition 15, it must be true that $\angle 6$ equals $\angle 3$ by Common Notion 1. But these two equal angles are alternate (interior) angles. Therefore, by Proposition 27, *AB* is parallel to *CD*, as required.

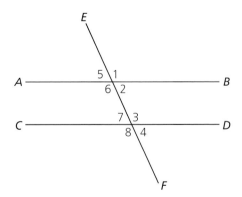

Propositions 28 and 29

Display 8.11

8.26 Prove part (b) of Proposition 28. If you do it the way Euclid did, these reasons will justify your steps: Proposition 13, Common Notion 3, Proposition 27.

8.27 Is the proof of part (a) of Proposition 28 direct or indirect? Explain.

Propositions 27 and 28 describe properties which guarantee that pairs of lines are parallel. But do *all* pairs of parallel lines have these properties? In other words, are the converses of these two propositions true? In Proposition 29, Euclid proves that they are. Can you state these converses before reading on?

Proposition 29 A transversal across parallel straight lines makes the alternate interior angles equal to each other, each exterior angle equal to the opposite interior angle, and the sum of the interior angles on the same side equal to two right angles.

Proof See Display 8.11 again. Suppose that *EF* crosses parallel lines *AB* and *CD*. We must prove that

(1) the alternate interior angles are equal
(2) each exterior angle is equal to the opposite interior angle
(3) the sum of the interior angles on the same side is equal to two right angles.

For part (1), suppose that the alternate interior angles, $\angle 3$ and $\angle 6$, are not equal. Then one of these angles, say $\angle 3$, is the smaller angle. Add $\angle 2$ to each.

(a) Then $\angle 2 + \angle 3$ is smaller than $\angle 2 + \angle 6$. (This step is allowed by Euclid's Common Notions. Do you see how?)
(b) But $\angle 2 + \angle 6$ equals two right angles. Why?
(c) By substitution, $\angle 2 + \angle 3$ is less than two right angles. This means that AB and CD, if extended indefinitely, meet. Why?
(d) But they do not meet because they are parallel. How do we know this?

Therefore, the initial supposition that $\angle 3$ and $\angle 6$ are not equal must be false. That is, the alternate interior angles, $\angle 3$ and $\angle 6$, are equal, as required.

The proofs of parts (2) and (3) are left as exercises for you. See questions 2 and 3 that follow.

1. Justify steps (b), (c), and (d) in the proof of part (1) of Proposition 29 with a reason that is allowable within Euclid's axiomatic system. The only propositions you will need are ones stated in this section or in Section 8.2.

8.28

2. Prove part (2) of Proposition 29. Start with $\angle 1$ as a typical exterior angle. Then use part (a), Proposition 15, and Common Notion 1 to get the result you need.

3. Prove part (3) of Proposition 29 for the interior angles 2 and 3 by using part (2), Common Notion 2, Proposition 13, and Common Notion 1.

Where in the proof of Propostion 29 is the Parallel Postulate used? Is it needed for all three parts? Why or why not?

8.29

Proposition 30 Straight lines parallel to the same straight line are also parallel to each other.

The proof of Proposition 30 follows easily from Propositions 27 and 29. It is left as an exercise for you; see problem 4 in the Problem Set.

Finally, in Proposition 31, Euclid proves that parallel lines can be constructed. Starting with a line segment and a point not on that segment, he uses Proposition 27 to construct a line parallel to the given line, as follows.

Proposition 31 (Construction) How to draw a straight line through a given point parallel to a given line.

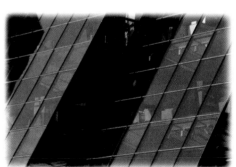

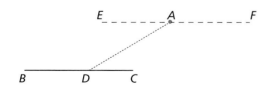

Proposition 31: Constructing a line parallel to a line

Display 8.12

Proof Let *A* be the given point and *BC* the given straight line. To construct a straight line parallel to *BC* passing through *A*, begin by choosing at random a point *D* on *BC*.

(a) Draw *AD*.
(b) At point *A* on line *AD*, construct an angle, ∠*DAE*, equal to ∠*ADC*.
(c) Extend *EA* through *A* to some point *F*.
(d) Since the line *AD* falling on the two lines *BC* and *EF* has made the alternate interior angles *EAD* and *ADC* equal, the lines *EF* and *BC* must be parallel.

Therefore, *EF* is parallel to *BC*, as required.

8.30 Justify each step in the proof of Proposition 31 by an axiom, a definition, or a lower-numbered proposition.

8.31 Does Proposition 31 guarantee that parallel lines exist? Why or why not?

The next proposition is a fundamental theorem of plane geometry that was known to the Pythagoreans and others, perhaps as much as 300 years before Euclid. You have used this fact often earlier in **MATH** *Connections*. Euclid's proof shows clearly how it is linked with the idea of parallel lines. This connection is very important, as we shall see later.

8.32 Work through the following proof of Proposition 32 by drawing the diagram described and giving a reason to justify each numbered step. Be sure that the diagram you draw allows all the steps of this proof to make sense!

Proposition 32 In any triangle, if one side is extended, the exterior angle is equal to the sum of the two opposite interior angles, and the sum of the three interior angles of the triangle equals two right angles.

Proof Suppose that *ABC* is a triangle. Extend one side of it, say *BC*, in a straight line to a point, *D*. We must show that

(1) the exterior angle, ∠*ACD*, is equal to the sum of the two opposite interior angles, ∠*BAC* and ∠*ABC*, and

(2) the sum of the three interior angles— ∠*BCA*, ∠*BAC*, and ∠*ABC*— equals two right angles. Number these three interior angles 1, 2, and 3, respectively.

(a) Draw *CE* through *C* parallel to side *AB* in such a way that ∠2 and ∠*ACE* are alternate interior angles.

(b) Since *AB* is parallel to *CE*, these alternate interior angles, ∠2 and ∠*ACE*, are equal.

(c) Since *AB* is parallel to *CE*, the exterior angle ∠*ECD* equals the opposite interior angle, ∠3.

(d) Therefore, ∠*ACD*, which is ∠*ACE* + ∠*ECD*, is also ∠2 + ∠3, as required by part (a).

(e) Adding ∠1 to each, we have

$$\angle 1 + \angle ACD = \angle 1 + \angle 2 + \angle 3$$

the sum of the three interior angles.

(f) But ∠1 + ∠*ACD* equals two right angles.

(g) Therefore, the sum of the three interior angles also equals two right angles, as required by part (2).

8.33

1. **How much is two right angles in degrees? In radians?**

2. **Think back to MATH** *Connections* **Year 2. Identify at least two useful facts or processes that depend on the fact that the sum of the angles of a triangle equals two right angles.**

With the next proposition, Euclid moves from parallel lines to parallelograms. They, in turn, lead to the construction of squares, the basic building blocks for the theory of area.

Proposition 34 The opposite sides and opposite angles of a parallelogram are equal to each other, and the diagonals bisect the area.

8.34 Assuming that *polygon* has already been defined, define *parallelogram* as you think Euclid did. Make sure that your definition allows the statement of Proposition 34 to make sense.

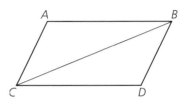

Proposition 34

Display 8.13

Proof Here is a summary of this proof. Parts of it are left for you, as problem 5 of the Problem Set. Let *ABCD* be a parallelogram with diagonal *BC*, as in Display 8.13. Since *BC* falls on both pairs of parallel sides, it forms two sets of equal alternate interior angles. These equal angles, together with the common side *BC*, make $\triangle ABC$ and $\triangle DCB$ congruent, implying that the pairs of opposite sides are equal, the opposite angles are equal, and the areas are equal.

In Propositions 35 through 45, Euclid proves various properties of parallelograms and of triangles that are related to parallel lines in one way or another. Then, just before proving the Pythagorean Theorem, he presents the construction of a *square*, which he defines as a quadrilateral with four equal sides and four right angles.

8.35
1. What do squares have to do with the Pythagorean Theorem?

2. Work through the proof of Proposition 46 by drawing the diagram described and justifying each numbered step by an axiom, a definition, or a lower-numbered proposition stated in this section or in Section 8.2.

Proposition 46 (Construction) How to construct a square on a given line segment.

Proof Let *AB* be a given line segment. We must construct a square with side *AB*.

(a) Draw line *AC* at right angles to *AB* from *A*.

(b) On line *AC*, mark a point *D* so that *AD* equals *AB*.

(c) Through *D* draw a line parallel to *AB*, and through *B* draw a line parallel to *AD*.

In step (c) label as *E* the intersection point of the two lines.

(d) Then *ADEB* is a parallelogram.

(e) Therefore, *AB* = *DE*, and *AD* = *BE*.

(f) But *AB* also equals *AD* (by step (b)), so all four sides of *ADEB* are equal.

(g) Now, since *AD* falls on parallels *AB* and *DE*, $\angle BAD + \angle ADE$ equals two right angles.

(h) But $\angle BAD$ is a right angle (by step (a)), so $\angle ADE$ is also a right angle.

(i) In parallelograms, opposite angles are equal, so $\angle ABE$ and $\angle DEB$ are also right angles.

Thus, since all four sides are equal and all four angles are right angles, *ADEB* is a square with side *AB*, as required.

Book I of Euclid's *The Elements* ends with this construction of a square and the proof of the Pythagorean Theorem and its converse. At this point, Euclid has established the basic properties of triangles, squares, and parallelograms. Of course, there is much, much more in the *The Elements*, including properties of other polygons, areas of figures, similarity, and so on. If you like this way of looking at geometry, you might try studying Euclid's *The Elements* on your own. President Abraham Lincoln did! Your library should have several books that can take you further into this fascinating, powerful axiomatic system.

Next we are going to look at a great historical puzzle, a mathematical mystery story. This mystery is about something that Euclid could not prove—the Parallel Postulate. To many people this statement looked more like a theorem than a postulate. It's not as simple or self evident as his other four postulates, and yet there was no doubt that it must be true for the Greeks' system of geometry. A lot of important facts depend on it, including the angle sum of a triangle, the existence of squares, and the Pythagorean Theorem.

Euclid was very good at proving theorems and organizing ideas. Why couldn't he prove this statement? For more than 2000 years, scholars were convinced that it was because Euclid just wasn't quite clever enough. They were convinced that the Parallel Postulate was really a theorem, and many of them proposed proofs for it. In every case, however, these proofs were incorrect. Sections 8.4 and 8.5 tell you the rest of this story and its surprise ending.

Problem Set: 8.3

1. Write out the "Similarly ..." part of the proof of Proposition 27.

2. In his proof of Proposition 29, Euclid adds the same angle to unequal angles and asserts that the sums must be unequal. He doesn't give a reason to justify this step. Explain how this step is allowed by Euclid's Common Notions. Be careful.

3. Referring to Display 8.14, Euclid's proof of Proposition 30 begins this way:

   > Suppose that each of the straight lines *AB* and *CD* is parallel to *EF*. We must show that *AB* is parallel to *CD*. Draw a transversal *GH* across all three of these lines. Since *AB* is parallel to *EF*, ...

   Use Propositions 29 and 27 to finish his proof.

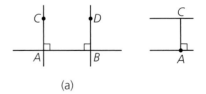

(a)

Proposition 30

Display 8.14

4. Use Proposition 30 to prove that there cannot be more than one line through point *A* that is parallel to line *BC*. (*Hint:* What if there were two?)

5. These questions refer to the proof of Proposition 34, which was summarized in the section. Use Display 8.13 to help you.

    (a) Prove that △ *ABC* and △ *DCB* are congruent. Justify each step you take.
    (b) Prove that the opposite angles *ABD* and *DCA* are equal.

6. (a) Prove that two lines that are perpendicular to the same line are parallel to each other. (*Hint:* If you draw a diagram and look at it just right, a proposition from this section does the trick.)
    (b) Prove that parallel lines are everywhere equidistant. (*Hint:* Apply Proposition 34 somehow. To do that, you'll have to refine the problem a bit.)

8.4 Can There Be Too Many Axioms? Independence

Learning Outcomes

After studying this section you will be able to:

Explain the difference between a dependent axiom and an independent axiom

Prove that axioms of a system are independent.

8.36

1. Look at the rules of Quick Six. Would it make sense to add the following rule?

   > If the sum of the numbers showing is 3, the player who put down the 1 takes both cards.

   What do you think "make sense" means here? What does it mean to you?

2. Section 8.3 says: "For more than 2000 years, scholars were convinced that...the Parallel Postulate was really a theorem, and many of them proposed proofs for it." Why should anyone care whether the Parallel Postulate was an axiom or a theorem? Why do you think this problem interested so many people for such a long time?

3. How are questions 1 and 2 related?

The Parallel Postulate question is a famous example of a general question about axiomatic systems.

> Which axioms add information that is not contained in the other axioms of the system?

This is a question of simple efficiency. For instance, consider the following five axiomatic systems.

Undefined terms: point, line, on
Axioms
A1   There is at least one point.
A2   Every point is on at least two lines.
A3   Every point is on at least two lines.
A4   Every line is on at least two points.
A5   Given any two points, there is exactly one line on both of them.

What seems senseless about this set of axioms?

8.37

You noticed, right? Axiom 3 adds no information to the system because it is the same as Axiom 2. Repeating an axiom is a waste of time and effort. It's a piece of useless clutter that should be thrown away.

Here is a less obvious example.

Undefined terms: point, line, on

Axioms

A1   There is at least one point.

A2   Every point is on at least two lines.

A3   Every line is on at least two points.

A4   Given any two points, there is exactly one line on both of them.

A5   For any given line, there is at least one point not on that line.

Does Axiom 5 add new information that is not contained in the other four? How can you tell? What do you think "contained in" means here?

8.38

Saying that Axiom 5 adds new information means that Axiom 5 cannot be deduced logically from the other axioms. That is, it cannot be proved as a theorem using only Axioms 1–4. But how can we be sure that *nobody* could prove it? Here's one way: If we could find an instance of Axioms 1–4 for which Axiom 5 is false, then you would be sure that Axiom 5 could not be proved as a theorem.

Can you find such an instance?

8.39

We didn't think so. Here's how we knew. The first four axioms of this system are System **A**, from the project at the end of Section 6.1. The fifth axiom here actually appears as a theorem in that project. Since it's a theorem, it must be true in *every* instance of Axioms 1–4. This means that Axiom 5 does not add any new information. It can be thrown away without changing the information contained in this system.

Words to Know: An axiom that can be proved from the other axioms of the system is said to be **dependent** on the other axioms. An axiom that cannot be proved from the other axioms of the system is said to be **independent** of the other axioms.

A Phrase to Know: An independent axiomatic system is a system in which *every* axiom is independent of the others.

Axiom 5 of the previous example is a dependent axiom. But what about the other four axioms of this system? Are they all independent, or is there another dependent one? It's time to find out.

Here is System **A** again.

Undefined terms: point, line, on
Axioms
A1   There is at least one point.
A2   Every point is on at least two lines.
A3   Every line is on at least two points.
A4   Given any two points, there is exactly one line on both of them.

The project at the end of Section 6.1 describes four different instances of System **A**. Any one of them is enough to guarantee that this is a consistent system. That is, there are situations in which all four axioms are true.

To see if Axiom **A4** is independent of the other three axioms, we also need an instance in which Axioms **A1**, **A2** and **A3** are true, but **A4** is false. Let's try to build one, step-by-step.

- The first thing to do is to choose meanings for the undefined terms. In this case, we'll make some dots for *points*, draw some straight streaks for *lines*, and let *on* mean a streak passing through a dot.

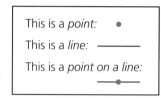

This is a *point:* •
This is a *line:* ———
This is a *point on a line:* ——•——

Remember that the only *points* and *lines* of our instance will be the dots and streaks we choose to draw.

- Now we'll use these meanings to make a situation in which **A1**, **A2**, and **A3** are true, starting with A1 and then checking the other axioms one at a time. Axiom **A1** says "There is at least one point." What if our entire instance is just one point? Then **A1** is true, but **A2** is not.

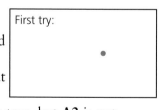

First try:

That's not good enough; we need to add something.

- Axiom **A2** says "Every point is on at least two lines." How about adding two streaks that cross at the dot? Now both **A1** and **A2** are true, but **A3** is not. Still not good enough.

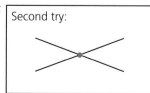

Second try:

- Axiom **A3** says "Every line is on at least two points." Adding another dot on each streak makes **A3** a true statement. Moreover, **A1** is still true, but now **A2** is false. Can we fix that without making **A4** true?

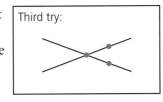

Third try:

- We want **A4** to be false, so just adding a third line through the two new points won't work. We need at least two more lines—one through each of the new points. Then two more points are needed to satisfy **A3**, placed carefully to keep **A2** satisfied. The Fourth try box shows one way to do that.

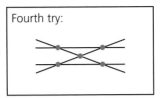

Fourth try:

Success! Axioms **A1**, **A2**, and **A3** are true statements about the Fourth try diagram, but **A4** is false. There is no line on the pair of points at the left or on the pair of points at the right. This diagram is an instance that proves Axiom **A4** independent.

> **Display 8.15 shows two more instances (using the same meanings for the undefined terms) that prove the independence of A4. All four axioms of System A are true for one of them. For the other, A1, A2, and A3 are true, but A4 is false. Which is which? Justify your answer.**

8.40

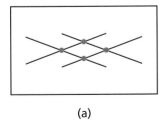

(a)

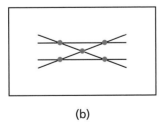

(b)

Display 8.15

Finding an instance to prove the independence of an axiom is often a quicker, simpler process than what we just did for **A4**. We wrote out each small step in painful detail to show you how to start looking for an instance. There are times when it is not obvious how to make or find what you need, or even whether or not it can exist. But sometimes you'll see what you need right away, as in this quick proof that **A3** is independent.

Axioms, Geometry, and Choice

8.4 Can There Be Too Many Axioms? Independence

- Again, the first thing to do is to choose meanings for the undefined terms. We'll use what we used before—dots for *points*, straight streaks for *lines*, and *on* meaning that a streak passes through a dot.

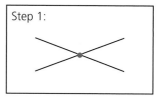

This is a *point:* •
This is a *line:* ———
This is a *point on a line:*
———•———

- Now, we know that we want Axioms **A1** and **A2** to be true, so we'll begin with the Second try diagram from before, and then adjust it.

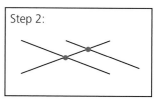

Step 1:

- We also want Axiom **A4** to be true, but **A3** to be false. This suggests the Step 2 diagram shown here. Check the axioms; you'll see that it works. Axioms **A1**, **A2** and **A4** are true, but **A3** is false, so **A3** is independent of the other three axioms.

Step 2:

8.41 **Now it's your turn. Prove that A2 is independent of the other three axioms.**

To prove Axiom **A1** independent, we need an instance in which **A1** is false, but **A2**, **A3** and **A4** are true. At first glance, this seems impossible. After all, if every line is on at least two points (Axiom **A3**), then isn't there at least one point? Not necessarily! Axiom **A3** is a universal statement. In Section 6.3 you learned that a universal statement is a conditional in disguise. In this case, we have

A3 If something is a *line*, then it is on at least two *points*.

Now, a false conditional must have both a true hypothesis and a false conclusion. But if there are no lines in the instance, then the hypothesis of **A3** is false. This makes that conditional statement true! An instance for the independence of **A1** appears in Display 8.16. It uses the dot and streak meanings for the undefined terms, as before.

Instance:

The independence of A1

Display 8.16

Explain how Display 8.16 is an instance for the independence of Axiom A1. (*Hint:* Start by rewriting the other three axioms as conditionals.)

8.42

We have just proved that System **A** is an independent axiomatic system. Each of its four axioms is independent of the other three.

"Yeah," mumbles somebody in the back row, "but you did it with a bunch of little, artificial instances. What good is that?"

It's actually *very* good. It's part of the power of abstraction.

> A proof that an axiom is independent using *any* instance means that the axiom is independent in *every* instance.

This means that you can make up little, artificial instances to establish the independence of axioms that model important, real-world systems. Problem 3 of the **Problem Set** shows you such an example. It contains an axiomatic system for projective geometry, the basis of perspective drawing and much of computer graphics. You can prove that the axioms of this powerful system are independent by making little dot and streak instances.

Here is a summary of the main ideas and methods of this section.

- A good axiom adds new information to its system. Such an axiom is *independent* of the other axioms.

- An axiom that does not add new information to the system is *dependent* on the other axioms.

- To prove that an axiom is dependent, you must prove it as a theorem derived from the other axioms.

- To prove that an axiom is independent, you must find or construct two instances.

  - In one, all the axioms must be true statements. This proves that the system is consistent.

  - In the other, the axiom in question must be false, while all the other axioms are true.

- To prove that an entire axiomatic system is independent, you must prove the independence of each axiom.

Note that the logical trick used to prove the independence of **A1** works with any statement that can be written in the form

If [hypothesis], then [conclusion].

For such a statement to be false, its hypothesis must be true and its conclusion must be false. For example,

> If there are two points, then they must be on exactly one line

is false only if there actually are two points and they are not on exactly one line. Thus,

> If you construct an instance in which the hypothesis of an axiom is not true, then that axiom *cannot be false* in that instance, so it must be true.

In other words, you can show that a conditional statement is true in either of two ways,

– by showing that both its hypothesis and its conclusion are true, *or*

– by showing that its hypothesis is false.

If the second way is used, the statement is said to be **vacuously satisfied**.

Problem Set: 8.4

1. Consider this set of axioms.

   Undefined terms: point, line, on
   Axioms
   A1 There are at least four points.
   A2 At least two lines are on equally many points.

A3 At least two lines are not on the same point.
A4 Each line is on at least two points.
A5 Not all lines are on the same number of points.

(a) Prove that Axiom 5 is independent.
(b) One of these axioms is dependent. Which is it? Justify your answer.

2. Using the dot and streak meanings for the undefined terms of System **A**, is the diagram in Display 8.17 an instance that proves the independence of Axiom **A2**? Explain.

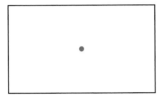

Problem 2

Display 8.17

3. Here is a set of axioms for projective geometry.

Undefined terms: point, line, on
Axioms
P1 There are at least one point and one line.
P2 Given any two (distinct) points, there is exactly one line on both of them.
P3 Given any two (distinct) lines, there is exactly one point on both of them.
P4 Every line is on at least three points.
P5 Not all points are on the same line.

(a) Prove that Axiom **P4** is independent. Explain your solution clearly.
(b) Prove that Axiom **P5** is independent. Explain your solution clearly.

4. This problem refers to the four axioms for a group, we studied earlier in Chapter 6. Here again are the axioms for a group, along with the standard names for the special elements they describe.

    A **group**, $(G, \diamond)$, is a set G together with an operation $\diamond$ for which these four axioms are true.

    Axioms

    G1 For any elements a and b of G, the result $a \diamond b$ is also an element of G. This property is called **closure.**

    G2 For any elements a, b, and c of G,

    $$(a \diamond b) \diamond c = a \diamond (b \diamond c)$$

    That is, the operation $\diamond$ is *associative* on G.

    G3 There is an element z in G such that, for every element a of G,

    $$z \diamond a = a \quad \text{and} \quad a \diamond z = a$$

    This element z is called an **identity** element of the group.

    G4 For each element a of G, there is an element a' in G such that

    $$a \diamond a' = z \quad \text{and} \quad a' \diamond a = z$$

    the element a' is an **inverse** of the element a.

    (a) Prove that the axiom about inverses is independent.
    (b) Prove that the associativity axiom is independent.
    (c) Suppose that we added this as a fifth axiom: "The operation is commutative." Would it be independent or dependent? Explain your answer.
    (d) Suppose, instead, that we added this as a fifth axiom. "The Cancellation Laws hold." Would it be independent or dependent? Explain your answer.

8.5 The World Through Different Eyes: Non-Euclidean Geometries

Here is the rest of the story about Euclid's fifth postulate. At the end of Section 8.3, we told you that people tried unsuccessfully to prove it for more than 2000 years. In the language of Section 8.4, they were trying to prove that the fifth postulate was dependent on the other four. There were many "near misses" —proofs that were accepted as valid for a few years or a few decades, but eventually found to be wrong in one way or another.

Some mathematicians proposed substitute statements that were logically equivalent to Euclid's fifth postulate, but were clearer or easier to use. The most famous of these substitutes is known as *Playfair's Postulate*. It is named after the Scottish scientist John Playfair, who made it popular in the 18th century.[†]

Playfair's Form of the Parallel Postulate: Through a point not on a line, there is exactly one line parallel to the given line.

What does it mean to say that two statements are "logically equivalent"?

8.43

Playfair's Postulate is so well known that it now appears in many geometry books as the Parallel Postulate, in place of Euclid's original statement. We are going to do the same thing. For the rest of this story, we shall use Playfair's form of the Parallel Postulate.

Early in the 18th century, an Italian teacher and scholar named Girolamo Saccheri tried a clever new approach to the Parallel Postulate question. Saccheri reasoned like this:

Learning Outcomes

After studying this section you will be able to:

Describe how different forms of the Parallel Postulate result in different systems of geometry

Identify some basic geometric facts that are true in all of these geometries

Identify some basic facts of Euclidean geometry that are false in the non-Euclidean geometries

Describe an instance of a non-Euclidean geometry.

[†]This substitute form was known many, many centuries before Playfair was born. The Greek mathematician Proclus stated and worked with it in the fifth century A.D.

1. We know that Euclid's axioms are consistent because we have instances of the system.

2. We believe that the Parallel Postulate is dependent on Euclid's other axioms, but so far no one has been able to prove it.

3. Suppose it is dependent. Then, if we replace the Parallel Postulate by its negation, we will be putting a contradiction into the system.

4. Therefore, if we use the negation of the Parallel Postulate as an axiom and can find a contradiction in this new system, we will have shown that the Parallel Postulate can be proved from the other axioms.

8.44

1. What does it mean to say that an axiomatic system is *consistent*?

2. What does it mean to say that an axiom is *dependent* on the other axioms of a system?

3. What is the *negation* of a statement? If the negation of a statement is false, what can you say about the truth or falsity of the original statement?

4. What is the Law of Contradiction?

5. Explain steps 3 and 4 in Saccheri's reasoning. Exactly how would a contradiction somewhere in his new system show that the Parallel Postulate can be proved?

The negation of Playfair's form of the Parallel Postulate has two parts.

Through a point not on a line, either

(1) there are no lines parallel to the given line

or

(2) there is more than one line parallel to the given line.

Saccheri had to show that each of these two cases results in a contradiction. Now, recall that Euclid avoided talking about parallel lines entirely until Proposition 27, and he didn't actually use the Parallel Postulate until Proposition 29. This meant that Saccheri could assume Euclid's first 28 propositions to be true in these two cases, as well.

He began by constructing an *isosceles birectangular quadrilateral*—a four-sided polygon with two right angles at its base and two equal sides. See Display 8.18. This figure, now known as a **Saccheri quadrilateral,** can be constructed using only Euclid's first 26 propositions. Therefore, it makes sense with or without the Parallel Postulate.

In Euclid's geometry, a Saccheri quadrilateral is a rectangle. Proving this, however, requires facts developed after Proposition 28. Therefore, the claim that ∠1 and ∠2 are right angles depends on the Parallel Postulate. Saccheri proved that, when the Parallel Postulate is not true,

> if part (1) of its negation holds, then ∠1 and ∠2 are larger than right angles, and

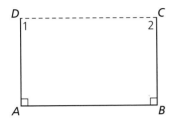

A Saccheri quadrilateral

Display 8.18

> if part (2) of the negation holds, then ∠1 and ∠2 are smaller than right angles.

These two situations would have seemed obviously absurd to Euclid, but if we think of *straight line* as an undefined term of the axiomatic system, then nothing is obvious at all.

> **Explain how Propositions 28, 33, and 34 can be used to prove that, in Euclid's geometry, a Saccheri quadrilateral is a rectangle.**

8.45

Saccheri used his quadrilateral to find a contradiction from part (1) of the negation. However, in doing so, he assumed that Euclid's Postulate 2—"A finite straight line can be extended continuously in a straight line"—meant that straight lines must be infinite. We'll come back to this curious fact later.

Part (2) of the negation was a more stubborn case. Saccheri proved many interesting results, but he could not seem to find a clear contradiction. He finally twisted a weak result into something that vaguely resembled a contradiction, but it convinced almost no one. In 1733, his results were published in a book called *Euclid Freed from Every Flaw,* but his proof was promptly forgotten for almost 100 years.

Early in the 19th century, Saccheri's approach was revived by four people. Three of them started by assuming Euclid's first four postulates and part (2) of the negation of the Parallel Postulate. That is, they considered this question:

> Can there be a system of plane geometry in which, through a point not on a line, there is more than one line parallel to the given line?

The great German mathematician Karl Friedrich Gauss explored this possibility around 1810. However, he didn't publish any of his findings, so almost nobody knew about his work then. The first published investigation of such a geometry appeared in 1829. It was written by Nicolai Lobachevsky, a Russian mathematician who devoted much of his life to studying it. At about the same time, Janos Bolyai, a young Hungarian army officer, was working out the same ideas, which he published in 1832. All of them came to the same surprising conclusion.

> If the Parallel Postulate is replaced in Euclid's axioms by part (2) of its negation, the resulting axiomatic system contains no contradictions!

That settled, once and for all, the 2000-year old question about Euclid's fifth postulate.

> The Parallel Postulate is an independent axiom.

In fact, it led to an entirely new plane geometry. A system that is not a model of the usual plane of Euclid's imagination (and ours). Instead, it has perfectly good instances of its own. We shall describe one of them for you, as soon as you answer the next questions.

8.46

1. **What are the main undefined terms of plane geometry? Think back to what was said in Section 8.2 about Euclid's definitions.**

2. **How are *parallel lines* defined?**

To construct an instance of Lobachevsky's geometry, we must assign meanings to the undefined terms *point, line, plane,* and *on.* Of these, the strangest one will be the meaning of *plane,* the surface on which all the figures of this system must exist.

Imagine a little child walking along, pulling a toy attached to a string. If the child makes a sharp left turn, the toy will trail behind, not making a sharp corner, but slowly curving around until it is almost directly behind once more. The curved path of the toy can be used to make the surface we want. We take two opposite copies of it, as shown in Display 8.19(a), and rotate this double curve around the line *AB*, as in Display 8.19(b). The resulting surface is called a *pseudosphere*. It looks like two trumpets joined together, with the narrow part of each one tapering gradually as it becomes infinitely long.

About Words

The prefix *pseudo-* is used to signify something pretended, fake, or deceptively like something else. A *pseudonym* is an *alias*, a name other than one's real name. *Pseudoscience* is something that pretends to be science, but is not.

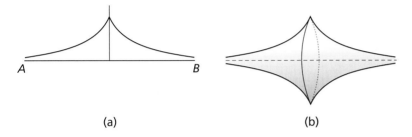

(a)   (b)

Forming a pseudosphere

Display 8.19

The pseudosphere is the *plane* of our instance, *points* are locations on it, and *on* has its usual meaning. A path on this surface is *straight* if it traces out the shortest distance between its endpoints. A (*straight*) line is an infinite extension of such a segment; it represents the shortest path between any two of its points.

It is very difficult to draw or visualize pictures on the pseudosphere. This surface has the property that through a point not on a line there are many parallels to a given line. That is, there are "straight" lines—lines that are the shortest paths between any two of their points—that intersect each other, but never meet a given line.

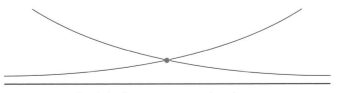

Straight lines on a pseudosphere

Display 8.20

Display 8.20 suggests how such lines would look on a flat surface. Both the crossing lines (as well as the lines between them) are parallel to the bottom line. They approach the bottom line

asymptotically; that is, they get closer and closer, but they never touch it. Remember that parallel lines in this geometry do not have to be everywhere equidistant from each other. If this picture were wrapped around the pseudosphere, all these lines would be straight.

The fourth person in the 19th century to follow in Saccheri's footsteps was Bernhard Riemann. Looking at part (1) of the negation of the Parallel Postulate, he wondered,

> Can there be a system of plane geometry in which, through a point not on a line, there are no parallels to the given line?

Saccheri had found a contradiction in this case, but it depended on assuming that lines are infinite. This assumption rested on Euclid's Postulate 2, which said that a finite straight line can be extended continuously in a straight line. Riemann observed that "extended continuously" did not necessarily imply "infinitely long." In particular, an arc of a circle can be extended continuously as far as we please. There is no endpoint, but its length is finite.

8.47 Someone in the front of the room objects: "How can Riemann talk about circles here? Euclid's Postulate 2 refers to straight lines!" Respond to this objection.

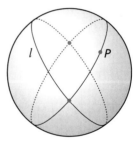

Any "straight line" through *P* must intersect *l*.

Display 8.21

8.48 Riemann constructed an instance of Euclid's first four postulates and part (1) of the negation of the Parallel Postulate by using a sphere as the *plane*. *Points* are locations on the sphere. The (*straight*) lines of this system are the great circles—circles that divide the sphere into two equal parts. Because the shortest path between any two points on a sphere is an arc of a great circle through those points, such circles are analogous to straight lines on a flat surface. The Equator is one example of a great circle on the sphere of Earth; the lines of longitude also are arcs of great circles. These meanings provide an instance of Euclid's first four postulates, but there are no parallel lines because any two great circles intersect [†]. Thus, given a point P not on a great circle l, any great circle through P must intersect l. See Display 8.21.

8.49

1. On a globe of the Earth, choose two cities that are fairly far apart—Chicago and Tokyo, for example. Using a string or a measuring tape, find the shortest path on the globe between these two cities. Then extend your string all the way around the globe, forming a circle. Measure the circumference of this circle.

2. Repeat part 1, using two different cities. How does the circumference of this circle compare with the one of part 1?

3. At what places do your great circles from parts 1 and 2 intersect?

4. Try to find a circle on the globe with a circumference larger than the ones you have already measured. In the term *great circle,* what does the word "great" signify?

5. When an airline advertises that it flies a great circle route from the U. S. to Europe or Asia, what does that mean? Why do you think they bother to advertise this? Why should their customers care?

6. Think of the Equator as a typical great circle. Why is there no great circle that does not cross the equator?

Riemann published his new geometry in 1854. Thus, by the middle of the 19th century there were three different kinds of geometry, distinguished from each other by the way they treat parallel lines. The new systems of Lobachevsky and Riemann were called **non-Euclidean geometries** to distinguish them from Euclidean geometry.

All three of these geometries are consistent systems, but their disagreement about parallelism gives them *very* different properties. For instance, only in Euclidean geometry is it possible

---

[†] Riemann's instance is actually a more abstract version of this, which avoids the problem of two diametrically opposite points having many great circles through them.

to have two triangles that are similar, but not congruent. In the non-Euclidean geometries, if the corresponding angles of two triangles are equal, then the triangles must be congruent.

8.50   Another strange difference among these geometries is that the angle sum of a triangle is not always 180°. In fact, the angle sum of a triangle can be used to tell you which geometry you are in! Imagine a *plane* for each of the three geometries—a flat surface for Euclid's, a sphere for Riemann's, and a pseudosphere for Lobachevsky's. Now picture in your mind's eye how you would draw a Saccheri quadrilateral on each of these surfaces in turn. On each surface, draw a line segment *AB*, construct equal perpendicular segments *AD* and *BC* at each end, and draw *CD* to connect the endpoints of those segments. How is your mind's eye doing? Compare what you are imagining to Display 8.22.

    The figure on the flat surface is a rectangle; *CD* = *AB* and the angles at *C* and *D* are right angles. On the sphere, however, *CD* is shorter than *AB,* and the angles at *C* and *D* are obtuse. Visualize the size of an angle by imagining tangents to its sides at the vertex. On the pseudosphere, *CD* is longer than *AB,* and the angles at *C* and *D* are acute. These pictures illustrate distinctive properties of the three geometries.

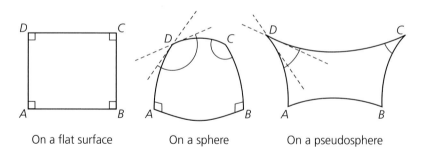

On a flat surface   On a sphere   On a pseudosphere

A Saccheri quadrilateral on each kind of plane

Display 8.22

- In Euclidean geometry, the other two angles of a Saccheri quadrilateral are right angles
- In Riemannian geometry, the other two angles of a Saccheri quadrilateral are larger than right angles
- In Lobachevskian geometry, the other two angles of a Saccheri quadrilateral are smaller than right angles.

8.51

1. What is an *obtuse* angle?

2. What is an *acute* angle?

3. In degrees, what is the sum of two right angles?

This information can be used to see how the angle sum of a triangle depends on the geometry you're using. Work through the following argument, and notice that none of the steps depend on the Parallel Postulate. This means that they work in all three geometries. Display 8.23 is not necessarily flat. It will look about the same on a Euclidean plane or on a very small portion of a sphere or a pseudosphere.

Start with any triangle—call it $\triangle ABC$.

1. Label the midpoints of sides AC and AB as D and E, respectively. Draw line DE, as shown in Display 8.23(a).
2. Draw perpendiculars AF, BG, and CH from the three vertices of the triangle to line DE, as shown in Display 8.23(b).
3. $\triangle AEF$ and $\triangle BEG$ are congruent (see Step 2), so $\angle 1 = \angle 2$.

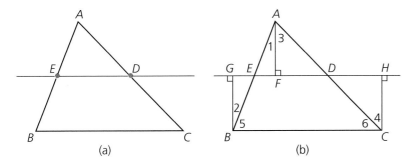

(a)   (b)

Finding the sum of the angles of a triangle

Display 8.23

4. $\triangle ADF$ and $\triangle CDH$ are congruent (see Step 2), so $\angle 3 = \angle 4$.
5. Notice that $GBCH$ is a Saccheri quadrilateral. Do you see why? Think of it upside down. Therefore, $\angle GBC$ and $\angle HCB$ are right angles in Euclidean geometry, obtuse angles in Riemannian geometry, and acute angles in Lobachevskian geometry.
6. Now, the sum of the angles of $\triangle ABC$ can be written as

$$\angle 1 + \angle 5 + \angle 6 + \angle 3$$

7. Substituting the information of Steps 3 and 4 into Step 6, we can rewrite the sum of the angles of $\triangle ABC$ as

$$\angle 2 + \angle 5 + \angle 6 + \angle 4$$

8. But the first two angles in this sum form $\angle GBC$ and the other two form $\angle HCB$. These are the two angles of the Saccheri quadrilateral $GBCH$ that are right angles in Euclidean geometry, obtuse angles in Riemannian geometry, and acute angles in Lobachevskian geometry.

Therefore,

Theorem The sum of the angles of a triangle is

– equal to 180° in Euclidean geometry,

– greater than 180° in Riemannian geometry, and

– less than 180° in Lobachevskian geometry.

Problem Set: 8.5

1. Explain how to construct a Saccheri quadrilateral using only what is permitted by Euclid's axioms and Propositions 1—26.

2. These questions refer to the argument at the end of this section about the sum of the angles of a triangle and to Display 8.23.

   (a) Prove that $\triangle AEF$ and $\triangle BEG$ are congruent.
   (b) Prove that $\triangle ADF$ and $\triangle CDH$ are congruent.
   (c) Explain step 5. Why is $GBCH$ a Saccheri quadrilateral?

3. These questions refer to Riemannian geometry on a sphere. You can think of a globe model of the Earth, if it helps you visualize what's going on.

   (a) Describe a triangle with three right angles.
   (b) Can you describe a triangle with an angle sum of more than 270° ? If so, do it. If not, explain why not.

4. Euclid defined a *square* as a quadrilateral with all four sides equal and four right angles.

   (a) Explain why, by this definition, there are no squares in either Riemannian or Lobachevskian geometry. (*Hint:* Think about Saccheri quadrilaterals.)

   (b) Adjust Euclid's definition of *square* so that it still describes the usual squares of Euclidean geometry and it also describes figures that actually exist in the non-Euclidean geometries.

   (c) Using your new definition, what can be said about the sum of the angles of a square in Riemannian geometry? In Lobachevskian geometry? Give a reason to support your answers. (*Hint:* Look back at Display 8.22; then try to visualize what a square should look like in each of these geometries.)

5. Label each of the following statements with one or more of these letters, as follows:

   E if it is true in Euclidean geometry

   L if it is true in Lobachevskian geometry

   R if it is true in Riemannian geometry

   N if it is not true in any of these geometries.

   (a) Through a point not on a line, there is at least one line parallel to the given line.

   (b) Through a point not on a line, there is at most one line parallel to the given line.

   (c) Whenever two straight lines intersect, they form equal vertical angles.

   (d) Every pair of (straight) lines intersect.

   (e) If two lines are parallel to a third line, then they are parallel to each other.

   (f) The sum of the angles of a triangle equals two right angles.

   (g) All triangles have the same angle sum.

   (h) In a right triangle, the sum of the two other angles is less than 90°.

   (i) All right angles are equal.

   (j) Every quadrilateral contains at least one right angle.

   (k) There exists a quadrilateral with four right angles.

   (l) There exists a quadrilateral with four equal angles.

6. Most of these questions refer to Riemannian geometry on a sphere. You can think of a globe model of the Earth, if it helps you visualize what's going on. Assume that the term *circle* is defined as in Euclid's geometry.

   (a) What is the definition of a circle?
   (b) Is every *straight* line a circle in Riemannian geometry? Justify your answer with a reason or a counterexample.
   (c) Is every *circle* a *straight* line in Riemannian geometry? Justify your answer with a reason or a counterexample.
   (d) In Euclidean geometry, is the ratio of the circumference of a circle to its diameter the same for all circles? If so, what is it? If not, give an example of two circles with different circumference/diameter ratios.
   (e) In the Riemannian geometry of the sphere, what is the circumference/diameter ratio of a great circle? Justify your answer.
   (f) Describe a circle on the sphere that has a circumference/diameter ratio different from that of a great circle. How large could such a ratio be? How small could it be? Justify your answers.

7. Which of the three geometries described in this section do you think is best for describing the world we live in? Give reasons to support your opinions. This question may not have a single right answer. In any event, it probably needs to be shaped and focused better before you answer it.

8.6 Mathematics and Our World

Let's summarize the main ideas of the previous section—three different systems of geometry based on Euclid's first four postulates—Euclidean Geometry, Riemannian Geometry, and Lobachevskian Geometry.

- These three systems are equally consistent. If there was a contradiction in either non-Euclidean geometry, there would also have to be a contradiction in Euclidean geometry.

- The three systems differ in what they assume about parallel lines.

  — Euclid assumed: Through a point not on a line, there is exactly one line parallel to that line.

  — Riemann assumed: Through a point not on a line, there is no line parallel to that line.

  — Lobachevsky assumed: Through a point not on a line, there is more than one line parallel to that line.

- Since these three different postulates about parallel lines contradict each other, the three different geometries are incompatible.

Faced with three geometric systems that conflict with each other, it is tempting to think of the old, familiar one as the "right" geometry and the other two as made up oddities. But why? Just because Euclid's system came first, does that make it the "right" one? After all, the words *point*, *line*, and *plane* are undefined terms in these geometries. Even though Euclid was thinking about the real world when he made up his postulates, how do we know that his meanings for those basic words make his postulates true statements about the real world?

In the spirit of Euclid, we might think of straight lines as sight lines from one point to another, like a surveyor's view of a marker through a transit. Sight lines are determined by light rays traveling to our eyes from the objects we see, so it is reasonable to interpret a straight line as the path of a light ray. How can we tell which parallel postulate holds for these lines? To verify that two light rays really are parallel, we would have to see infinitely far, following them beyond our solar system and past the most distant galaxies. That's impossible without

Learning Outcomes

After studying this section, you probably will not be able to do anything that you couldn't do before, but— if you think hard about it—you just might understand the world you live in a little bit better.

the use of satellites or technology yet to come. There is another approach.

The theorem at the end of Section 8.5 says that the sum of the angles of a triangle depends on the geometry (Euclidean, Riemannian, Lobachevskian). Only in Euclidean geometry is that sum exactly 180°. Maybe if we measure a large triangle very carefully, we can find out if the geometry of our world is really Euclidean.

8.52 Take out a blank piece of paper. Using a very sharp pencil or fine point pen and a good ruler, draw as large a triangle as you can. Then measure its three angles with a protractor.

1. Write down the three angle measurements to the nearest tenth of a degree, if you can. What do you think is your margin of measurement error? That is, how far off might each of your measurements be, one way or another?

2. Find the sum of these three angles. Using your margin of error estimate, what are the largest and the smallest possible values for the actual angle sum of this triangle?

3. Can you conclude from your measurements that we live in a Euclidean world? Why or why not?

8.53 When the mathematician Karl Friedrich Gauss was directing a land survey of the kingdom of Hanover in Germany, he measured a very large triangle very carefully. His triangle measured 69 by 85 by 197 kilometers. What are these lengths in miles? Its vertices were points on three mountaintops. He placed mirrors at these vertices to reflect light rays from a signal fire. Then he carefully measured the angles of the triangle formed by the reflected light rays. The sum of these measurements was 180.004125°. Its difference from 180° was so small that it was well within the margin of measurement error of the tools used.

8.54
1. Does Gauss's experiment prove that Euclidean geometry must be the true geometry of the world? After all, the sum of his measurements was *very* close to 180°. Explain your thinking.

2. Suppose that the margin of error for Gauss's measurements was ±0.5° and that the triangle had had an angle sum of 181°. Would this have proved that we live in a Riemannian world? Explain your thinking.

The hypothetical case of question 2 you just discussed is similar to something that actually occurred in 1919. The results of an astronomical experiment showed that, even after accounting for possible measurement error, the path of light from a distant star was *not* a Euclidean straight line. That is, the experiment showed that the light rays from the star appeared to be curved. This can be explained in either of two ways,

- the universe really is Euclidean, but light rays are not straight, or

- light rays follow the shortest paths from source to destination, and hence are actually straight lines in a non-Euclidean universe.

Asking which of these alternatives is true is an unanswerable question. To put it bluntly, the bottom line, as folks say, is not what's true, but what works. Geometries are tools, designed by humans, to help us deal with a wide variety of theoretical or practical circumstances. Like any other tools, some work better for one job, some for another.

- If you are building a house, marking out a basketball court, designing airports or automobiles or dress patterns, then Euclidean geometry is by far the simplest to use. It works well for such things.

- If you are an astronomer studying distant galaxies, you might prefer Riemannian geometry. It works better than Euclidean geometry for such things.

- If you are studying binocular vision, Lobachevskian geometry might work best for you.

In any case, a geometry is a tool chosen by the worker, not a fixed feature of the job site.

More than any other single event, the invention of the non-Euclidean geometries made people realize choice, not necessity, lies at the heart of the scientific method. The scientists' job is not to dig up hidden scientific truths, much as an archaeologist unearths a dinosaur skeleton or a prospector strikes gold. Instead, their job is to *make up* scientific laws, to invent principles that bring some order to our puzzling world. Whether or not these laws are *true* in any absolute sense is unknowable and irrelevant. We should ask only whether or not these laws help us to predict how things in our world will behave tomorrow or next week or next year. If they do that well, then they are properly a part of our world.

REFLECT

This chapter is about a 19th century solution to a 2200-year old question about a geometry axiom. Its main feature is Euclid's axiomatic system of plane geometry. You saw how Euclid constructed a powerful, dependable system from a handful of commonsense assumptions about points and lines in a plane. Efforts to resolve the question of whether or not Euclid's Parallel Postulate was independent of his other axioms and postulates led to the development of two different types of non-Euclidean geometry, one by Riemann, the other by Lobachevsky and Bolyai. Finally, you saw how the construction of these geometries led to the understanding that there is no single "right" geometry. Like any mathematical systems, different geometries are tools to help us understand different aspects of our world.

PROJECTS

1. Is the following statement true or false in your everyday world?

   "Parallel lines are everywhere equidistant."

   Take a stance (true or false) and write an essay rationalizing your choice.

2. Study and report on a type of geometry not discussed in this text.

3. Fashion a "game" using the rules of axiomatic systems, present it to the class and play it.

4. Create a geometry for a specific three-dimensional figure found in everyday life (e.g., football, donut, etc.). List the undefined terms, definitions, axioms and at least one theorem for your system.

5. What is the best model (instance) of the real world: Euclidean Geometry, Lobachevskian Geometry, or Riemannian Geometry? Write a paper rationalizing your choice.

6. Write about

   "Time and again history has shown man's judgment as to whether something agrees or disagrees with experience is largely a matter of habit of thought and like most habits can be changed."[1]

---

[1]Hollis R. Cooley, et al., *Introduction to Mathematics*. 2nd ed. Boston: Houghton Mifflin, 1949, p. 548.

Appendix A: Using a **TI-84 Plus (TI-83 Plus)** Graphing Calculator

A graphing calculator is a useful tool for doing many different mathematical things. Once you begin to use it, you'll find that it is powerful, fast, and friendly. In fact, your biggest difficulty may be just getting started for the first time! Because this machine can do a lot, it has lots of complicated looking buttons. But you don't have to know about *all* of them before you start to use *any* of them! The sooner you make friends with your electronic assistant, the more it will be able to help you. Let us introduce you to each other by trying a few simple things.

The Cover

The face of the calculator is protected from dirt and scratches by a cover that slides on and off from the top. When you're using the calculator, this cover slips on the back so that you won't lose it. Always put the cover back over the face of the calculator when you finish using it.

On, Off, [2nd] , and Clear

To get the calculator's attention, just press [ON] (at the lower left corner of the calculator). What happens? Do you see a dark block blinking in the upper left corner of the screen? That's the *cursor*, which tells you where you are on the screen. The cursor is always at the spot that will be affected by the next button you push.

Notice that the word [OFF] is printed in blue above the [ON] button. Notice also that there is one key of the same color. It is the key marked [2nd] at the top of the first column of buttons.

When you push [2nd] , it makes the next key that you push behave like what is marked above it in blue.

Try it. Push [2nd] . What has happened to the cursor? Do you see an up arrow ↑ inside it as it blinks? That's to remind you that [2nd] key has been pushed and will affect the next key you choose. Now push [ON] . What happens? Did the cursor disappear? You should have a blank screen; the calculator should be off.

It's always a good idea to turn your calculator off when you finish using it. If you forget, the calculator will turn itself off after a few minutes to save its batteries. Sometimes when you are using it, you may put it aside and do something else for a little while. If it is off when you pick it up again, don't worry; just press [ON].The screen will show what was there before it shut down.

Pressing [CLEAR] gives you a blank screen that is ready for new work. But the last thing you did is still stored. Press [2nd] then [ENTER] (bottom right corner) to bring it back.

Basic Arithmetic

Doing arithmetic on a graphing calculator is no harder than on a simpler calculator. In fact, it's easier. This calculator has a screen that lets you keep track of the problem as you enter it. Let's try a few simple exercises. Turn your calculator on.

- Pick two 3-digit numbers and add them. To do this, just key in the first number, press [+] and then key in the second number. Your addition problem will appear on the screen. Press [ENTER] to get the answer.

If you make a mistake when entering a number, you can go back and fix it. The [◄] key lets you move back (left) one space at a time. When you get to your mistake, just key in the correct number over the wrong one. Then move forward (right) to the end of the line by using the [►] key.

For instance, to add 123 and 456, press 1 2 3 [+] 4 5 6 [ENTER]. The screen will show your question on the first line and the answer at the right side of the second line, as in Display A.1.

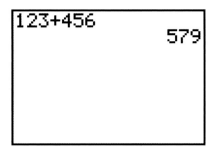

Display A.1

- Now let's try the other three basic arithmetic operations. To clear the screen, press CLEAR. Then try subtracting, multiplying, and dividing your two 3-digit numbers. For instance, if your numbers are 123 and 456, press

$$1 \ 2 \ 3 \ \boxed{-} \ 4 \ 5 \ 6 \ \boxed{ENTER}$$

$$1 \ 2 \ 3 \ \boxed{\times} \ 4 \ 5 \ 6 \ \boxed{ENTER}$$

$$1 \ 2 \ 3 \ \boxed{\div} \ 4 \ 5 \ 6 \ \boxed{ENTER}$$

Your screen should look like Display A.2.

Notice that the display uses ∗ for multiplication (so that it is not confused with the letter x) and / for division.

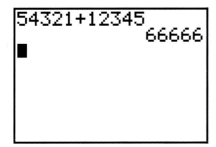

Display A.2

- Here are two button-pushing shortcuts.

If you don't want to redo a problem with just a small change in it, you don't have to reenter the whole thing. 2nd ENTER will bring back the last problem you entered. Just move to the place you want to change, key in the change, and press ENTER. For instance, add 54321 and 12345, as in Display A.3.

```
54321+12345
            66666
█
```

Display A.3

Now, to subtract 12345 from 54321, press [2nd] [ENTER]; the next line will show 54321 + 12345. Move your cursor back to the + sign (using [◀]) and press [−] ; then press [ENTER]. Did you try it? Your screen should look like Display A.4.

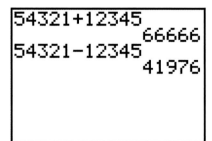

Display A.4

Let's check to see that 41976 is the correct answer by adding 12345 to it and seeing if we get the first number back again. Since you want to do something to the last answer, *you don't have to reenter it.* Press ⊞. Does your calculator show Ans+ and the cursor? It should. If you press an operation key right after doing a calculation, the machine assumes that you want to perform this operation on the last answer. It shows that last answer as Ans. Now key in 12345 and press [ENTER]. You should get back the first number, 54321.

1. Pick two seven-digit numbers and add them. What do you get?

2. Now subtract the second number from the first. Can you do it without rekeying the numbers? What do you get?

3. Now multiply your two seven-digit numbers. What do you get? What does the E mean?

4. Check the last answer by dividing the second of your seven-digit numbers into it. Do it without rekeying the last answer. Do you get your first number back again?

Multiply 98765432 by 123456. Now check the product in two ways.

a

- Divide by pressing ⊡ then entering 123456. Does it check?

- First reenter the product; then divide it by 123456. The product is in scientific notation. To enter it as a regular number, remember that the positive number after the E tells you to move the decimal that many places to the right. Does it check?

1. Divide 97533 by 525 and by 625. One of the answers you get will be exactly right, and the other one will be a very close approximation.

b

- Which is which?

- How can you tell?

- If you hadn't been told that one of the answers is an approximation, how could you know?

2. When an answer is too long to be displayed with ten digits, the calculator shows a ten-digit approximation. Does it do this by just chopping off (truncating) the rest of the digits, or by rounding off? What test would you give your calculator to tell which way it does this?

1. Pick any three-digit number and note it down.

c

2. Repeat its digits in the same order to form a six-digit number (like 123123, for example). Key this number into your calculator.

3. Divide your number by 7.

4. Divide your answer by 11. How do you do this without reentering the answer?

5. Divide the last number by 13. What do you notice about the result? Do you think that it is just a coincidence?

6. Pick another three-digit number and repeat steps 2–5.

7. Try to beat the system; see if you can pick a three-digit number that doesn't work this way. What might you try? Why?

8. Can you actually prove that the pattern you see *works every time*? How might you try to do this?

The Two Minus Signs

The calculator has two minus signs. The one on the gray key looks like ⊟ and the one on the white key looks like ⟨⁻⟩ . The gray one, on the right, is for subtraction. It is grouped with the keys for the other arithmetic operations. To subtract 3764 from 8902, for example, you would key in

8 9 0 2 ⊟ 3 7 6 4 ENTER

Go ahead; do it. Do you get 5138?

The white minus key, to the left of the ENTER key at the bottom, is for making a number negative. It is grouped with the digit keys and the decimal point. To add the numbers ⁻273, 5280, and ⁻2116, for example, you would key in

⟨⁻⟩ 2 7 3 ⊞ 5 2 8 0 ⊞ ⟨⁻⟩ 2 1 1 6 ENTER

Try it. Notice that the display shows these negative signs without the parentheses, but they are smaller and raised a little. To see the difference between this negative sign and the subtraction sign, try subtracting the negative number ⁻567 from 1234. Here are the keystrokes:

1234 ⊟ ⟨⁻⟩ 567

The display should look like this:

1234 − ⁻567

Raising to a Power

To raise a number to a power, press ⌃ (just above the divsion sign) before entering the exponent. Thus, to compute 738^5, press

7 3 8 ⌃ 5 ENTER

The screen should look like Display A.5.

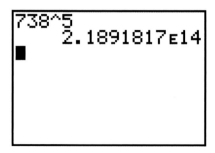

Display A.5

The Menu Keys

Many keys bring a menu to the screen. A menu is a list of functions—things that the calculator is ready to do for you. For instance, press each of the keys across the row that starts with MATH. Don't worry about what all those lists say; just pick one out and look at it as you read the rest of this paragraph. Notice that it is actually a double menu. There are two cursors on it, shown as dark blocks. The one in the top left corner can be moved along the top line by using the ◀ and ▶ keys. Each time you move it to a new place on the top line, the menu below changes. The items in each lower menu are reached by using the other cursor, which can be moved up and down along the left side of the screen by using the ▲ and ▼ keys.

Once you have put the cursor on the choice you want, you actually make the choice by pressing ENTER. This makes the calculator go back to its "home" screen and display your choice. To make the calculator do what you have chosen, press ENTER again.

1. How many separate calculator functions can be reached through the menus of the MATH key?

2. How many separate calculator functions can be reached through the menus of the MATRIX key?

Entering Data in a List

The data handling tools are found through the statistics menu.

- Turn your calculator on and press STAT. You'll see a menu that looks like Display A.6.

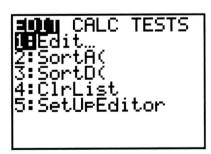

TI-84 Plus/TI-83 Plus

Display A.6

• To enter data, make sure that the top cursor is on EDIT and the left cursor is on 1: . Then press ENTER. Your screen display should look like Display A.7, with the cursor right under L1.

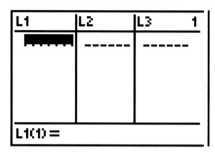

Display A.7

Note that if the display shows numbers in the L1 column, you'll have to clear the data memory. There are two ways to do this.

Get out of this display (by pressing 2nd [QUIT]) and go back to the STAT menu. Press 4. When ClrList appears, press 2nd 1 then ENTER; Done will appear. Now go back to the STAT screen and choose 1:Edit .

or

Without leaving this display, use the ▲ and ◄ keys to move your cursor to the top of the column and highlight L1. Press CLEAR and then the ▼ key. List L1 should be cleared.

If you are missing a list in L1 to L6, go back to the STAT menu and press 5 and ENTER. This will reset the calculator to list columns 1 through 6.

• Now it's time to enter the data. Let's use a set of test scores {90, 85, 95, 87, 86, 92, 88, 75, 81, 92} The calculator stores in its memory each data number you enter, along with an L1 label for that entry. The first number is called L1(1), and the second is called L1(2), and so on. We'll ignore the L2 and L3 labels for now. Key in the first data number, then press ENTER. Notice that L1(2) now appears at the bottom of the screen. Key in the second data number and press ENTER; and so on, until you have put in all the data. If you make a mistake, just use the arrow keys to move the cursor to your error, type over it correctly, then move back to where you were.

At this point, the calculator has all your data stored in a way that is easy to use, and the data will stay stored even after the calculator is turned off.

Summaries of 1-Variable Data

It is easy to get summary information about data that is stored in a single list.

- Bring up the STAT menu.
- Move the top cursor to CALC. The side cursor should be on 1:1-Var Stats. Press ENTER.
- 1:1-Var Stats will appear on your screen. Enter the list you want the calculator to summarize. For instance, if you want a summary of the data in list L1, press 2nd 1; then press ENTER.

That's all there is to it! A screenful of information will appear. Sections 1.3–1.7 in Chapter 1 of Year 1 explain how to interpret that information.

Putting Data in Size Order

The TI-84 Plus (TI-83 Plus) have built-in programs that will put your data in size order automatically. Let's order the test scores that you just entered.

1. Go to the STAT menu and choose 2:SortA(then press ENTER.

2. Tell the calculator to sort the L1 list by pressing 2nd 1 then ENTER. Your calculator screen should now say DONE.

3. To see what it has done, reopen List 1 (using STAT 1:Edit). Your data should now be listed in ascending order — that is, from smallest to largest as you read down the list. The A in SortA(stands for ascending order.

Now go back to the STAT menu and choose 3:SortD(then press ENTER. Tell the calculator to sort the L1 list again. (Press 2nd 1 ENTER.)

1. When the screen says Done, what has your calculator done? Look at L1 again to help you answer this question.

2. What does the "D" in SortD(stand for?

Once the data are in size order, it is easy to find the median. For example, if you have 21 data items in all, the median is just the 11th one in the sorted list. Scroll through the data (using the ▲ key) until you find L1(11). Its value is the median. If you have 20 data items, the median is halfway between the 10th and 11th items in the sorted list. Scroll through the data until you find L1(10) and L1(11). Then calculate the number halfway between them.

Finding the mode is just as easy. Count repeated items in this list. The one that is repeated the most times is the mode.

The Graph Window

This kind of calculator is called a graphing calculator because it can *draw graphs*. The screen on a graphing calculator can show line drawings of mathematical relationships. It does this with two kinds of coordinate systems—*rectangular coordinates* or *polar coordinates*. In this part we shall use only rectangular coordinates; polar coordinates will appear much later. If you are not familiar with the idea of a rectangular coordinate system, you should review the first section of Chapter 3 in Year 1 now.

Your calculator leaves the factory with standard coordinate axes built in. To see what they look like, turn on your calculator and press GRAPH (in the upper right corner). You should see a horizontal and a vertical axis crossing the middle of the screen. The horizontal axis is called the *x*-**axis**, and the vertical axis is called the *y*-**axis**. If your screen doesn't show this, press ZOOM and choose 6:ZStandard. Examine this display carefully; then answer the following questions.

1. Assuming that the dots along each axis mark the integer points, what is the largest possible value on the *x*-axis? On the *y*-axis?

2. What is the smallest possible value on the *x*-axis? On the *y*-axis?

3. Does it look as if the same unit of measure is being used on both axes?

4. Why do you suppose the spacing between the units is not exactly the same everywhere on an axis? Do you think that this might cause a problem?

The standard coordinate axis setting can be changed in several ways. This is done using the menu that appears when you press WINDOW. Try that now. You should get Display A.8.

TI-84 Plus/TI-83 Plus

Display A.8

Xmin and Xmax are the smallest and largest values on the *x*-axis (the horizontal axis); Ymin and Ymax are the smallest and largest values on the *y*-axis (the vertical axis).

Xscl and Yscl are the scales for marking off points on the axes. The setting 1 means that each single integer value on the axis is marked. To see how the scale value works, change Xscl to 2. Move the cursor down, using ▾, then just key in 2 in place of 1. Now press GRAPH. What change do you notice? Now go back to the WINDOW menu (press WINDOW) and change Yscl to 5. Return to the graph (press GRAPH). What has changed?

The Xres = 1 line indicates the resolution of the graph. It can be set to an integer from 1 to 8. At Xres = 1, it evaluates a function at each of the 94 pixels on the *x*-axis. At Xres = 8, it evaluates the function at every eighth pixel.

Change the WINDOW settings so that they look like Display A.9. Then look at the graph and answer these questions.

1. Where on the screen is the origin of the coordinate system?

2. Does it look as if the same unit of measure is being used on both axes?

3. Does it look as if the spacing between the units is the same everywhere on an axis?

4. What happens when you press ▴ then ▾?

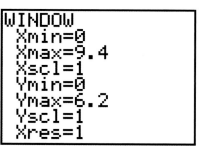

TI-84 Plus/TI-83 Plus

Display A.9

If you have worked through the previous questions, you found that pressing ▲, ▼ puts a cross exactly in the middle of your screen and two numbers at the bottom. The cross is the cursor for the graphing screen, and the numbers are the coordinates of the point at its center. In this case, the cursor is at (4.7, 3.1). It can be moved to any point on the graph by using the four arrow keys ▲, ▼, ◄, ► at the upper right of the keypad.

Move the cursor to the point (4, 3). How far does the cursor move each time you press ◄ or ►? How far does it move each time you press ▲ or ▼? Now move the cursor directly down to the bottom of the screen. What are the coordinates of the lowest point you can reach?

These new WINDOW settings are better than the standard one in some ways, and worse in others. Let's look again at the Standard coordinate system and compare it with the one we just saw. To get back to the standard settings, press ZOOM, then press 6 to choose ZStandard. The Standard coordinate axes should appear immediately.

These questions refer to the Standard coordinate axes.

1. Where is the cursor to begin with? How do you find it if you can't remember?

2. Try to move the cursor to the point (4, 3). How close can you get to it?

3. How far does the cursor move each time you press ◄ or ►?

4. How far does it move each time you press ▲ or ▼?

5. Move the cursor directly down to the bottom of the screen. What are the coordinates of the lowest point you can reach?

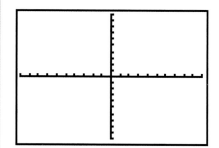

6. In what ways is this coordinate system better than the one we set up for the previous set of questions? In what ways is it worse?

7. How might we fix the bad features of this system without losing the good ones?

Another useful WINDOW setting is 8:ZInteger in the ZOOM menu. When you press [8], coordinate axes appear, but they are still the standard ones. Press [ENTER] to get the Integer settings.

These questions refer to the Integer coordinate axes.

1. Try to move the cursor to the point (4, 3). How close can you get to it?

2. How far does the cursor move each time you press [◄] or [►]?

3. How far does it move each time you press [▲] or [▼]?

4. Why is this setting named Integer?

To plot a point (mark its location) on the graphing screen, go to the point-drawing part of the DRAW menu, like this.

```
DRAW POINTS STO
1:ClrDraw
2:Line(
3:Horizontal
4:Vertical
5:Tangent(
6:DrawF
7↓Shade(
```

Draw Menu

```
DRAW POINTS STO
1:Pt-On(
2:Pt-Off(
3:Pt-Change(
4:Pxl-On(
5:Pxl-Off(
6:Pxl-Change(
7:Pxl-Test(
```

Points Menu

Press [2nd] [PRGM] and move the top cursor to POINTS.

Choose 1 to make the [ENTER] key mark cursor locations. If you want to mark some points and erase others, choose 3. This lets the [ENTER] key change the state of any point the cursor is on; it will mark one that isn't already marked, and will unmark one that is. (*Hint:* If you have plotted too many points and you want to start over, you can go to Draw menu and enter 1 for ClearDraw. This will wipe out everything you have plotted and return to the Standard coordinate settings. If you were using different coordinate settings, you will have to redo them in the WINDOW menu. If you want to erase some points, see Drawing Points in the graph section of the TI Guidebook).

Problem Set: Appendix A

1. What WINDOW settings do you need in order to put the origin at the upper right corner of your screen? What can you say about the coordinates of the points that can be plotted on this screen?

2. What WINDOW settings do you need in order to put the origin at the upper left corner of your screen? What can you say about the coordinates of the points that can be plotted on this screen?

3. Choose the Integer setting for the coordinate axes and plot the points (30, 14), (-5, 20), (-26, -11), and (6, -30). Then write the coordinates of two points that lie within the area of the graph window but cannot be plotted exactly with this setting.

4. Find WINDOW settings to form a coordinate system such that the points (120, 80) and (-60, -40) are within the window frame.

   (a) How far does the cursor move each time you press ◀ or ▶?

   (b) How far does it move each time you press ▲ or ▼?

   (c) Can you put the cursor exactly on (120, 80)? If not, how close can you come? Plot this point as closely as you can.

   (d) Can you put the cursor exactly on (-60, -40)? If not, how close can you come? Plot this point as closely as you can.

   (e) Can you put the cursor exactly on (0, 0)? If not, how close can you come?

5. Find WINDOW settings to form a coordinate system such that the cursor can be put exactly on the points (20, 24.5) and (-17.3, -14).

   (a) What is the initial position of the cursor?

   (b) How far does it move each time you press ◀ or ▶?

   (c) How far does it move each time you press ▲ or ▼?

   (d) Can you put the cursor exactly on (0, 0)? If not, how close can you come?

Drawing Histograms

Drawing a histogram is very easy. All you have to do is choose a few numbers to tell the calculator how wide and how tall to make the bars, as follows. Turn your calculator on and press WINDOW. The screen should look like Display A.10, maybe with different numbers.

TI-84 Plus/TI-83 Plus

Display A.10

The numbers in this WINDOW list tell the calculator how to set the horizontal (X) and vertical (Y) scales.

- Xmin, an abbreviation of *X minimum*, is the smallest data value the picture will show. You should set it at some convenient value less than or equal to the smallest value in your data set.

- Xmax, an abbreviation of *X maximum*, is the largest data value the picture will show. Set it at some convenient value greater than or equal to the largest value in your data set.

- Xscl, an abbreviation of *X scale*, says how to group the data. It is the size of the base interval at the bottom of each bar of the histogram. For instance, Xscl = 10 will group the data by 10s, starting from the value of Xmin that you chose.

- Ymin is the smallest frequency of any data group. It is never less than 0, which usually is a good choice for it.

- Ymax represents the length of the longest bar. Choose a convenient number that is not less than the largest frequency of any data group, but not much larger.

- Yscl determines the size of the steps to be marked on the vertical (frequency) scale. For small data sets, set it to 1. If your setting for Ymax is much larger than 10, you might want to set Yscl larger than 1. A little experimenting will show you how to choose a helpful setting.

- Leave Xres=1.

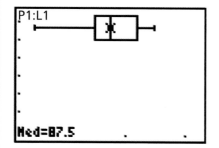

Now your calculator is ready to draw a histogram.

- Press [STAT PLOT] ([2nd] [Y=]), choose 1 and press [ENTER].

- Choose these settings from each row by moving the cursor to them with the arrow keys and pressing [ENTER] each time.

    – Highlight On.

    – Highlight the histogram picture.

    – Set Xlist to the list containing your data (L1, L2, etc.).

    – Set Freq:1.

Now press [GRAPH] — and there it is!

Drawing Boxplots

The TI-84 Plus (TI-83 Plus) calculators can draw boxplots. All they need are the data and a few sizing instructions. Here's how to do it.

- Turn the calculator on, press [STAT] and choose 1:Edit... from the EDIT menu. Check which list contains the data you want to use. Let's assume it's in L1.

- Press [WINDOW] and set the horizontal (X) and vertical (Y) scales. If you have forgotten how to set your WINDOW, refer to "The Graph Window" section. Choose convenient numbers for the X range—Xmin less than your smallest data value and Xmax greater than your largest data value, but not too small or too large. You don't want the picture to get squeezed into something you can't see well! Also set Xscl to some convenient size.

- The Y settings don't matter as much. Ymin = –2 and Ymax = 3 work a little better.

- Press [STAT PLOT] ([2nd] [Y=]), choose 1: and press [ENTER]. Select these settings from each row by moving the cursor to them with the arrow keys and pressing [ENTER] each time.

    On; the boxplot picture; L1 from the Xlist; 1 from Freq

- Now press [GRAPH] —and there it is!

- To read the five-number summary, press [TRACE] and use the [◄] and [►] to display the five numbers one at a time.

Graphing and Tracing Lines

If you want the calculator to graph a line or a curve, you must first be able to describe the line or curve by an algebraic equation. Once you have the equation for what you want to draw, you must put it in the form

$$y = [\text{something}]$$

For a straight line, that's not a problem; we often put the equation in this form, anyway. For some other kinds of curves, putting them in this form can be a little messy. In this section we shall deal only with straight lines.

All graphing begins with the Y= key. When you press this key for the first time, you get the screen in Display A.11.

```
Plot1  Plot2  Plot3
\Y1=
\Y2=
\Y3=
\Y4=
\Y5=
\Y6=
\Y7=
```

TI-84 Plus/TI-83 Plus

Display A.11

These lines allow you to put in as many as ten different algebraic equations for things you want drawn. The subscript number gives you a way to keep track of which equation goes with which picture on the graph. To see how the process works, we'll make the first example simple—two straight lines through the origin.

> Key in -.5X on the $Y_1 =$ line, *using the* X,T,Θ,*n* *key to make the* X; then press ENTER.

It is important to use X,T,Θ,*n* for X because that's how the calculator knows that you are referring to the horizontal axis.

> Key in -.25X on the Y2= line and ENTER it.

Be sure to use the (-) key for the negative sign. If you don't, you'll get an error message when you ask for the graph. If you want to wipe out one of these equations and redo it, just move the cursor back to the equation and press CLEAR.

```
Plot1  Plot2  Plot3
\Y1=-.5X
\Y2=-.25X▪
\Y3=
\Y4=
\Y5=
\Y6=
\Y7=
```

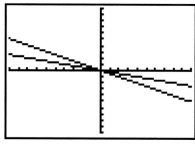

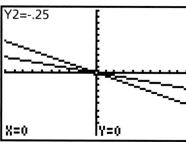

Now your work is done. Press GRAPH and just watch as the calculator draws the lines. If you forget which line goes with which equation, or if you want to see the coordinates of the points along your lines, press TRACE and then move the cursor with the ◄ and ► keys. When you do this, the coordinates of the cursor's position appear at the bottom of the screen. The equation appears in the upper left hand corner. In this example, when you press TRACE you will be on $Y_1 = -.5X$, the first of the two lines we entered. Try it. To switch from one line to another, use the ▲ and ▼ keys. Notice that, in this case, either of these keys gets you to the other line. That's because we are only graphing two equations. If we were graphing more than two, these keys would move up and down the *list of equations*, regardless of where the graphs appeared on the screen.

There is a way to remove the graph of an equation from the screen without erasing the equation from your list. For example, let us remove the line Y1 = -.5X from the picture. Go back to the Y= list. Notice that the = sign of each equation appears in a dark block. This shows that the graph of this equation is turned on. To turn it off, move the cursor to the = sign and press ENTER. The dark block will disappear. To turn it back on, put the cursor back on = and press ENTER again.

Approximating Data by a Line

This section refers to a situation that commonly arises in the analysis of two-variable data. Such data can be represented as points on a coordinate plane, and it is often useful to know if the pattern of points can be approximated by a straight line. A common way of doing this is called *least-squares approximation*. An explanation of this process and its use appears in Chapter 4 of Year 1. This calculator section provides a simple example of how to get the TI-84 Plus (TI-83 Plus) to give you a least-squares approximation of a set of data.

Let's look at a very small, simple data set. The process is exactly the same for bigger, more complicated data sets. Here are four points of two-variable data.

$$(1, 2) \quad (2, 3) \quad (3, 5) \quad (4, 6)$$

If you plot these points on a coordinate plane, you will see that they don't all lie on the same line. Don't just take our word for it; make a sketch! The calculator uses the least-squares method to find automatically the line of "best fit."

Section 4.3 (in Chapter 4) describes how this method works and what best fit means. These are the instructions for getting the calculator to do all the tedious work for you.

First of all, you need to have the data entered in two *separate data storage lists*. You get to these lists by pressing STAT and choosing 1:EDIT... from the EDIT menu. When you press ENTER, you should get Display A.12.

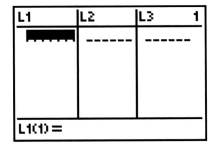

Display A.12

If the columns already contain data that you don't want, you can clear them out in either of two ways.

- Press STAT and choose 4:ClrList from the menu that appears. When the message ClrList appears, enter the name of the list you want to clear. (Press 2nd 1 for L1, 2nd 2 for L2, etc.) Then press ENTER ; the screen will say Done. Now press STAT to return to the process of entering data.

- Go to the first element in your list L1(1) and press DEL. Continue to do this until the list is gone. This is a reasonable method as long as the list is short.

Enter the first coordinate of each data point into list L1; put its second coordinate in list L2. The four data points of our example should appear as shown in Display A.13.

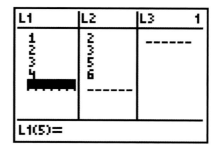

Display A.13

Now we are almost done. Press $\boxed{\text{STAT}}$ and go to the CALC menu. Choose LinReg(ax + b). When you press $\boxed{\text{ENTER}}$, the screen will display an algebraic description of the line of best fit. For our example, it looks like Display A.14.

- The second line, y = ax + b, just tells you that the information is for slope-intercept form. Notice that the TI-84 Plus (TI-83 Plus) use *a*, not *m*, for the slope here.

- The third line says that the slope is 1.4.

- The fourth line says that the *y*-intercept is .5.

Note that the last two lines may show the *correlation coefficient r*, and the *coefficient of determination r²*. The correlation coefficient is not discussed in your textbook. A detailed explanation of how it works will have to wait until you study statistics in more depth. But, in case you are curious about it, here is a little more information. The correlation coefficient is always a number between −1 and 1, inclusive. 1 and −1 stand for a perfect fit, with all points exactly on the line. (1 is for lines with positive slope; −1 is for lines with negative slope.) The closer *r* is to 0, the worse the fit.

```
LinReg
 y=ax+b
 a=1.4
 b=.5
 r²=.98
 r=.9899494937
```

TI-84 Plus/TI-83 Plus

Display A.14

Putting together this information about our example, we see that the least-squares line is described by the equation

$$y = 1.4x + .5$$

Graph the line $y = 1.4x + .5$. Are any of the four data points on it? How can you be sure?

a

Using Formulas to Make Lists

Sometimes it is useful to make a new list of data from an old one by doing the same thing to each data value. For instance, you might want to add a fixed number to each value, square each value, or find the distance of each value from some particular number. Instead of computing the new list one entry at a time, you can do it all at once if you can express your process as a formula.

Here's how the process works.

- Go to the STAT menu. Enter a list of data in L1, and then clear L2 and L3.

- To add 5 to each entry in L1, move the cursor over to the second column, then up to the heading, L2. The bottom line of your display should read L2= (without any number in parentheses).

- The trick here is to let the symbol L1 stand for each element of the list L1. That is, we make L1 *a variable*. Key in L1 + 5; the bottom of your screen should read L2 = L1 + 5.

- Now press ENTER and watch the entire column for L2 fill out automatically!

- To list in L2, the square of each entry in L1, put the cursor on L2 (at the top of the column). Then enter L1^2 (or L1 * L1).

- Now let us list in L3 the midpoint between the L1 entry and the L2 entry. Put the cursor back on L3 at the top of the column and press CLEAR. This removes the old formula. Now key in (L1 + L2)/2 and press ENTER.

    1. **List at least 10 data values in L1.**

    b

    2. **Write a formula to list in L2 the distance between 17 and each entry in L1. Remember: Distances are never negative numbers. Then use it.**

3. Write a formula to list in L3 the square of the difference (which may be negative) between each entry in L1 and 17. Then use it.

4. Write a formula to list in L4 the square root of each entry in L3. Then use it.

5. How are columns L2 and L4 related? Explain.

Drawing Circles

To draw circles directly on a graph, use 9:Circle(in the DRAW menu. (The [DRAW] menu appears when you press [2nd] [PRGM].) 2:Line(can be used to draw segments, which lets you add radii, diameters, and other segments to your drawings of circles.

Before beginning, make sure that all the functions on your Y= screen are turned off. If they are not, their graphs will appear when you draw circles and segments. Also make sure that all STAT PLOTS are turned off.

Follow these instructions to draw a circle directly on a graph.

1. From the ZOOM menu, choose ZStandard (to clear any unusual WINDOW settings). Then choose ZSquare or ZInteger, which displays the graph window.

2. From the DRAW menu, choose 9:Circle(.

3. Choose a point for the center by moving the cursor to this point and pressing [ENTER].

4. Choose the radius for your circle by moving the cursor this many units away from the center and pressing [ENTER]

You can continue to draw circles by repeating the last two steps. To clear the screen before drawing a new circle, use :ClrDraw in the DRAW menu. If you want to stop drawing circles, press [CLEAR].

 Follow the steps above to draw each of these items.

1. a circle with center (0, 10) and radius 5

2. a circle with center (12, -7) and radius 15

3. four circles with center (0, 0)

You can also draw a circle from the Home Screen (the calculator's primary display WINDOW) by following these instructions. You can use this same method to draw circles from a program.

1. From the Home Screen, choose Circle(from the DRAW menu.

2. Input the coordinates of the center, followed by the radius; then press ENTER. For example, if you enter (0, 10, 5), the calculator will draw a circle with center at (0, 10) and radius 5, using whatever ZOOM WINDOW setting is current.

3. To return to the Home Screen, press CLEAR.

1. Draw a circle with center (3, 2) and radius 7 directly from the Home Screen. If your graph does not look like a circle, how can you adjust the graph WINDOW so that it does?

2. Draw four concentric circles around (0, 0) directly from the Home Screen. Earlier you were asked to draw this figure directly on a graph. Which method is easier for you? Why?

Appendix B: Using a Spreadsheet

Computers give us many different tools for doing and using mathematics. One of these tools is called a **spreadsheet**. These days, a spreadsheet is an easy-to-use and very powerful computer program, but the idea of a spreadsheet is really much simpler and older than computers. Originally, a spreadsheet was just an oversized piece of paper, with lines and columns that made it easier for accountants and bookkeepers to keep their work in order.

You can make a spreadsheet on a lined piece of paper.

- Make a narrow border across the top and down the left side of the sheet.

- Divide the rest of the paper into columns from top to bottom. Six columns of about equal width will do for now.

- In the left margin, number the lines, beginning with 1, to the bottom of the page.

- Across the top margin, name each column with a letter from A to F in alphabetical order.

Your paper should look something like Display B.1.

	A	B	C	D	E	F
1						
2						
3						
4						
5						
6						
⋮						

Display B.1

The Cell Names

Each box in this grid has its own address — the letter of its column followed by the number of its row. For instance, C4 refers to the box, third column (column C), on the fourth line (row). The electronic spreadsheets that computers handle look just like this, and each position in them is addressed in just the same way. Electronic spreadsheet manuals often call the boxes **cells**. We'll do the same thing, so that you become used to the term.

> Here are a couple of questions to get you comfortable with the way cells are addressed.
>
> - Make a copy of Display B.1 and shade in these cells: **A2, B3, C4, D5, E6, A6, B5, D3, E2**. What shape do you get?
>
> - If you wanted Display B.1 to be shaded in a checkerboard pattern, with alternating cells filled in, which cells would you shade? Write out all their addresses. There's more than one way to do this.

The advantage of electronic spreadsheets over handmade ones is that the electronic ones do the computations for you, *IF* you ask them properly. If you know how to speak the language of your spreadsheet program, you can get it to do all the hard work very quickly. The main idea to remember is

> A spreadsheet is powerful because it can find and work with numbers that appear anywhere on it by using the cell names.

Therefore,

> When working with a spreadsheet, always try to build what you want, step-by-step, from the first data you enter. The fewer numbers you have to enter, the easier it is for the spreadsheet to do your work.

The rest of this appendix shows you how to get an electronic spreadsheet to work for you. For practice, each new process will be introduced by using it to deal with this problem.

> You are sent to the local supermarket to buy at least 2 pounds of potato chips for a club picnic. The club treasurer tells you to spend as little money as possible.

Now, there are many different brands of potato chips, and each brand comes in several different size bags. How can you compare prices in a useful way? Well, the bag sizes are measured in ounces. If you divide the price of the bag by the number of ounces, you'll get the price per ounce (this approach is called *unit* pricing). We'll set up a spreadsheet to tell you the price per ounce of every kind of potato chip bag your market sells.

> *Don't just read the rest of this appendix*: **DO IT! Work along with the instructions using your own spreadsheet.**

Entering Numbers and Text

There are three different kinds of things you can put in a cell — numbers, text, and formulas. Most spreadsheets distinguish between numbers and text automatically.

1. If you enter numerical symbols only, the entry is treated as a number.

2. If you begin an entry with letters or other symbols not related to numbers (even if numbers are entered along with them), the entry is treated as text.

Note that if you want a number (such as a date or a year) or a number related symbol (such as $) to be treated as a text entry, you have to tell the machine somehow. Check your user's manual for the way your spreadsheet program does it.

Display B.2 lists the prices of different brands and sizes of potato chips, including the special sale prices for the day. These are actual data from a supermarket. To enter these data in their most useful form, you should use *three* columns—one for the brand, one for the weights (in ounces), and one for the prices. Put the information of Display B.2 into columns A, B, and C now.

Brand of Chip	No. of Ounces	$Cost of Bag
Cape Cod	11 oz.	2.49
Eagle Thins	9.5 oz.	1.99
Humpty Dumpty	6 oz.	1.19
Humpty Dumpty	10 oz.	1.68
Lay's	6 oz.	0.95
Lay's	14 oz.	2.79
O'Boisies	14.5 oz.	2.79
Ruffles	6 oz.	1.39
Ruffles	14 oz.	2.79
Tom's	6 oz.	1.39
Tom's	11 oz.	1.69
Wise	6 oz.	1.39
Wise	10 oz.	1.48

Display B.2

The standard column width of your spreadsheet probably is not big enough to handle some of the brand names. Find the Column Width command and adjust the width of column A to 15 spaces. While you're at it, you might as well adjust the width of column B (the ounces) and column C (the price) each seven spaces wide. This will make the display look a little neater.

Entering Formulas

If you want the spreadsheet to calculate an entry from other data, you have to give it a formula to use. You also have to begin with a special symbol to let it know that a formula is about to be entered. The special symbol depends on the type of spreadsheet you have. Excel uses the symbol = ; Lotus 1-2-3 uses the symbol + ; your software might use something else.

Calculate the price per ounce of Cape Cod chips by entering the formula C1/B1 into cell D1. As soon as you enter it, the number 0.226363 should appear. This is correct, but more accurate than we need. Three decimal places should be enough. Find the spreadsheet command that fixes the number of decimal places and use it to set the column D display to 3 places.

Copying Formulas

To get the price per ounce of Eagle Thins, all you have to do is copy the formula from cell D1 to cell D2. Do that. Check the spreadsheet manual to see how to copy from one cell to another. As soon as you do it, the number 0.209 will appear. Now look at the formula itself. Notice that it says C2/B2; that is, when you copied the formula one cell below where it started, the spreadsheet automatically changed the cell addresses inside it by that amount. This automatic adjustment process is one of the most powerful features of the spreadsheet. Next we'll use it to get the price per ounce of *all* the other kinds of chips at once!

Repeated Copying

You can copy a cell entry over and over again, all at once, along as much of a row or column as you mark out. If the entry is a formula, the spreadsheet will automatically adjust the cell addresses in it at each step. In some spreadsheet programs (such as Excel), this is done by the Fill command. In others (such as Lotus 1-2-3), it is done as part of the Copy command, by highlighting the entire region of cells into which you want the formula copied.

Find out how this works for your spreadsheet. Then copy what's in D2 into cells D3 through D13 and watch all the per ounce prices appear immediately. At this point, your spreadsheet should look something like Display B.3.

	A	B	C	D
1	Cape Cod	11	2.49	0.226
2	Eagle Thins	9.5	1.99	0.209
3	Humpty Dumpty	6	1.19	0.198
4	Humpty Dumpty	10	1.68	0.168
5	Lay's	6	0.95	0.158
6	Lay's	14	2.79	0.199
7	O'Boisies	14.5	2.79	0.192
8	Ruffles	6	1.39	0.232
9	Ruffles	14	2.79	0.199
10	Tom's	6	1.39	0.232
11	Tom's	11	1.69	0.154
12	Wise	6	1.39	0.232
13	Wise	10	1.48	0.148

Display B.3

What *formula* is being used in cell D3? In D7? In D13?

Inserting Rows and Columns

Now let's put in column headings so that the spreadsheet is easier to understand. Move the cursor to the beginning of row 1 and use the Insert Row command of your spreadsheet to put in two rows at the very top. Cape Cod should now be in cell A3. We'll use the first row for headings and leave the second row blank. Enter Brand in A1, ounce in B1, price in C1 and enter $/oz. in D1. Change the width of column D to 7 spaces.

Because we've moved everything down, the row numbers no longer correspond to the number of brands listed. Make space to renumber the rows that list the brands, like this: Move the cursor to the top of the first column and use the Insert Column command to put two new columns at the far left. Cape Cod should now be in cell C3.

Numbering Rows

Now let's try a little experiment. We'll number the brands in two different ways. Make the two new columns, A and B, only 4 spaces wide. Now put the numbers 1 through 13 down these two columns, starting at the third row, in these two ways.

- In column A, enter each number by hand—the number 1 in A3, the number 2 in A4, and so on, down to the number 13 in A15.

- In column B, enter the formula B2+1 in cell B3. The number 1 will appear because the spreadsheet treats the empty cell B2 as if it had 0 in it. Now copy this formula into all the cells from B3 through B15.

Do columns A and B match? They should. If they don't, ask your teacher to help you find what went wrong. At this point, your display should look like Display B.4.

	A	B	C	D	E	F
1			Brand	oz.	$/bag	$/oz.
2						
3	1	1	Cape Cod	11	2.49	0.226
4	2	2	Eagle Thins	9.5	1.99	0.209
5	3	3	Humpty Dumpty	6	1.19	0.198
6	4	4	Humpty Dumpty	10	1.68	0.168
7	5	5	Lay's	6	0.95	0.158
8	6	6	Lay's	14	2.79	0.199
9	7	7	O'Boisies	14.5	2.79	0.192
10	8	8	Ruffles	6	1.39	0.232
11	9	9	Ruffles	14	2.79	0.199
12	10	10	Tom's	6	1.39	0.232
13	11	11	Tom's	11	1.69	0.154
14	12	12	Wise	6	1.39	0.232
15	13	13	Wise	10	1.48	0.148

Display B.4

Ordering Data

Another handy feature of an electronic spreadsheet is that it can put in order data that is listed in a column. It can put numbers in size order, either increasing or decreasing. Most spreadsheets can also put text entries in alphabetical order. To do this, you need to find the Sort command and tell it what list of data you want to rearrange. In Excel, Sort is in the Data menu; in Lotus 1–2–3, it's in the Select menu. The computer prompts you for a little more information, such as whether you want ascending or descending order, then does the sorting.

Note that some spreadsheets move entire rows when they sort; others can be told just to rearrange the data in a single column. Check your user's manual to see how your spreadsheet works. In this example, we assume that the spreadsheet moves entire rows when it sorts.

Let's rearrange the potato chip list according to the price per ounce, from most expensive to least expensive. Follow your spreadsheet's instructions to sort the per ounce prices in column F in ascending order. Which kind of potato chip is the best buy? Which is the worst buy?

> **Look at columns A and B.**
>
> 1. **Do they still match? What has happened? Explain.**
>
> 2. **What would have happened if you had entered the number 1 in B3, then entered the formula =B3+1 in B4? Explain.**

Now that we have all this information, how do we find out how much it will cost the club for the 2 pounds of potato chips? Here's one plan.

- Compute the number of ounces in 2 pounds.

- Multiply the cost of 1 ounce by the total number of ounces needed.

Warning: There's something wrong with this approach; what is it?

> **We'll do this on the spreadsheet because it provides an example of a different way to use cell addresses. To find the total number of ounces, we just multiply the number of pounds (2) by 16. Make these entries on the spreadsheet.**

- In C17, enter number of lbs.; in D17, enter 2.

- In C18, enter number of oz.; in D18, put the formula that multiplies the entry in D17 by 16. (What is that value?)

Constant Cell Addresses

To find out how much 2 pounds of each kind of potato chip will cost, first set column G to display in currency format. Then move the cursor to cell G3. This should be the first blank cell at the end of row 3. We want this cell to show the number of ounces to be bought (in D18) multiplied by the price per ounce (in F3). Let's try it.

- Enter the formula D18*F3 in G3. The result should be $4.74.
  Is your first kind the Wise 10 oz. bag?

- So far, so good. Now copy this formula to the next line, in G4. What do you get? $0.00? How come?

- Look at the formula as it appears in G4. Does it say D19*F4? What happened?

Remember that when you shift a formula from one location to another, the spreadsheet automatically shifts every cell address in exactly the same way. We copied this formula to a location one row down from where it was, so the spreadsheet added the number 1 to the row number of each cell address in the formula. Now, we want that to happen to one of these addresses, but not to the other. That is, the cost of the kind of potato chip in row 4 should use the price per ounce in F4, but it should still use the total number of ounces from D18.

 To prevent the spreadsheet from automatically adjusting a cell address when a formula is moved, enter the cell address with a $ in front of its column letter and a $ in front of its row number.

This means that you should go back to cell G3 and enter the multiplication formula $D$18*F3. Now copy this to G4. Do you get $4.92? Good. If not, what went wrong? Ask your teacher if you need help figuring it out. Now copy this formula into cells G5 through G15. Column G now should show the cost for 2 pounds of each kind of potato chip in your list.

Go to G1, make this column 7 spaces wide and enter the word cost as the column heading.

1. According to column G, which kind of potato chip is the best buy?

2. Why is that *not* necessarily the best buy for your club?

3. What's wrong with letting this answer tell you what kind to buy? *Hint*: How many *bags* would you have to buy?

The INT Function

As the hint in the box above suggests, using the information in column G to guide your choice may not be a good idea because the supermarket sells potato chips by the bag. In order to know how much it will cost to get at least 2 pounds of chips, you first must know how many bags you'll need.

How do you do that? Easy, right? Just divide 32 oz. (2 lbs.) by the number of ounces in a single bag. If you get a mixed number, add 1 to the whole number part.

For example, if you want at least 32 oz. in 10 oz. bags, divide 32 by 10. You get 3.2 as an answer, but, since you can't buy 0.2 of a bag of chips, you need 4 bags.

There's a spreadsheet function—called INT—that makes this very easy to compute automatically. The INT function gives you the greatest integer less than or equal to the number you put into it. For instance.

$$\text{INT}\left(3\frac{1}{3}\right) = 3$$

$$\text{INT}(2.98) = 2$$

$$\text{INT}(5) =$$

Let's use this function to carry out the computation we just did, finding how many 10 oz. bags of Wise potato chips we need in order to have at least 2 pounds. But instead of entering the numbers in separately, we'll get them from other cells on the spreadsheet. Move to cell H3 and enter the formula

$$\text{INT}(\$D\$18/D3) + 1$$

Just to make sure you understand what we're doing, answer these questions before moving on.

1. What does $D$18 stand for?

2. Why are the $ symbols there?

3. What does D3 stand for?

4. What number is $D$18/D3?

5. What number is INT($D$18/D3)?

6. What number is INT($D$18/D3)+1?

7. If you copy this formula to cell H4, how will it read?

Now use the Fill command to copy this formula into cells H4 through H15. For each kind, the number you get says how many bags you need in order to have at least two pounds of chips. Put the heading bags at the top of this column H, and make the column 5 spaces wide.

Now we can finish the problem. To find the cost of at least 2 lbs. of each kind of chip, multiply the number of bags you need by the cost of a single bag. Enter a formula in I3 that does this; then copy it into I3 through I15. Finish your spreadsheet display by renaming column G cost 1 and naming column I cost 2 and changing the width of column I to 6 spaces.

1. If you *must* get at least 2 lbs. of chips and you want to spend as little as possible, which kind do you buy?

2. How many bags do you buy?

3. What does it cost you?

The next questions show the power of spreadsheets for testing out different variations of a situation. Each part is exactly the same as above, except that the total number of pounds of chips is different. Answer each one by changing as little as possible on your spreadsheet.

1. If you *must* get at least 3 lbs. of chips and you want to spend as little as possible, which kind do you buy? How many bags do you buy? What does it cost you?

2. If you *must* get at least 4 lbs. of chips and you want to spend as little as possible, which kind do you buy? How many bags do you buy? What does it cost you?

3. If you *must* get at least 5 lbs. of chips and you want to spend as little as possible, which kind do you buy? How many bags do you buy? What does it cost you?

Problem Set: Appendix B

1. These two questions refer to the potato chip spreadsheet that you just made.

    (a) Add a column J that shows the total number of ounces of potato chips of each kind that you get when you buy enough bags to get at least two pounds of potato chips. What formula will compute these numbers?

    (b) Add a column K that shows the number of *extra* ounces (more than 2 pounds) that you get when you buy enough bags to get at least two pounds of potato chips. What formula will compute these numbers?

2. Make a spreadsheet like the one for the potato chips to deal with this problem.

    (a) Your favorite aunt runs a shelter for homeless cats. As a present for her birthday, you decide to give her 5 pounds of canned cat food. You want to spend as little money as possible. The brands, sizes, and prices for the canned cat food at the supermarket are shown in Display B.5. What brand and size is the best buy, and how many cans of it should you get? What will it cost?

    (b) Your best friend thinks you have a great idea. She decides to buy your aunt 5 pounds of canned cat food, too. If you both chip in and buy a combined present of 10 pounds of canned cat food, what is the best buy of canned cat food for your combined present? Explain your answer.

Brand of Cat Food	No. of Ounces	Cost
Alpo	6 oz.	3 for $1.00
Alpo	13.75 oz.	$ .65
Figaro	5.5 oz.	$ .37
Figaro	12 oz.	$ .66
Friskies	6 oz.	$ .35
Friskies	13 oz.	$ .58
Kal Kan	5.5 oz.	4 for $1.00
Puss 'n Boots	14 oz.	$ .55
9 Lives	5.5 oz.	3 for $ .88
9 Lives	13 oz.	$ .48
Whiskas	5.5 oz.	3 for $1.00
Whiskas	12.3 oz.	$ .55

Display B.5

3. Here's a bonus question.

   (a) Invent a problem about breakfast foods that is like the potato chip and cat food problems.

   (b) Go to your local supermarket and gather the brand, size, and price information that you will need to solve your problem.

   (c) Using the data you gather for part (b), set up a spreadsheet that solves the problem you invented in part (a).

Appendix C: Programming the **TI-82 (TI-83)**

After you have been using the TI-82 (TI-83) for a while, you may notice that you are repeating certain tasks on your calculator over and over. Often you are repeating the same sequence of keystrokes, which can become very tiresome. Programs give you a way to carry out long sequences of keystrokes all at once, saving you a great deal of time and energy.

In this appendix we will show you some simple TI-82 (TI-83) programs and how to enter and use them. In the textbook, there are some other programs which you will find useful in solving problems.

Correcting Mistakes

When you enter a program you will almost surely make some keying mistakes. You can use the arrow keys to back up and key over any mistakes. To insert something new, rather than keying over what is already there, give the insert command (INS above the [DEL] key) by keying

[2nd] [DEL]

Use the [DEL] key to delete the current character.

Entering Programs

To enter a program, give the [NEW] command under the [PRGM] menu by keying

[PRGM] [◁] [ENTER]

Your calculator should look like Display C.1. You are now in program writing mode. Whatever you key in will be stored in the program you are creating, rather than being executed directly. To get out of program writing mode, give the QUIT command.

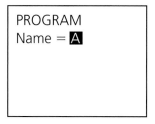

Display C.1

Next you need to name your program so that you can use it. We will start with a very short and not very useful program just to test your ability to enter a program and run it. Give your program the name ADD. Normally, to enter the capital letters that are above and to the right of some of the keys you must press the [ALPHA] key first. When naming a program, however, the calculator goes into ALPHA mode automatically. This means you *don't* have to press the [ALPHA] key when entering the letters in the program name. Key in

Your calculator screen should now look like Display C.2

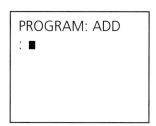

Display C.2

We now need to enter the actual program commands. Our test program will ask for two numbers and then add them. Each line of the program begins with a colon. At the end of each line of the program press [ENTER] . The first line of our program asks for the first of the two numbers it will add. The two numbers that we tell the calculator to add are called the *input* for the program. The Input command is the first item under the I/O section of the PRGM menu. We will store the input in memory A. Key in

The TI screen should now look like Display C.3.

```
PROGRAM: ADD
: Input A
: ■
```

Display C.3

The next line in the program asks for another number and stores it in memory location B. Enter the second line now, based on the way you entered the first line. Your screen should now look like Display C.4.

```
PROGRAM: ADD
: Input A
: Input B
```

Display C.4

The third line adds the numbers stored in memories A and B and stores the result in memory C. Key in

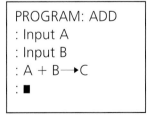

The new screen is in Display C.5.

```
PROGRAM: ADD
: Input A
: Input B
: A + B→C
: ■
```

Display C.5

We finish our program with a statement which displays the result of adding the two numbers (now stored in memory C). The display command Disp is the third item under the I/O section of the PRGM menu.

Key in

[PRGM] [▷] [3] [ALPHA] [C]

The resulting screen is in Display C.6

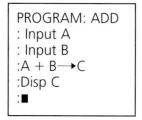

```
PROGRAM: ADD
: Input A
: Input B
:A + B→C
:Disp C
:■
```

Display C.6

We are done writing the program! To quit programming mode use the [QUIT] key (above the [MODE] key). The program is automatically saved. Key in

[2nd] [QUIT]

You are now back to the Home Screen, where you started.

Running Programs

To run the program we just keyed in, we go to the EXEC section of the PRGM menu, key in the number of the program we want to run, and then press [ENTER]. We will assume that the program named ADD that we just entered is program number 1. Key in

[PRGM] [1] [ENTER]

If you entered the program correctly, a question mark appears asking for input. If there is an error, look at the next section on editing programs. This question mark is produced by the first line of your program. You are being requested to type in the first of two numbers, which will then be added by the program. Let's suppose that we want to add the numbers 4 and 5. Press [4] then press [ENTER]. A second question mark appears asking for the second number. Press [5] and press [ENTER] again. The result, 9, should appear. The screen now looks like Display C.7.

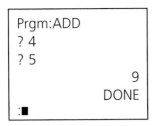

Display C.7

To run the program again, just press the ⎡ENTER⎤ key. You don't have to go through the PRGM menu to run the program the second time, as long as no other calculations have been performed in between. Try adding two other numbers to see how this works.

Quitting Programs

If you are in the middle of running a program and you want to stop the program, press ⎡ON⎤ key. To try this out, run the ADD program again, but this time when the first question mark appears, press ⎡ON⎤. The screen should look like Display C.8.

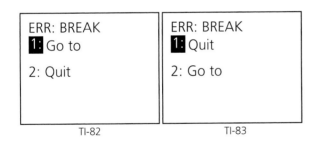

Display C.8

Press ⎡2⎤ to quit the program and return to the Home Screen. Pressing ⎡1⎤ puts you back in program writing mode at the point in the program where you stopped the program.

Editing Programs

If your program doesn't work, or if you just want to make changes to a program, you use the EDIT section of the PRGM menu. Key in

This should put you back in the ADD program (assuming it is program 1). Your screen should look just as it did when you left the program writing mode (see Display C.6). Use the arrow keys and the insert ⟨ INS ⟩ and delete ⟨ DEL ⟩ keys as explained in the Correcting Mistakes section.

To open space for a new line, put the cursor at the beginning of a line, give the insert command ⟨ INS ⟩ and then press ⟨ ENTER ⟩. To try this on your ADD program, use the arrow keys to put the cursor at the beginning of the second line of the program and key in

⟨ 2nd ⟩   ⟨ DEL ⟩   ⟨ ENTER ⟩

Your screen should look like Display C.9.

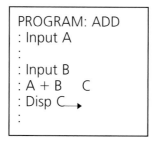

```
PROGRAM: ADD
: Input A
:
: Input B
: A + B    C
: Disp C⟶
:
```

Display C.9

The blank line we just created will not affect the program, so we can just give the QUIT command to leave the program writing mode.

A Useful Program

Now that you have some practice with writing, editing, and running programs, let's take a look at a program that you might really find useful.

Graphing With Parameters

Suppose that we want to graph the equation of a straight line, say $y = ax + 5$, for several values of a. The constant a is called a *parameter*. First we can enter the expression AX + 5 as expression Y1 under the Y= menu. We can then store numbers in memory A and press ⟨ GRAPH ⟩. The problem is that we only see the graph for one value of a at a time. The following program allows you to easily produce graphs for many values of a and keep all of the graphs on the screen together.

Enter the program shown in Display C.10, using what you
learned from the **Entering Programs** section. Name the program
PARAMS. Note: DrawF is item 6 under the DRAW menu
(above the [PRGM] key) for the TI-82. Y₁ is item number 1 of
the Function sub menu under the Y-vars menu (above the
[DRAW] [VARS] key). For the TI-83, Y₁ is found by keys
[VARS] [▷] [1] [1] [ENTER] .

```
PROGRAM: PARAMS
: Input  A
: DrawF  Y₁
: ■
```

Display C.10

The program is simple, but saves quite a few keystrokes. You
put in a value for *a*, and then the function is graphed using the
DrawF command.

To use this program you must store your function in function
memory Y_1 and then *turn off* Y_1 (put the cursor on the = and
press ENTER). Your Y= WINDOW should look like
Display C.11. Notice that the = is *not* highlighted, indicating
the function is off.

```
Y₁ = AX + 5
Y₂ =
Y₃ =
Y₄ =
Y₅ =
Y₆ =
Y₇ =
Y₈ =
```

Display C.11

To set the graph WINDOW to the Standard setting, press the 6
under the ZOOM menu. Your WINDOW settings should appear
as in Display C.12.

WINDOW FORMAT	WINDOW FORMAT
Xmin = -10	Xmin = -10
Xmax = 10	Xmax = 10
Xscl = 1	Xscl = 1
Ymin = -10	Ymin = -10
Ymax = 10	Ymax = 10
Yscl = 1	Yscl = 1
	Xres = 1
TI-82	TI-83

Display C.12

Now run the program. Try starting with an a value of 1. Press $\boxed{1}$ then $\boxed{\text{ENTER}}$ in response to the question mark. You should see a graph of the function $y = 1x + 5$. To run the program again, first press the $\boxed{\text{CLEAR}}$ key (to get back to the Home Screen) then $\boxed{\text{ENTER}}$. Try an a with a value of -2 this time. Now both the graphs of $y = ax + b$ for $a = 1$ and for $a = -2$ should be on the screen, as shown in Display C.13.

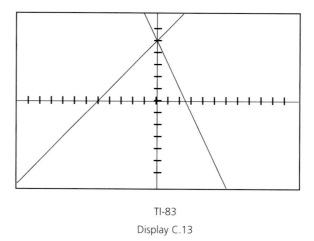

TI-83

Display C.13

If you want to clear the graph screen, use ClrDraw, which is item 1 under the DRAW menu.

You only need to change the function stored in Y_1 to graph any other function with one parameter. For instance, try graphing the function $y = a^x$ for various a values.

Appendix D: Linear Programming With Excel

The graphical method of solving Linear Programming problems is explained in the text. The limitation of this method is that it is applicable only to problems with two variables.

Linear Programming is one of the most used mathematical methods in real-world problem solving. Only rarely are two variables present in a realistic problem. Mathematicians have developed methods to solve Linear Programming problems with any number of variables; a computer program is then needed to carry out the computations. One commonly used computer program which solves Linear Programming problems is called LINDO™.

Several spreadsheet programs can solve Linear Programming problems. Microsoft Excel, Lotus 1-2-3, and Quattro Pro are such spreadsheet programs. We will look at how Excel 5.0 solves linear programming problems, but we will not explain the method Excel uses. This is known as treating the program as something mysterious—we can follow the instructions for using the program, but we don't know how the program gives a solution to the problem. Knowing how to solve simple problems graphically helps us to understand the output from the program, even if we don't understand the exact method the computer is using. Just imagine that Excel is using a method similar to the one you learned for two variable problems.

Our first example will be a very simple problem with only two variables. Then we can solve the problem graphically as in the textbook and check our answer against the answer from the computer. We will then extend the problem to three variables; here a graphical solution is not possible.

Problem

A new housing development is being built near Bart's house. Bart has noticed that the construction workers often leave the site to get lunch. Always on the lookout to earn money, Bart figures that he can make lunches for the workers and sell them at a profit. We will assume there are enough workers and Bart can sell all of the sandwiches that he can make.

Bart decides to make two types of lunches. The first lunch will have two sodas and one sandwich (the Thirsty Worker Lunch) and the second type of lunch will have two sandwiches and one soda (the Hungry Worker Lunch). Bart plans to buy the sandwiches and sodas from a local deli for $3.00 per sandwich and $0.50 per can of soda. He will sell the Thirsty Worker Lunches for $5.00 and the Hungry Worker Lunches for $8.00. This means that Bart's profit for each Thirsty Worker Lunch is $1.00 and his profit on each Hungry Worker Lunch is $1.50.

Bart has one problem. The deli doesn't open until 11:30 a.m., which is too late to make lunches and have them ready for the workers. He figures he needs to buy his supplies the night before, but that means he needs to keep the (24 cans) of soda in the family refrigerator. Bart finds a cooler in the basement that will hold 20 sandwiches.

How many Hungry Worker Lunches and how many Thirsty Worker Lunches should Bart prepare in order to make the most money? His constraints are that he can use only 20 sandwiches and 24 sodas as explained above.

Solution

SETUP

First we need to formulate the problem as a linear programming problem. Let x represent the number of Thirsty Worker Lunches and y the number of Hungry Worker Lunches that Bart prepares. Then Bart's profit P is

$$P = 1.00x + 1.50y$$

The soda constraint would be

$$2x + y \leq 24$$

and the sandwich constraint would be

$$x + 2y \leq 20$$

The other two constraints which we don't want to forget are

$$x \geq 0 \text{ and } y \geq 0$$

Computer Solution

Our goal is to set up the spreadsheet as shown in Displays D.1 and D.2 and to show the formulas that you actually key into each cell. Display D.2 shows what the result should look like on your spreadsheet. To get this result, follow the steps below.

1. Key in a title for the spreadsheet in cell A1; we used "Bart's Lunch Business." Don't key in any quotation marks. We dressed up the title a bit by making the font larger (12 point) and using the Outline style; just select cell A1 and choose Font from the Format menu.

2. Key in x in cell A3, y in cell B3 and P = 1.00x + 1.50y in cell C3.

3. Cells A4 and B4 will represent the initial guess for x and y. These guesses don't have to be good; they just have to make sense. The easiest guesses are 0 for both x and y, since they satisfy all the constraints. Therefore, key in 0 in A4 and 0 in B4.

4. Key in = 1.00 * A4 + 150 * B4 in cell C4. This represents the profit for the x and y you chose. You should see 0 appear since x and y are now 0.

5. Key in the word constraints in cell A6. We will use row 7 to label the constraints, and row 8 to put in the constraints as formulas.

6. Key in x + 2y < = 20 into cell A7 and 2x + y < = 24 into cell B7 as labels for the sandwich and soda constraints.

7. Key in the **left side only** of the sandwich constraint into cell A8. Therefore you key in = A4 + 2 * B4 into cell B7. Similarly key in = 2 * A4 + B4 into cell B8. At this point zeros should appear in these cells since x and y are both 0.

	A	B	C
1	Bart's Lunch Business		
2			
3	x	y	P=1.00x+1.50y
4	0	0	=1*A4+1.5*B4
5			
6	constraints		
7	x+2y<=20	2x+y<=24	
8	=A4+2*B4	=2*A4+B4	

Display D.1

8. Select cells A3 through C8 and choose CELLS: Alignment from the Format menu. Choose center for horizontal alignment. Then choose CELLS: Number from the Format menu and select 0.00. Your spreadsheet should now look like Display D.2

	A	B	C
1	Bart's Lunch Business		
2			
3	x	y	P=1.00x+1.50y
4	0.00	0.00	0.00
5			
6	constraints		
7	x+2y<=20	2x+y<=24	
8	0.00	0.00	

Display D.2

We are now ready to tell the computer to find the solution to our linear programming problem. We use a capability of Excel called the Solver to get the solution. You may have noticed that we have not actually specified all of the information for the constraints. In particular, we need to tell Excel that cells A4 and B4 need to be positive (x and y should be positive), that cell A8 should be less than 20 and cell B8 should be less than 24 (the sandwich and soda constraints). We do this as shown below.

9. Choose Solver from the Tools menu. The goal is to get the Solver dialogue box to look like Display D.3.

10. Type C4 in the Set Target Cell box. You don't need to type the $s; they will be added by Excel automatically. This box tells the computer which cell to maximize; in our problem C4 is the cell that represents Bart's profit.

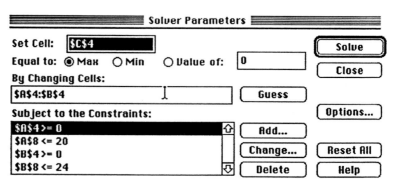

Display D.3

11. Type A4:B4 in the By Changing Cells box. This instructs the computer to adjust the cells in this range (the number of

Thirsty Worker and Hungry Worker Lunches in our problem) until cell C4 is at a maximum.

12. Put the constraints into the Subject to the Constraints box. For each you must click the Add button, which brings up another dialogue box as shown in Display D.4. Key in the Cell Reference and the Constraint value (the right-hand side of the constraint inequality). Click on the < = drop-down menu to choose < = or > = (you can also choose = or int for integer).

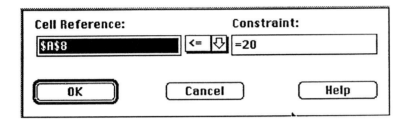

Display D.4

13. Click the Max button in the Equal To line to indicate that this is a maximization problem (it is probably already chosen).

14. Click the Solve button, and Excel will attempt to solve the problem. Excel will then report whether it found a solution or not. If a solution was found, just click OK in the dialogue box that pops up, and the values of the variables which provide the solution will have replaced the initial guesses that you gave in step 3.

Bart's Lunch Business

x	y	P=1.00x+1.50y
9.33	5.33	17.33

Constraints:

x+2y<=20	2x+y<=24
20.00	24.00

Display D.5

15. Summarize your findings and explain the spreadsheet for someone who might not be familiar with the problem. Display D.5 shows the solution to our problem, as well as a short verbal description of the results. We also dressed up

our report with a little formatting (using Borders from the Format menu and turning off the gridlines with Display from the Option menu). Note that, in this problem, we needed to round our results since fractional parts of a lunch do not make sense.

Summary of Findings

Bart is going to sell two types of lunches. We let x represent the number of Thirsty Worker Lunches, which contain two sodas and one sandwich. We let y represent the number of Hungry Worker Lunches, which contain one soda and two sandwiches. Bart's constraints are that he can use at most 20 sandwiches and 24 sodas. His profit P is $1.00 on each Thirsty Worker Lunch and $1.50 on each Hungry Worker Lunch.

The tables in Display D.5 resulted from performing a linear programming analysis of the problem. What they show is that Bart should make nine Thirsty Worker Lunches and five Hungry Worker Lunches. The values in the table need to be rounded since Bart can't make a fraction of a lunch. His profit will be less than the $17.33 shown in the table; his actual profit will be

$$1(9) + 1.5(5) = \$16.50$$

Extension to Three Variables

Suppose that Bart decided to make a third type of lunch with 2 sandwiches and 2 sodas (Super Lunches). Let z represent the number of Super Lunches. Bart will sell Super Lunches for $9.00; his profit on these lunches would be $2.00. Then the new profit formula would be

$$P = 1.00x + 1.50y + 2.00z$$

The new constraints would be

$$2x + y + 2z \leq 24 \text{ and } x + 2y + 2z \leq 20$$

for soda and sandwiches. Display D.6 shows what formulas you would type into the cells. Display D.7 shows how the spreadsheet would look before solving.

	A	B	C	D
1	Bart's Lunch Business			
2				
3	x	y	z	P=1.00x+1.50y+2.00z
4	0	0	0	=1*A4+1.5*B4+2*C4
5				
6	constraints			
7	x+2y+2z<=20	2x+y+2z<=24		
8	=A4+2*B4+2*C4	=2*A4+B4+2*C4		

Display D.6

	A	B	C	D	E
1	Bart's Lunch Business				
2					
3	x	y	z	P=1.00x+1.50y+2.00z	
4	0.00	0.00	0.00	0.00	
5					
6	constraints				
7	x+2y+2z<=20	2x+y+2z<=24			
8	0.00	0.00			

Display D.7

When you now invoke the Solver, there are several changes you must make in the Solver dialogue box. You need to add the constraint C4 > = 0 ($z \geq 0$ in the problem) into the Subject to Constraints box, change the By Changing Cells box to A4:C4, and change the Set Target Cell box to D4. After these changes, click Solve; the spreadsheet displays the solution to the new problem as shown in Display D.8.

	A	B	C	D	E
1	Bart's Lunch Business				
2					
3	x	y	z	P=1.00x+1.50y+2.00z	
4	4.00	0.00	8.00	20.00	
5					
6	constraints				
7	x+2y+2z<=20	2x+y+2z<=24			
8	20.00	24.00			

Display D.8

We see by looking at Display D.8 that the addition of a new type of lunch has a significant effect on the solution to Bart's problem. Now Bart should make four Thirsty Worker Lunches and eight Super Lunches and no Hungry Worker Lunches. His profit goes up from $16.50 to $20. We don't need to round this time since the values of the variables come out as whole numbers.

A big advantage to using the computer solution for this type of problem (besides being able to solve problems with more than two variables) is that we can easily change any part of the problem and get instant feedback on how the answer changes. For example, if Bart increases the amount he charges for the Hungry Worker Lunches, common sense tells us that at some number it would become profitable to make some of these lunches. What is that number?

To answer the previous question, you could try increasing the selling price of Hungry Worker Lunches to $8.60 to see if this changes the solution. This changes the profit on these lunches to $2.10. The only change in the problem is that the new profit formula is

$$P = 1.00x + 2.10y + 2.00z$$

Just change cells D3 and D4 to reflect the new information and run the Solver again. We find that, indeed, it is now profitable to provide some Hungry Worker Lunches (the result is interesting—check it out). With more guess and check we could pin down exactly the point where the y variable enters the problem.

Follow up Exercise

Carry out the process that was started. Keeping all other quantities in the problem constant, try different values for the price for the Hungry Worker Lunches until you find the number at which it just becomes profitable to make some of these lunches. Thus, it should be the case that if you lower the price of these lunches by any small amount, the solution to the Linear Programming problem has $y = 0$ in it, but if you increase the price by any small amount the solution for y is greater than 0. Discuss what happens to all variables and the total profit as you make these changes.

GLOSSARY

and-statement A statement of the form "p and q." It is true if p and q are both true; it is false otherwise.

arithmetic mean For two numbers, a and b, it is represented by $\frac{(a + b)}{2}$.

asymptote A line that part of a curve approaches but does not intersect.

axiom A statement that is assumed to be true without proof. Axioms are the starting point assumptions of an axiomatic system.

axiomatic system A mathematical system derived by logic from a set of axioms.

axis of symmetry A line that divides a figure in half so that each half is a mirror image of the other.

basic arithmetic-geometric mean inequality is defined by $\frac{(a + b)}{2} \geq \sqrt{ab}$, where a and b are nonnegative.

break-even point The value at which revenue and expenses are equal, i.e., profit is zero.

Chaos Game A game based on random rolls of a die which turns out to have a well defined pattern of results when graphed.

characteristic property A condition clear enough for us to decide whether or not any given object satisfies it.

circular definition A definition in which the defining condition is described by using words whose meanings depend on the word being defined.

closure The property whereby applying an operation to elements of a set always results in an element of that same set.

complex number A number that can be written in the form $a + bi$, where a and b are real numbers and $i = \sqrt{-1}$.

conclusion The statement q in a conditional statement that can be put in the form, "If p, then q."

conditional statement A statement that can be put into the form, "if p, then q," where p and q are statements. It is false if p is true and q is false; it is true otherwise.

conjecture A statement that has not been proved true or false.

conjunction An *and* statement of the form "*p and q.*"

connected (graph) A graph in which one can reach any vertex from any other by traveling along the edges.

consistent axiomatic system An axiomatic system that does not contain any contradictions.

consistent statements Statements that do not contradict each other.

constraint A condition that restricts your actions with regard to solutions to problems.

contradiction A statement that is always false.

cost line A straight line in a coordinate plane along which cost is a constant.

countable set A set that can be put into one-to-one correspondence with the natural numbers.

counterexample An example that proves a universal or conditional statement false.

cycle A path of edges in a graph that starts and ends at the same vertex but that does not pass through any edge or vertex, other than the starting point, more than once.

deductive reasoning The process of using logic to prove statements from other statements that are known or assumed to be true.

defined term A word that is explicitly described within an axiomatic system, using the undefined terms and/or words defined previously.

dense set (of numbers) A set of numbers with the property that there is another member of the set between any two members.

dependent axiom An axiom that can be proved from the other axioms of the axiomatic system.

disjunction A statement of the form "*p or q.*" It is false if p and q are both false; it is true otherwise.

domain The set of possible x-values (dependent variable values) for an equation or a function.

e An irrational number that is the limit of $(1 + \frac{1}{a})^a$ as a increases; $e \approx 2.718$.

edge One of the segments connecting pairs of vertices in a graph.

equivalent statements Two statements that always have the same truth values. They are formally called "logically equivalent statements."

Euclidean tools Unmarked compass and straightedge.

event A subset of a sample space.

existential statement A statement asserting the existence of at least one thing that satisfies some condition.

feasible region (in a plane) The set of points in a coordinate plane corresponding to the feasible solutions of a Linear Programming problem.

feasible solution A solution to a problem that leads to an action that is capable of being completed.

field A set with two associative and commutative operations and identities for both operations; every element has a first-operation inverse; every element except the first-operation identity has a second-operation inverse; and the second operation is distributive over the first.

fractal The name given to pictorial representations of certain geometrical shapes that are self-similar and have a fractional dimension.

geometric mean For two nonnegative numbers, a and b, it is represented by $\sqrt{ab}$.

geometric series A series in which the ratio of any two consecutive terms is always the same.

graph (as in Graph Theory) A system consisting of a set of points, called vertices, and a set of segments, called edges, that connect pairs of vertices.

group A closed set with an associative operation, an identity element, and an inverse for each element.

hypothesis The statement p in a conditional statement that can be put in the form, "if p, then q."

identity element An element z in a set with an operation such that z combined with any element of the set leaves that element unchanged.

inconsistent axiomatic system An axiomatic system that contains a contradiction.

independent axiom An axiom that cannot be proved from the other axioms of the axiomatic system.

independent axiomatic system An axiomatic system in which every axiom is independent of the others.

inductive reasoning The process of looking at particular examples and abstracting a general statement that appears to be true about all of them.

infinite process Any process that can be repeated infinitely many times.

instance (of an axiomatic system) The assignment of meaning to the undefined terms of an axiomatic system in such a way that all the axioms become true statements about those meanings.

integer A member of the set {..., –3, –2, –1, 0, 1, 2, 3, ...}.

integral calculus A branch of calculus that includes finding lengths, volumes, and areas under curves.

inverse (of an element) A number or variable in a set with an operation and element a' that, when combined with a, results in the identity element.

irrational number A number that can be expressed as a nonrepeating, nonterminating decimal.

Linear Programming model A mathematical model consisting of a linear objective function and a set of linear constraints. All variables are assumed to be nonnegative.

Method of Exhaustion A method devised by Archimedes for finding the sum of certain infinite series.

model (mathematical) A mathematical example or object that is used to describe a situation outside of mathematics.

modular addition The process of combining numbers by adding them and then taking the remainder of the sum divided by the modulus as the answer.

modulus A designated number used to define the operations of a particular instance of modular arithmetic.

natural number A member of the set of counting numbers {1, 2, 3, ...}.

negation A statement whose truth value is always opposite to the truth value of a given statement.

non-Euclidean geometry A geometry based on Euclid's first four postulates and the negation of the Parallel Postulate.

objective function A function that represents the goal in solving a problem; i.e., the profit function is an objective function when one wants to maximize profit.

operation Any rule or process that assigns to each ordered pair of elements of a set exactly one element of that same set.

or-statement A statement of the form *"p or q."* It is false if *p* and *q* are both false; it is true otherwise.

particular statement A nonquantified statement about one or more specific things.

postulate A specific assumption about a particular subject; an axiom.

profit line A straight line in a coordinate plane along which profit is a constant.

proposition A statement that is assumed to be true within an axiomatic system (i.e., following from the axioms by a valid argument).

quantified statement A statement containing a quantifier.

quantifier A word indicating how many of some kind of thing is being considered.

rational number A member of the set of numbers that can be expressed in the form $\frac{a}{b}$, where *a* and *b* are integers and $b \neq 0$.

real number A member of the set of all rational and irrational numbers.

Saccheri quadrilateral An isosceles birectangular quadrilateral; that is, a four-sided polygon with two right angles at its base and two equal sides.

statement A sentence that has a truth value.

symmetry (rotational) A movement of a plane figure that returns it to its original outline in the plane after a finite number of rotations about a point.

theorem A statement that can be proved from the axioms of an axiomatic system.

tree A connected graph with no cycles.

truth values *True* and *false*, used as labels applied to statements.

unbounded quantity Something that has no limit.

undefined term One of the "starting point" words of an axiomatic system. Its meaning is inferred from its use in the axioms, but it is not formally defined within the system.

universal statement A statement asserting that all things of a certain kind satisfy some condition.

vacuously satisfied axiom A conditional axiom that becomes a true statement in an instance because its hypothesis is never true.

valid argument A deductive argument for that the conclusion is guaranteed to be true whenever all of the hypotheses are true.

Index

3b.

Index 3b.

A

About Words
attract, 424
bisect, 568
conjecture, 483
consistent, 546
constraint, 318
contract, 424
distract, 424
elements, 554
existentialism, 400
extract, 424
for instance, 390
fractal, 502
infinity, 476
junction, 406
modulate, 443
paradox, 476
postulate, 555
pseudo-, 595
pseudonym, 595
pseudoscience, 595
quantifier, 400
quantity, 400
root, 424
slack, 334
subtract, 424
universal statement, 400
universe, 400
Abstract, 424
Abstraction, 405, 441, 458
Alice in Wonderland, 412
Alternate exterior angles, 573
Alternate interior angles, 573
and statement, 404-408
conjunction, 406
Aquinas, St. Thomas, 553
Archimedes, 428, 513, 525, 530
Aristotle, 553
Area approximations,
lower bound, 529
under the curve, 525, 527
upper bound, 529
Arithmetic-geometric mean
inequality, 374, 375, 377,
379
Associative, 437-440, 491, 590

Axiom, 388, 389, 392, 393, 399,
424, 428, 432, 433, 437, 543,
544, 548, 549, 555, 582-584,
588-590
dependent, 583, 589
independent, 582, 583, 587
of field, 467, 468
of group, 589, 590
Axiomatic system, 388, 392,
393, 399, 545, 548
consistent, 543, 546
inconsistent, 546
independent, 582, 583

B

Basic arithmetic-geometric
mean inequality, 374, 375
Basic variables, 336
Bellman, Richard, 302
Biconditional statement, 413
Binary operation, 431
Bisect, 568
Block diagram, 299-308
Bolyai, Janos, 594
Bound
bounded, 529
lower, 529
unbounded, 482
upper, 529
Brute Force Method, 300

C

Calculus, 530, 584
Cancellation, 451
Cancellation Laws, 452
Cantor, Georg, 534
Center, 556
Chaos Game, 500
Chaos Theory, 502
Characteristic property, 395
Circle, 397, 552
Circular definition, 395
Clock addition, 443
Closure, 437, 438, 464, 470
Closure property, 437-439, 491
Common multiplier, 516, 518
Common Notions, 554, 557
Common ratio, 518

Commutative, 453, 459, 491
Complex numbers, 468, 509
Composition, 432, 458, 459
Conclusion, 410, 411
Conditional statement, 410,
411, 418, 588
biconditional, 413
Conjecture, 483, 484
Conjunction, 406
and statement, 406
Connected, 363
Connectives, 404-406
and, 404-408
if ... then, 404, 405, 409,
410, 588
or, 404-408
Consistent, 543, 546, 592
Consistent axiomatic
system, 543
Constraints, 318-324, 329,
348-350
Construction, 557, 558
Contour lines, 325
Contradiction, 419, 545, 546
Contrapositive, 421, 545
Converse, 412, 561
Cost line, 351
slope, 351
Cost schedule, 354
Countable sets, 534
Counterexample, 419, 459
Cycle, 364

D

Dantzig, George, 334, 341
simplex method, 334
Decimals
finite, 496
infinite, 496
Decision variables, 317
Deductive reasoning, 417
Defined term, 388
Definition, 395, 397
characteristic, 395
circular, 395
noncircular, 395
De Morgan, Augustus, 408
De Morgan's Laws, 408

I-1